THE COMPL SBEE

The History of t ...e First Official Price Guide

by

Victor A. Malafronte

The Original World Frisbee Champion

Edited by F. Davis Johnson

The Complete Book Of Frisbee
The History Of The Sport & The First Official Price Guide
By Victor A. Malafronte

Published by: American Trends Publishing Co.
909 Marina Village Parkway, #321
Alameda, CA 94501
510 814-9639

Copyright © 1998 by Victor A. Malafronte
First Edition
Editor: F. Davis Johnson
Art Director: Bobbi Alexander, Designwest/Graphics
Illustrator: Rachel Forbes
Printed in Korea
Library Of Congress Cataloging in Publication Data.
Malafronte, Victor, A.

THE COMPLETE BOOK OF FRISBEE – The History of the Sport/The First Official Price Guide/The Frisbee Conspiracy by Victor A. Malafronte-Copyright 1998. (All Rights Reserved)

Includes bibliography and index.
1. The History of Frisbee. How & What to Collect with Price Guide. 3. Frisbee Conspiracy.
ISBN: 0-9663855-2-7

FRISBIE'S is a registered trademark of the Frisbie Pie Co. (Table Talk Pies).

DISC GOLF: Disc Golf was a registered trademark of the Disc Golf Association. Founder, "Steady Ed" Headrick, donated the term Disc Golf to the public domain.

FRISBEE is a Registered Trademark of the Wham-O Inc. for flying discs used in toss games.

As a matter of social commentary and responsibility, the word "FRISBEE" in this book, will appear the way I have found it used throughout history, as a generic term describing toss and catch games played with a round flying disc: Frisbie, Frizby, Phrisbee, Frisbey, Frisbees!

TABLE OF CONTENTS

THE HISTORY OF FRISBEE PLAYING: The First Definitive Study Conducted on the Origin of Frisbee Playing

INTRODUCTION

EARLY HISTORY OF FLYING DISC OBJECTS AND GAMES
>
> Discus Throwing
> The Chacarani/Chakram
> Quoits
> Throwing Rings
> Disc and Cross
> Japanese Bird Disc
> Hoop and Spear
> Kinxe
> Trapshooting
> Skittles

MODERN DAY FRISBEE GAMES

UNFETTERED METAL:
COOKIE LIDS AND PIE TINS VIE FOR AIR SUPREMACY

FRISBEE COLLECTING TODAY

MAJOR FLYING DISC CLASSIFICATIONS

Listing of 20 different classifications covering 25,000 discs
with a general price guideline for each class.

CHAPTER V   107
COLLECTIBLE FRISBEES

INTRODUCTION

THE FIRST OFFICIAL COMPLETE BOOK OF FRISBEE PRICE GUIDE

A listing and description of nearly 400 collectible flying discs
and accessories with price guidelines.

THE ART OF FRISBEE

THE $50,000 FRISBIE PIE SAFE

CHAPTER VII   205
THE FRISBEE CONSPIRACY

A major investigation revealing that Wham-O may have wrongly applied for a registered trademark on the generic term "frisbee"!

ACKNOWLEDGMENTS

A special thank you to the following people who played important roles in providing research and/or materials for the completion of this book:

Amy Antman: Dartmouth College, NH
Tom Atkins: Amherst, MA
Bob Beckerer: Bridgeport, CT
Alona Burnett: Brentwood, CA
Kevin Cotchen: Gibsonia, PA
Daria D'Arienzo: Amherst College Library-Special Collections
Coszette Eneix: San Francisco, CA
Hal Erickson: Berkeley, CA
Sam Ferrans: Tokyo, Japan
Nora G. Frisbie: Claremont, CA
Dudley Gaman: Portola Valley, CA
Jerome Gundrun: Windsor, CT
Steve Hartwell: North Reading, MA
Steady Ed Headrick: Watsonville, CA
Dave Johnson: Monson, MA
Irv Kalb: Mountain View, CA
Phil Kennedy: Wethersfield, CT
Tom Kennedy: Santa Barbara, CA
John Kirkland: San Luis Obispo, CA
Diane Kurtz: Bridgeport Public Library, Bridgeport, CT
Robert J. Malafronte: Chicago, IL
Mary McMullin: New Haven, CT
David Oberlander: Richardson, TX
Patent Clearinghouse Staff: Sunnyvale, CA
Tex Robertson: Camp Longhorn, Inks Lake, Burnet, TX
Dan "Stork" Roddick: Pasadena, CA
Tom Schot: Capitola, CA
Tim Selinske: Covina, CA
Lowell Shields: Mount Lake Terrace, WA
Kevin Sparkman: Toronto, Canada
Walter H. White: Moscow, Russia
Tom Whiffen: Franklin, MA
Ralph Williamson: Seattle, WA
Douglas C. Wilson: Amherst College Public Affairs Office
Nanci A. Young: Princeton University Archives

A very special thank you to the following frisbee collectors who helped establish the price guidelines for this book:

Donn Blake: Las Vegas, NV
Tiina Booth: Amherst, MA
Paul Brenner: Freeville, NY
Dave Griffin: Centreville, VA
Phil Heilman: Durham, NC
Tom Ingle: Kansas City, MO
Tom Monroe: Gainesville, FL
Rick Neil: Tulsa, OK

Jim Palmeri: Rochester, NY
Rich Rand: Chicago, IL
Lowell Shields: Mountlake Terrace, WA
Steve Trauger: Erlanger, KY
David Vescio: Jupiter, FL
Wil West: Anaheim, CA
Ralph Williamson: Seattle, WA
Bruce Willis: Huntsville, AL

A special thank you to the following people for their letters on the early days of frisbee playing and personal accounts of the games they played:

Harry T. Ambrose
Ellis B. Baker
Shirley E. Banta
Margaret Beathold
Bob Beckerer
Henry F. Bedford
Putnam W. Blodgett
Bert Bond
Kenneth R. Bondi
John Borkowski
Ezra Bowen
Charlie Broad
Wilbur W. Bullen Jr.
Thomas E. Byrne, III.
Louis Cherepy
Margaret Cole
Phil C. Cooke
R. Wilson Cozby Jr.
L. Wallace Dean III
Edouard L. Desrochers

William Dohrmann
Marie Dorok
Priscilla Douglas
Meta Dziedzic
Paul S. Eriksson
Richard Frisbee
Ronald F. Gibson
Peter H. Gott
Ace Hall
S. Hamill Horne
Richard A. Howe
James P. Hunsicker
Graham Hunter
Millie LaConte
Stephen A. Langford
William F. Loomis
Kenneth Lundstrom
Judge James F. McClure Jr.
Dr. Thomas H. Moore
Mayor Griff Morris

Richard Mount
David H. Oberlander
William J. O'Connell
Jean M. Peck
Sam Carr Polk
John Register
Chuck Reul
Paul Rippner
Rick Rotolo
Don Ryan
Mary Schow
Clark Sharick
George L. Snow
Judge Kevin Tierney
Ira Townsend
Al Veerhoff
Karl R. Wiegand Jr.
Webster Wilde Jr.
Barbara Wilt
Richard R. Wood Jr.

This book is for all who have dared launch their dreams like frisbees and follow them where they may...

INTRODUCTION

Think for a moment of plastic. No, not of the covering on your great aunt's sofa. Nor, for that matter of its frequent association with everything fake, passing and disposable in our culture. Not of plastic as Dustin Hoffmann thought of it in *The Graduate*, as the ultimate symbol of stifling conformity.

Think rather of plastic as a liberating force of flightful joy for millions! Think of it as an expression of man's eternal urge to soar with the birds— to defy gravity and see the world as it's never been seen before. Think of it as the means by which baby boomers and countless others have acted out mankind's greatest dream— to fly. Think of plastic in these ways, and you'll be thinking of the frisbee, and its many spin-off brothers and sisters!

Now, come back to earth for a moment to musty cellars, gritty flea markets, and attic nooks. In any one of these "hangers" may be a grounded memory, a swirl of plastic that once in the near or distant past soared in profile to sunsets, rose on beach breezes, or was wobbled to and fro in the first awkward flirtations of a boy and a girl. Of such are memories made. Embedded in the spheroid form of the flying disc are countless individual memories as well as the collective dreams of a generation that's reached the moon and beyond. "Pluto Platter;" "Sailing Satellite;" "Mars Platter;" "Magic Saucer;" these are all names of flying discs, names that reflect our longing to power beyond this world at warp drive, off into the great adventure.

This book is all about the adventure that awaits anyone willing to take the trip, right here on terra firma, to locate and liberate 100 years worth of a vast and varied assortment of flying discs from their musty, often forgotten "hangers." The rewards are obvious. Collecting is all about nostalgia, the aura of happy association. Few objects have more joy attached to them than the flying disc. It is truly plastic in its finest form. For the collector who seeks, the rewards are obvious— not least in the considerable monetary value many old discs have accrued, as shall be detailed in this book.

They've been taken to outer space, tossed off the Great Wall of China, been "sacrificed" off of Himalayan peaks, and taken flight at just about every park and beach in the world. Flying discs have been thrown over 600 feet, as well as been tossed aloft and hovered for better than sixteen seconds before settling back into the hand of the thrower. Frisbee play has become a healthy way of life for people of all nationalities. Many players identify themselves as part of the "Frisbee Family" who find in their shared enthusiasm for frisbee sports, sympatico souls wherever they go.

Once thought of as a fad as passing as the eating goldfish/stuffing Volkswagens fancies, frisbees are now said to annually outsell baseballs, basketballs and footballs combined! In fact you'll hear from disc aficionados that "when a ball dreams, it dreams it is a frisbee!" This inexpensive and simple "genius of a toy" has become as All-American as baseball and hotdogs, and is aerodynamic to boot.

Disc play has also strongly impacted many other cultures. Worldwide on every beach and park in season there are legions of casual participants doing just what the famous slogan on the underside of frisbee has ever exhorted them to do; "Play Catch—Invent Games!" In addition, several hundred flying disc tournaments are held throughout the world annually, attracting thousands of participants and spectators of all ages. There are more than 700 disc golf courses located in 13 countries. In 1995, more than 17,000 people took part in "The World's Biggest Golf Weekend" held to introduce new players to the sport. In this country, three national disc golf publications are published catering to the interests of disc golfers, and there are many other publications nationwide which serve local/regional players.

Disc golf's growing ascendance reflects a general trend of frisbee sports gaining in grassroots appeal with every passing year. The running/passing disc game known as "Ultimate Frisbee" is also increasingly popular— nearly 600 colleges and universities participate nationally in competitive leagues.

Organizers, promoters and manufacturers have been lobbying to have these "new age games" of disc golf and Ultimate accepted as an Olympic demonstration sport as Ultimate was for the 1982 Goodwill games. It is only a matter of time before the Olympic committee will realize that these athletic, non-contact and user friendly games should be considered as prime representatives of an ethos of recreation that shall dominate the twenty first century. Also, look for frisbee to become a full medal sport at the 2001 International World Games in Akita, Japan.

The many diverse games/pastimes that have grown up over the 100 years that frisbees have been around, have spawned a tremendous variety of disc types for the collector to track down. For each of these sports/games, frisbees have been invented that cater to its needs—discs of various weights, shapes, colors, aerodynamics, hot stamps, etc. The result: for the collector, there is endless happy hunting to be had! One of the objectives of this book is to communicate to collectors and would

1974 and 1975 Women's World Frisbee Champion, Jo Cahow, showing off her winning form at the 1975 World Championships. Credit: Wham-O Inc.

be collectors that there are valuable treasures out there to be found. All you need to know is what to look for and where. This book will provide you with more than enough information to get you started and flyin'!

For the past 30 years one of the best kept secrets in America has been value and collectibility of the flying disc! One of my prime motivations in

Victor A. Malafronte, the Original World Frisbee Champion and charter member of the Frisbee Hall of Fame. Photo by: Anne Hodgkinson

writing this book is to enlighten the public about the world of collectible frisbees. Since 1968, most collectors have lain atop their growing piles of valuable plastic like dragons on their hordes, reluctant to let the word spread far of the lucrativeness of their newfangled "treasures Americanus." Many a collector seeing an old gem tossed about a park or beach has found it impossible to resist dangling a new, shiny disc in trade rather than educating people about the value of what they casually fling back and forth.

Similar to most others outside disc playing circles, toy dealers, show dealers and the like have generally been unaware of the market value of these antique discs, often parting with treasures such as a Space Saucer or Wham-O Pluto Platter for $20.00 or less. In turn, the flying disc dealer can sell such antique frisbees for up to 20 times what he/she paid for it! As for any collectible market, it's always helpful to have inside knowledge.

Historically, disc collectors have been privy to a whole underground culture that over the years has actively flourished around disc play. Casual tossers, and the rest of the general public have for the most part been unaware of just how large and encompassing disc culture has become. The result is that many a disc "prize" has been casually given up by its unknowing owner. Reading this book, you shall no longer remain in the dark.

Yes, at last, frisbee collecting is no longer a secret endeavor enjoyed by a few hundred people in the know. Come join us and share with us the excitement of tracking down these collectible toys! The time is right for you to go check the basement, garage, attic, and all your closets. Don't be shy about contacting your relatives either. Then ask all your friends to check for musty plastic treasures—even make the effort to turn a conversation with a casual acquaintance into a subtle request that he or she do a little purposeful spring cleaning!

A lot of what's here has been culled from the vast knowledge of disc collectors. Piecing together their knowledge and recollections, we've been able to determine pretty closely production years for antique discs. Also, by delving through the inventory of many collectors, we can ascertain if a certain disc is rare, due perhaps to color or some other odd variation that gives it uniqueness.

For you the reader, this book is the culmination of 30 years of frisbee collecting experience and expertise—contained herein is the most comprehensive, detailed and historically correct chronology of the flying disc from its origins right up to the present day. In fact, 1998 marks the 50th anniversary of the creation of the first plastic frisbee. It's also the 40th anniversary of the closing of the Frisbie Pie Company of Bridgeport, Connecticut whose tossed pie pans inspired both a pastime and the frisbee name by which it is universally recognized. If that's not enough, 1998 is also the 30th anniversary of the invention of the popular frisbee team game known as Ultimate. In celebration/homage of all this, nearly 300 people from all flight ways of discdom have contributed to this account, the first of its kind. Without their indispensable assistance and support this would have wobbled off the press heavy winged at best, grounded at worst! Turn the page— have we a tale to spin!

"A Hound of Frisbee" Frisbee dogs on campus! 1960. Credit: Seeley G. Mudd Manuscript Library. Department of Rare Books and Special Collections. Princeton University Libraries.

Chapter I

THE HISTORY OF FRISBEE PLAYING:
The First Definitive Study Conducted on the Origin of Frisbee Playing

Introduction

Can anyone determine who was the first person to throw a disc shaped object through the air? Of course not. It's pretty obvious that anything that's relatively flat, throwable and disc-like has more than likely been thrown by someone who likes to throw. Think back to your childhood especially if you have a history of liking to throw things, and think how unselfconsciously you first picked up that flat skipping stone, gave it a flip, and delighted in it skimming across the water. Throwing is a natural and spontaneous joy, and for some it never ends.

The editor of this book, my friend Dave Johnson, who went on to become the World Distance Champion, is told that at a very young age he was flipping the lids of Gerber baby food jars about. One of his earliest memories after the passage of Hurricane Carol in 1954, is flipping torn off shingles from his house off into the bushes till his parents advised him in no uncertain term to stop throwing away the mortgage. No doubt such temptations to toss anything even remotely deemed tossable have been consistent hallmarks (or at least sidebars!) of human evolution.

With this in mind, we will not try in this account to determine the impossible as to who first flipped what when. We will, however, try to separate fact from fiction and rumor from truth for the chronology that really counts— the evolution of modern disc play!

Becoming aware of our "roots" is an important goal for most of us. No less so for the sports that help define our lives. As a nation, we know the origins of baseball, basketball and volleyball. We believe that frisbee playing is no different than these other established sports that originated in America. It is part of Americana, part of our ever evolving culture, a sport that took off with the "Baby Boom" generation. Now, as a household name easily recognized by people around the world, it's time to set the record straight as to how frisbee play has come to be so much a part of us.

Over the years whenever I have read articles about the early history of frisbee playing, they have usually consisted of only one or two paragraphs of basically the same story with fanciful variations. So casual have these accounts been, that incorrect statements and misleading claims have been repeated over and over again with minor variations. Such chroniclers have traditionally regarded frisbee as something of a lark on the level of goldfish swallowing, something to be treated with but the lightest of passing fancy. It's no wonder, therefore, that the real history of the sport has been so misrepresented.

Be assured, our exhaustive research to set the record straight in this account is not an attempt solemnize a pastime that has been such a source of pure joy to millions. To the contrary, the joyful, irreverent, whimsical nature of frisbee play is precisely what makes this pastime so irresistible to millions world wide. Many a frustrated athlete who has felt alienated, out of his or her element in traditional sports, has found a home in disc play. Today with the increasing development of disc games, tournaments, and the specialized discs as well as organizational structures that have arisen to support these, there are to be found in frisbee sports as talented athletes as one will find in any competitive arena.

A good example of this is the Ultimate frisbee program at Amherst High School in Western Massachusetts. Coach, Tiina Booth, a premier disc player herself, has done such a good job of development that star players from "established" sports such as soccer are opting instead to play Ultimate, which needless to say has raised the ire of her fellow coaches!

But the Amherst athletic department is coming around. Tiina's Ultimate team has now been given varsity status, perhaps the first such program in the country to achieve such distinction. Tiina's coaching accomplishments have also attracted wider attention—she was featured in the August 18, 1997 *Sports Illustrated* feature "Faces in the Crowd." This ability to attract elite athletes is a tribute both to this coach, and to the challenging and fun nature of the flying disc game of Ultimate itself.

But, despite much evidence like this to the contrary, chroniclers of the frisbee phenomenon have for too long, inaccurately and unfairly made a mockery of the history of disc play. With frisbees and flying saucers of the extra terrestrial kind so closely linked in the popular mind, it's as if the flying disc mysteriously materialized one day from space with instructions to "throw me to your leader!" Until now, no serious attempt has been made to bring to light additional information that could document and enhance the true and full nature of this pastime.

There are quite a number of individuals and institutions that have made spirited and often worthy claims both to the invention of the flying disc and related games, as shall be shown. But first, let's spike the pretentious hearts of a few of the more persistent myths and distortions regarding the origins of disc play:

One is that frisbee tossing began at Yale University in New Haven as secular unrest against compulsory chapel. The story goes that in 1827, a certain early campus rebel by the name of Elihu Frisbee vigorously tossed a collection plate 200 feet across the Yale campus, thereby sparking a begging plate scaling fad that supposedly lasted until the "Great Collection Plate Shortage" of 1873. Of course, there is no record of an Elihu Frisbee ever attending Yale.

From whence does this legend arise? From the fertile mind of a Yale student as published in a letter forum in the *New York Times* on August 25, 1957. Enough said, one would think, but so casual to date has been investigation of frisbee's origins that this sophomoric explanation has taken on semi-gospel authenticity!

So too has the story that our sport was started by a celebrating student slipping on a bar tray in such a way that it was sent flying through the air sparking the fad. Add to this file of flippancy the story of students who in 1939, while fixing a flat tire, discovered a Frisbie pie pan in a corn field in Nebraska. Then there's the tale of two fur trappers (Chris and Fris) who fought off Indians with viciously spinning buffalo chips.

As we've noted, the flinging of anything flat and roundish that can be sent spinning should be considered as an early form of frisbee play, even though probably very few have deliberately played catch with a discus, or phonograph record for that matter. But somewhere, and farther back in time than most would imagine, two or more people probably got together and played their version of "keep away," or a variation of what's now known as frisbee golf using a cookie can cover, pie tin, or whatever. It is known, for instance, that college students played a prototype of what later evolved into frisbee football, using a serving tray.

In the spirit of improvisation, one game almost inevitably will lead to another. For instance, young people having first tossed potato chip can covers back and forth, then likely casually challenged each other to prove who could throw these the farthest. Such activities are all part of the origin and development of flying disc play and are more than likely to have occurred spontaneously at various times in many places worldwide.

But the most persistent and well documented story of the origin of frisbee throwing begins with the Frisbie Pie Company of Bridgeport, Connecticut in the early 1900's. There, workers on break made pie tin tossing a regular pastime. Conveniently located close to Yale University, the company's pie delivery routes nicely intersected other New England campuses as well. The Frisbie workers got the college students going. Then, because fads by nature travel with almost telepathic ease, Frisbie pie pan tossing spread to campuses throughout New England, especially the Ivy League ones. In any event, well prior to the mid 1950's, the word "frisbee" in various spellings had clearly become a familiar term among New England area college students, referring to the throwing of flying discs of various forms, as well as to related games. (See Chapters VI and VII for a full account of the Frisbie Pie Company, and of how the frisbee name evolved from regional to national recognition.)

There are, to be sure, a number of competing theories of frisbee origins. For instance, there's the cookie can cover school, and one must also acknowledge the potato chip, pretzel, cracker can cover, woven basket, even ice cream container cover, source claims. Each of these makeshift flying discs has in one account or another been claimed as the mother ship that spawned frisbee. There is even the west coast theory that workers in the motion picture industry tossing bottoms or tops of film canisters around Hollywood movie lots, spawned the frisbee epoch. No doubt they did toss canisters in such a manner. Who wouldn't in a idle moment? In fact, if one so wishes, flying disc origin stories can be traced all the way back to ancient Greece. In Myron's immortal statue, Discobolus is frozen in the middle of a fling!

Again, the objective of this historical account is not to find out who first threw the very first disc shaped whatever, but rather is a quest for a clear chronology of organized flying disc play, and how the term "frisbee" eventually came to be the universally accepted name for flying discs. Much of what you will read here of these origins has never been revealed before for a number of reasons which will be speculated on. My goal has been to pinpoint when and where flying disc play was first organized so it could be offered to other people! I've searched for believable, and documented foundation stories of our sport's origins, and have found several credible tales which will be shared here. This has been my main focus during these five years of research. I have also tried to determine what manner of flying disc was first utilized in these earliest of frisbee games. Let's begin on a cold trail that as we follow it becomes increasingly warm.

Early History of Flying Disc Objects and Games

Flying discs and disc like objects have been innovated and thrown by many cultures over the centuries for a variety of reasons including for sport, and use as weaponry. What follows are brief descriptions of various historical flying discs, their use(s), and descriptions of the gradual evolution over time of flying disc technology and innovation that has culminated in the frisbee.

Discus Throwing

Thousands of years prior to being liberated to soar in plastic form, flying discs likely made their ponderous debut in the form of the discus. Discus throwing was first chronicled in the verse of the great Greek poet, Homer around 700 B.C. The blind bard's account is likely the first of any disc shaped object being thrown by hand.

During the first Olympic Games in 776 B.C., discus throwing was one of the competitions of the pentathlon event, which also included the long jump, spear throwing, a sprint race, and wrestling. The early discus was made of unwrought bronze and iron, manufactured by pouring molten metal into the sand to produce the original raw pancake shape. The cooled ingot then had its surface area and edges smoothed out as it was made ready for competition. These discus ingots were highly revered by the Grecians of that era who felt they possessed godlike powers. The winner of the discus event received the actual discus as his prize.

Archeologists have uncovered discuses ranging from three to twelve pounds with weight averaging 5 lbs. 11 oz. However, a standardized discus was selected for major competitions, with all competitors required to throw the same weight. A lighter 3 pound discus was probably used by boys. The heaviest ones were specifically used for training purposes, much as the medicine ball is used for conditioning today. The standard size and shape of the early discus was very similar to that used by today's Olympians, which weighs in at 4 lbs. 6.5 oz.

The early Greek athletes through trial and error, discovered the proper "angle of flight" or "attack" for achieving long distance throws with these discs. However, the technique used to toss a discus at these early Greek Olympic games was not the whirling, "overhand wrist flip" used by today's athlete; it was instead thrown underhanded! The longest toss on record at the time was 105 feet, by the strong armed Phayllos. But the ancient applications of aerodynamics are nonetheless the same as those used by today's champion Olympic discus throwers. Even the far lighter discs utilized by frisbee competitors are thrown using similar principles pioneered by the Greeks.

The Chacarani /Chakram

Much as did James Bond's disc throwing adversary, Oddjob, 15th century soldiers from northern Delhi, India used a lethal throwing weapon called a Chacarani. The Chacarani was a flat steel ring with a sharpened edge. Although made in different sizes, most were approximately 9 inches in diameter and 1 inch in width. Soldiers could carry seven or eight of these nasty projectiles. They would hurl the Chacarani at the enemy by spinning them on their fingers, building momentum to fling them through the air. These were also thrown discus style.

A version of this weapon favored by Sikhs who had a well deserved reputation as fierce warriors, was known as the Chakram. Some Sikhs wore a turban that was tall and tented, allowing them to carry several of these Chakrams stacked on top of their heads.

Quoits

Quoits is the oldest known ring game in which the ring or disc is thrown, the object to land it on a peg, whereby the scorer gains a point. The word "quoit" can be traced to the French verb, "quoiter," meaning to stir-up. It was first played as a game in Scotland and England during the fourteenth century.

The game of quoits was easy to set up and could be played almost anywhere, even indoors (Parlor Quoits). Requiring very little equipment and a small court size, it quickly became popular with the laboring class of that time. In America, the game of quoits was most popular during the mid-nineteenth century. The first official U. S. rules were written in 1869. The game, though now almost forgotten, was played with some regularity at least into the early 1900's. In fact a 21 year old future president of the United

Fifteenth century chakram warrior.

States, Franklin Delano Roosevelt, enjoyed games of quoits as one of many shipboard diversions as he steamed to England aboard the Celtic in 1903.

The standard quoit court was 80 feet long by 25 feet wide, the pitching area between each stake or scoring area set at 54 feet. Each target area was 3 feet wide and filled with clay so that a thrown quoit could not eas-

Championship quoit game – 1800's

ily be dislodged by the next toss. Although there were many variations of the game, the main objective was to ring the thrown quoit onto or near a peg imbedded in the ground.

In quoit tournament play, 61 points won the game which often took up to 4 hours to play. At major competitions, most quoit game discs weighed three pounds or more. No doubt, as a result, players came to feel increasingly heavy handed as a long competition wore on. Tossing a three

Nineteenth century flying ring game.

pound iron disc over 50 feet for 3-4 hours in competition would tire out even today's professional athletes. This more or less eliminated women from play which was probably by design. Instead, wives, children and elders were expected to fulfill roles as appreciative spectators when Dad and Uncle Albert went off to play their game. Mom and Aunt Gloria became known as "quoit widows." No doubt some were as glad to be rid of their men for a time as are the golf widows of today! Family members left out of quoits competition eventually came up with a real ringer of a game to occupy their time. Now quoits has all but been forgotten, but the substitute game they invented, horseshoes, has gone on to become one of the most popular in America!

The patent history of the game of quoits documents technological improvements in the aerodynamics of the disc-rings, as well as the utilization of ever lighter materials in the manufacturing process. Over time, quoits of all sizes, weights, and designs became less ringlike, and ever more to resemble a flying disc. Increasingly, these game discs were optimally designed to be skillfully thrown or tossed through the air to the target with but a narrow hole in the center to allow them to settle around the peg. It's easy to perceive the game of quoits as a distant forbear of modern day frisbee sports, struggling to get off the ground.

Throwing Rings

Another design of the quoit was shaped like a ring. Some were forged from metal, some were molded of rubber, some were simply made by shellacking a twisted circular length of rope into a ring. Their weights ranged from a few ounces to three pounds. In the early 1900s, throwing rings became lighter, evolving into hollow tubes made of rubber, fabric, or leather. These rings were filled with materials which gave them varying weights. The throwing ring is a link in the frisbee ancestral line as having been used in an early nonspheroid "throw and catch" game.

Disc and Cross

The game of disc and cross, almost as venerable as quoits, originated in France during the early part of the 14th century. It was most popular during the reign of Louis-Philippe of Orleans (1830-1848). Disc and cross was played on a cross-shaped court marked out on a grassy surface. The target or "center of the square area" was marked by four painted posts. Two teams consisting of two players each would stand on the opposite ends of each cross section. The discs were brightly painted and constructed of wood measuring 12 inches in diameter and 5/8 of an inch in thickness. One team would start play by trying to "roll" its playing disc through the center of the square.

Meanwhile, the opposing team would try to disrupt the first team's attempt by rolling its disc to strike the other's just as it passed through the center

The popular nineteenth century disk and cross game.

of the square. Points were scored for each successful "hit" or "run." The scoring team would then go on offense. Before play began, both teams would agree on a point total to determine the winner of each match. This game was introduced to North America by early colonists and became very popular with Native Americans who created a ring target game.

Japanese rabbit hunter, fifteenth century.

Japanese Bird Disc

Sometime during the 15th century, Japanese rabbit hunters devised a flying disc designed to make a flapping sound. This flying disc, manufactured of straw, could imitate the sound made by the wings of a bird of prey. As the disc approached, the rabbit would automatically freeze in its tracks. The skillful hunter would close in on his prey by continuing to throw additional discs in the rabbit's direction. Eventually, the hunter would be able walk up and pick up the nearly paralyzed rabbit by its ears. This is an early example of the arresting powers of flying discs which have since mesmerized millions!

Hoop and Spear

One of the most popular games played by the Pomo Indians of California was Hoop and Spear. In most villages, a natural game field was created when the inhabitants laid out their wigwams and lodges. From all this activity would result a hard beaten plot of ground located at the center or near the edge of the village. On this plot, men and boys of the tribe would construct a set of "barriers" at fifteen feet apart. These barriers were made by stacking four or five logs or tree saplings on top of each other with stakes used to hold them in place.

Hoop and spear ring game, 1800's.

Two players, each with one hoop and spear, would stand inside their barriers. (Hoops were made of strips of wood with a bead attached. The wood strips were bent about and fastened into a circle 15 inches in diameter.)

One of the players would roll his wooden hoop along the ground. The other player's challenge was to run behind the hoop and attempt the throw his spear through the hoop before it reached the barrier wall. The player whose spear was closest to the colored bead was the winner of that game.

Kinxe

Another Native American version of Hoop and Spear was the Kinxe game from British Columbia. Two teams of equal numbers would stand opposite each other, 15 feet apart. Each player had a small hoop (3-5 inches in diameter) and a spear. The object of the game was for one team to throw or roll its hoops at the opposing team. The hoops could be thrown all at once or randomly. The opposing team would try to spear as many hoops as possible. This game was devised to mimic the hunting of birds from a blind.

In the kinxe game, rings were thrown into the air. 1800's.

Trapshooting

The sport of trapshooting was invented by the British in the late 17th century. The earliest account of trapshooting appeared in a 1773 British publication called *Sporting Magazine*. For early such competitions the targets were live pigeons, utilized both in competition and practice. These unfortunate birds were placed in holes dug into the earth. A box, the "trap," attached to a long string or cord, was placed over the hole to prevent the bird from escaping. When a marksman called, "pull," that was the signal for an attendant to literally pull on the string letting the pigeon go— most likely to kingdom-come as the "trap shooters" fired at will! Trapshooting became one of Britain's most popular sports. Many annual competitions were held and shooting clubs became common.

Trapshooting also caught on in the colonies early in the nineteenth century. In America, live targets were also used. These included sparrows, and most notably the passenger pigeon which at the time flew in flocks so vast that there are reports of their having darkened the sky. The first recorded formal trapshoot was held in Cincinnati, Ohio in 1831. But reacting to 10 years of live bird slaughter, early animal rights activists introduced state legislation against this sport.

In addition to this increasing opposition, there was the practical problem of pigeons and sparrows being difficult to capture. Compounding these drawbacks, live birds didn't always offer a consistently easy target. As it became obvious that winning serious prize money competitions was more a matter of luck than pure skill, standardization followed with the introduction of inanimate targets for all competitions. This is where the flying disc as "clay pigeon" entered the picture, and the flesh and blood version was left to less riskier pursuits such as delivering messages and pasting statues!

Whether by coincidence or not, in 1880, when the passenger pigeon was becoming extinct, George Ligowsky of Cincinnati introduced the first flat, disk shaped clay target. He also invented the first consistent method of manually throwing a "clay pigeon." The earliest examples of these "discs" were made of clay mixed with water and then baked. However, these were very hard and consequently didn't always break when hit. Consequently, clay pigeons made of river silt mixed with pitch were developed. A later innovation was limestone mixed with petroleum as a binder, the same form of pigeon used to this day. Now, clay pigeons are catapulted out of a mechanical launcher, but early models were designed to be thrown into the air with a hand held launcher. The thrower had to be skilled enough to make the clay disc travel in certain trajectories. To mimic the artful escape tactics of game birds, clay pigeons were designed to perform a variety of flight patterns. Continued experimentation refined aerodynamics. That and the introduction of lighter weight materials established the clay pigeon as a worthy predecessor of today's plastic flying discs. Take a close look at a clay pigeon and note many similar features to the frisbee, such as ridges and curved edges.

In the 1800's, frisbee shaped clay pigeons were skillfully thrown into the air with a hand held launcher.

Skittles

Skittles was an early nineteenth century British version of bowling, with players attempting to knock over nine pins by throwing or sliding a disk down an alley or across the living room floor. The skittle disk was a simple round piece of wood, flat on both sides. The wooden pins were set up as in a regulation bowling game, and usually measured 4 inches in diameter. Most players used the underhand method to throw the disk. A more challenging skittles game was played outdoors on grass where a player used a disk eight inches in diameter and one inch thick. The pins were set seventy five feet from the thrower. A player would usually use the discus throwing motion (or the overhand wrist flip) to knock over as many pins as possible. This grass version of the game was much more difficult to master. It was also played on ice during the winter months.

Skittles flying disc game was more challenging when played outdoors. 1900's.

Chapter II

MODERN DAY FRISBEE GAMES

Unfettered Metal: Cookie Lids and Pie Tins Vie for Air Supremacy

In the course of researching the history of disc throwing, I received many replies from those who remembered early flings with metallic discs. Interestingly, most of the people who responded described throwing games that utilized cookie tin covers as opposed to pie pans. There are a couple of good reasons that likely explain why the cookie cover beat the pie pan as disc of choice in that now unimaginable world without the plastic frisbee. First, cookie tin covers with their flat tops and deeper perpendicular edged rims were much more air worthy— players could perform a variety of throws with more control than with a pie pan.

Second, may have been the domestic factor. Hard bitten collectors of Frisbie pie pans can attest to the formidable challenge of smuggling a pie

The first frisbees. Pie pans, cookie can covers, woven baskets and ice cream lids. From these humble beginnings, a recreational pastime grew into an international sport!

pan out of a kitchen where it is often highly prized. For several good reasons, one should never cross a cook! Cookie tin covers on the other hand, lacking the utility of pie tins, were likely more expendable for trivial pursuits such as tossing.

But despite these factors, my research has shown that in most places Frisbie pie pan throw and catch games occurred simultaneously along with similar cookie cover diversions. In some areas where the cookie can cover game was popular, there was very little pie pan tossing activity, and vice versa. Assuring the pie pan remained prominent in such activities was its ready availability– a fresh pie could be purchased for only 50 cents whereas a large tin of cookies or potato chips was a much more expensive proposition for students.

Pre-plastic era. Two men tossing two pie tins on a southern California beach. 1940. Photo by: Wayne Miller. Courtesy of Wham-O Inc.

Cookie Can Cover Flight Characteristics

Easier and more comfortable to grip than a pie tin, cookie covers featured turned-down, straight edge rims which measured from 1/4 to one inch in depth. Their diameters varied from three to twelve inches, which allowed a greater choice of size than more standardized pie tins which average 9 and 5/8 inches in diameter. The overall shape and weight of the cookie can cover resulted in better drag which created more lift and better stability during flight than any pie pan could produce. In other words, the can cover could "catch more air," allowing a player to toss one with greater accuracy and distance than a pie pan.

But all these advantages aside, it is the cookie tin covers that have ended up with the more obscure billing in the history of disc throwing, not unlike how Beta-Max technology, though superior, lost out to the VCR. Research does indicate that Frisbie pie pan throwing as a fad preceded widespread cookie cover tossing. But as it always does, History decided in its inscrutable way, and the result? It is the Frisbie that has been forever immortalized as the pie pan that lent its name to a universally recognized pastime!

The early metal flingers like most pioneers, had to be hardy. Both pie tins and can covers were easily damaged when used on concrete, or on a parking lot surface. In particular the extending leading edge of pie pans could develop broken sharp edges that the catcher needed to be wary of. To avoid nasty nicks, players took to wearing gloves, or even taped the edge circumference of the pie pan/cookie cover for protection. (Some players got smart and stuck to grass for throwing surfaces.)

My research reveals that can cover and pie pan tossing, though quite widespread, occurred in different environments. Evidently, can cover activity was most prevalent and probably originated at summer camps and prep schools, with pie tin tossing more common on college campuses. When mom sent a tin of cookies in a care package to son or daughter, the cover might later be spied in flight across tree lined quadrangles and lawns. It seems some students at an age of peak sugar craving, valued cookie can covers over the contents!

Any mention of early cookie can cover activity must take into account all the other metal can covers that were available to be utilized as tin spin machines, including potato chip, fruit cake, dates, pretzel, and film can covers. These came in many sizes and varieties, and as shall be seen, were along with the pie tin, utilized in a number of different games. The most common activity enjoyed by the vast majority of metal can cover/pie tin enthusiasts, was the simple throw and catch game— just tossing for the heck of it, as do the vast majority of today's frisbee throwers. No rules, no scoring—just casual, fun diversion. The joy of tossing a flying object through the air and catching it was its own reward. But of course as in any casual activity, there are always those who progress on to more structured games.

Early Frisbee Games and Their Development into Modern Pastimes

Find yourself playing catch with some form of flying disc on a tree lined quadrangle, a statue here, a bench over there, a fire hydrant over by the access road, and several discreet trash cans scattered about. You may find that your mind, if fertile and not overly concerned with scholastics and other distractions, eventually comes up with the idea of frisbee golf, and you'll start formulating how many strokes would constitute par to hit, say, that statue or one of those trash cans. From early on, such musings spawned many informal types of frisbee golf activity played throughout the USA, mostly by college students who would get together on occasion to play their own patented versions of the game on campus. Because the metal tin covers and pie pans used during this early period were easily dented, players would waft gentle "putts" against the targets, the hitting of which were the objective of the game.

Usually, each "tee" and "hole" target was selected by each player in turn. The object of the game was to "hole out," meaning to strike the designated target in the fewest throws possible. Pins or targets could be whatever the imagination of the designer of that particular hole could conjure from the surroundings. Commonly selected "holes" included patches of grass, manhole covers, bushes, water fountains, trash cans, statues, light poles, trees, fire hydrants, perhaps even the dean of students out for a stroll! This activity also took place in parks and at playgrounds. Neighborhood children were known to use Hula Hoops on the ground as targets or pins. The average distance to these "holes" was around 100 feet which, with the less than dependable discs of the day, allowed for challenging pars. Here are some accounts I have gathered of early forms of frisbee golf, frisbee football, cover can tennis and guts frisbee. Also introduced are some of the major pioneers of frisbee sports and games.

Tex Robertson and the Sa-Lo Frizbee Game

In 1922, an eleven year old Tex Robertson always looked forward to playing the game of throw and catch. But not with a baseball or football! He and his buddies preferred to sail a metal cover from a one gallon container of Jewel Shortening. From his home town of Sweetwater, Texas, Tex traveled to Los Angeles in 1931, and introduced the "flying cover game" to the Los Angeles Junior College Physical Education Department. Unfortunately, all three metal can covers he brought were destroyed within 30 minutes, from striking the ground too many times.

Two years later, in 1933, Tex Robertson established the first organized "flying disc games" at the Wolverine Day Camp, then located in the vicinity of Ann Arbor, Michigan. Tex Robertson added some new twists to the camp activity menu: the flying disc games of Pitch-n-Catch, Hit The Runner and Keep Away. Discs consisted of paper covers from ice cream containers, attractive no doubt by sweet association in youngsters' minds. Coaching his charges in disc throwing techniques, Tex would repeatedly urge them to "sail it low and level," good advice for any beginning disc thrower. This saying, distilled down to Sa-Lo, became the name both for Tex's flying disc, and the games he invented utilizing it. Therefore, Camp Wolverine truly has claimed the right to be called the birthplace of organized frisbee playing.

By 1935, Tex had moved from Michigan to Austin, Texas, where he became swimming coach for the University of Texas, a po-

Nine year old Alfred L. (Skippy) Shepperd is showing off his advanced Sa-Lo sidearm technique with a metal can cover. 1948. Credit: Camp Longhorn

sition he held until 1951. In 1937, he and student/friend Jack Nendell, performed the perhaps first ever large scale flying disc demonstration before a capacity crowd at a University of Texas basketball game. The crowd was introduced to a game of Sa-Lo utilizing a cardboard "disc" reinforced around the rim with tape. A round piece of felt was glued to the top of the disc to add extra weight and stability.

Tex was also the announcer for the very popular and consequently always crowded swimming meet known as the Texas Aquatic Carnival. In order to receive the results of each swimming match more quickly, (there was no room for a runner), the scores were written on a Sa-Lo disc; then head judge Bob Tarlton with a flick of his wrist would "air mail" the results to the stage!

In 1939, Tex and his wife Pat started Camp Longhorn at Inks Lake locat-

Tex Robertson, founder of Camp Longhorn. Tex is the "father of organized Sa-Lo frizbee playing." Credit: Camp Longhorn. 1997.

ed in Burnet, TX. Part of his plan to recruit new campers was to ask youngsters in the neighborhood to take the "Sa-Lo challenge." This was a test of skill in throwing a Sa-Lo through a 3 foot hoop that Tex would place in the prospect's front yard. His fascination with flying disc games resulted in Sa-Lo becoming an important part of Camp Longhorn's summer activities. Soon, Tex introduced the game of Sa-Lo golf by laying out 5 hoop holes around the camp grounds to which the children tossed metal and paper Sa-Los. In addition, campers could choose from a menu of Sa-Lo tennis, distance competitions, and the catch and throw skills event.

Camp Longhorn only slowly caught on in the beginning. Some children even had to be "borrowed" for photographs in the first camp brochure. Although most of the campers enjoyed the thrill of playing Sa-Lo, some of their parents thought the game to be a little out of the ordinary. However, Tex stayed the course, and thanks to this southern gentleman, Sa-Lo represents the oldest organized flying disc game as an institutionalized activity offered to other people. Tex's Sa-Lo games continue to be played at Camp Longhorn to this day. "Salo-Frizbee," as it's now called, has been enjoyed by thousands of young people including President Bush's grandchildren. At the same time, Camp Longhorn has thrived and become one of the premier summer camps in the United States. It now offers 31 different activities for 3,200 campers to enjoy. With its optimum location on the shores of Inks Lake, it's always smooth sailing at Camp Longhorn whether on the water or through the air!

Tin Lid Golf

It is obvious from the responses I have received that variations of the disc golf game sprung up independently in many different locales across North America, and no doubt elsewhere. One such spontaneous eruption took place on the vast prairie of Western Canada in 1926. That year, ten year old Ronald F. Gibson and his friends began playing a game they called "Tin Lid Golf." They hailed from a mere dimple of a town, Bladworth, Saskatchewan (population 115), and attended the Bladworth Elementary School. Ronald and his playmates, to pass away the long idle hours of summer vacation, set up a tin lid golf course on the school grounds. There was ample acreage there to lay out 8 holes or "bases" as they dubbed them, with 150 foot "fairways" in between. The bases (or pins) were 4-5 foot diameter circles that were drawn in the sandy soil. In order to "hole out," the tin lid they used for a disc had to come to rest within the circle. Trees had to be avoided because they would dent the valuable and hard to come by metal can covers. Players kept count of how many throws it took to complete each hole. This golf game was played in regular sequence as one would progress on a prescribed course.

The metal can covers were lifted from 10 pound containers of lard or grease, the kind of utilitarian container one would expect to find in the hard scrabble western plains (as opposed to those dainty cookie samplers!) They were approximately 9-11 inches in diameter with a 3/4 to one inch edge. During the Depression years, even such humble tins as these were not readily available; therefore Ronald and his playmates to prevent favorite lids being claimed by a rival, went so far as to punch small holes in them with a nail to form their names or initials.

Ronald, to improve throwability, would bring the metal lids to his father's blacksmith shop to modify them for better gripping. Using a vise, he would crimp a 1 inch portion of the edge of the rim flat up against the underside. This allowed a player to better grip the lid with the thumb on top and the index finger clutching the flattened portion of the rim. The primary purpose of this modification was to more easily throw the lids backhanded, the sharp edge flattened to avoid painful shredding of skin. This modification also enabled the players to throw farther and with more accuracy. Gibson's is the earliest account of someone taking an existing metal can cover and modifying it for the purposes of improving its playing capabilities. This is also the earliest account of an informal disc golf game that I have received, one that Gibson and friends continued to play until they graduated from high school.

Disk Scaling Game

As innovator of a disc form of "pitch and putt" golf, Mr. Walter A. Darby of Great Neck, New York was a true pioneer. In 1937 Mr. Darby applied for a U. S. Patent (2,126,245) for his Disk Scaling Game. His game was played with a 2 tier, concave shaped disk that was machine formed of light weight metal, fiber or rubber. It was hollow on the underside in much the same manner as today's modern disc. There were four small holes located near the center of the top dome. The combination of the four holes and the hollow underside made these early disks quite sensitive to air buoyancy and friction during flight. In its hollowed out form, the Darby disk could entrap more air, causing uneven pressure which made the disk glide and wobble in irregular trajectories. With this knuckle ball like unpredictability it was quite a challenge for a player to sail the disk into the Darby "disk catcher" which was the object of his game. The disk catcher was similar in design to an adjustable laundry basket that was suspended and held open by a wire frame. Putting, therefore, was very tricky and depended on an accurate approach to the front of the basket; a player whose approach landed backside or on a difficult angle was guaranteed trouble.

Walter Darby's disk scaling game. Frisbee golf in 1937!

Mr. Darby describes an activity with obvious similarities to today's widely popular frisbee golf game— a number of his targets would be "laid out on a course having equal or unequal distances between the baskets. In this way, a number of people could play at the same time progressively around the course in tournament fashion." Clearly, Mr. Darby and friends had pioneered a formal and organized game of disc golf!

The Harvard Frisbee Golf Version

Disc golf no doubt sprang up serendipitously on many colleges campuses at various times. An early Harvard version of the game began with a simple flick of the wrist. George L. Snow along with fellow students was enjoying semester break in December of 1939 in a cabin in New Hampshire's White Mountains. In an idle moment, George flipped a cover from a round tin of crackers across the table. So began a can cover flinging fad that easily spread back to the Harvard campus and became rather established both in Harvard Yard, and along the banks of the nearby Charles River. Among a number of informal disc scaling games Snow and his friends innovated, was a form of disc golf they first played in 1939. Players mutually agreed on a target; then each with his can cover tried to hit it in the least number of throws. Pins could be a tree, bush, trash can, even a prominent rock. The idea was to pick out holes with challenges that required a variety of throws for both long and short accuracy.

George L. Snow of New London, NH, proudly poses with the 1957 Frisbee Field dedication plaque. Credit: George L Snow. (See page 230.)

Like many students of that era, Snow had to interrupt his studies for

George "Bud" Snow and his brother-in-law playing catch with a metal cookie can cover in 1946. Credit: George L. Snow

the more important task of preserving civilization in the epic struggle of World War II, but upon his postwar return to Harvard he resumed can cover scaling. Concluding his account on a romantic note, Snow tells of having been presented by his wedding ushers in 1950, one of the original pan covers of the type they had played with at Harvard. It was painted with fluorescent paint so the newlyweds could throw it back and forth on the beach at night while on their honeymoon in Bermuda. Primed with a table lamp before being taken to the beach, it shown brightly enough to attract a lot of attention from people who had never seen such a thing before. This was probably the first ever glow in the dark flying disc!

Phrisbee Football and the Creation of Ultimate Frisbee

When people are playing a friendly game of throw and catch with a flying disc, the inevitable errant throw entices players to run after the disc in order to make the grab. There is always a sense of accomplishment and athletic prowess when a player completes a long run, sometimes dodging trees, people, benches, and grasps the flying disc in its final throes of flight. Or, there's the leaping satisfaction of intercepting a disc at its apex, plucking it from the air with one's fingertips before it sails on. Such sensations are comparable to being a receiver in football, going out for the long pass, and making a "Hail Mary" reception in the end zone to win the game.

A number of frisbee games mimic or have been inspired by ball games we have long been familiar with. Though noting the similarities, the participant will soon come to appreciate how the flying disc opens up a whole new menu of possibilities for athletic play. It adds a dimension or two to flight that balls only dream of! Less fettered by the chains of gravity, the flying disc doesn't travel in the same predictable, parabolic arc that a ball must follow. A disc can hover, fly straight and fast, turn right or left, or even skip off a hard surface. The flying disc effortlessly outmaneuvers the ball in attitude, grace, and serendipity. Every casual player has seen a disc, seemingly within grasp, be suddenly wafted up and away by a prankster like puff of wind. Or, there are those epic moments where the seemingly uncatchable disc somehow is— plucked out of an eddy where hovering in place, it has overstayed its shelf life.

Consequently, it's easy to understand why the disc versions of ball games such as football and golf have developed, and as in the case of disc golf and Ultimate, become widespread. A flying disc offers more variation, plus, disc games allow participation at various levels of skill, which is not the case with established ball sports where the more gifted athletes hold sway. Frisbee sports, unlike ball sports, also require little outlay of money for participa-

Columbia High School Varsity Frisbee Team. The original creators of the Ultimate frisbee game. 1968. Photo by: Mark Epstein

tion. All that is really required is one frisbee for 20 people to play an organized game of Ultimate, no pads, helmets, jocks, and other accessories.

The Seeds of Ultimate

Ultimate frisbee, an organized team game that combines aspects of football, soccer and even basketball, is by far the most popular and widespread of team disc games. It evolved from "frisbee football" and other early makeshift team games associated with flying disc play. Such a game was being played in 1942 at Kenyon College in Gambier, Ohio, a "two hand touch" early version of frisbee football. Played with a large size Oven-Ex cake pan, the game was dubbed "Ace Ball." In 1950, the game again became a fad at Kenyon and one of the contests was photographed by Elliot Elisofon of *Life Magazine*.

Similar games sprang up at other college campuses. As early as 1953, and probably before, students at Amherst College also played an offbeat game of football minus the pigskin! Instead, a plastic or metal serving tray was used for play action passes and long bombs down field. In a letter to the editor, published in the January, 1958, *Amherst Alumni News*, Peter Schrag '53 describes this game, stating, "Rules have sprung up and although they

Namer Younan goes up high for Team Sweden but the U.S. Team went on to win the 1997 WFDF Ultimate Championships held in Jonkoping, Sweden. Photo by: Patrick Lundmark

vary, the game as now played is something like touch-tackle, each team trying to score goals by passing the tray down field. There are interceptions and I believe passing is unlimited. Thus a man may throw the frisbee to a receiver who in turn passes it to still another man. The opponents try to take over either by blocking the tray or intercepting it."

Here, Mr. Schrag has nicely summarized how today's modern game called Ultimate is played, though he's anticipated by better than 15 years its official invention and codification of rules! Amherst College, therefore, can rightfully claim to be the birthplace of a frisbee game that developed on lines very close to today's Ultimate.

Ultimate, the widely popular flying disc game that sprang from frisbee football and like activities, began as follows: In 1967, Joel Silver, of Maplewood, New Jersey attended the Mount Herman summer camp in Northfield, Massachusetts. With his friend, Buzzy Hellring, they enjoyed afternoon team games of frisbee football. That fall, Joel entered Maplewood's Columbia High School and brought with him his new found knowledge of "flyin' football," and also his penchant for mischief.

One day, to liven up a routine student council meeting, Joel moved that the council investigate the possibilities of establishing a frisbee team at Maplewood High. This was meant to be just one of those frivolous suggestions that drive parliamentarians mad. But to his surprise, the council weighed the matter, and after considerable discussion, passed his motion! Responding to this mandate, Joel along with the President of the Council, Gordon Chang, and members of the school newspaper, *The Columbian*, began to organize frisbee football games during their lunch periods in the Spring of 1968.

These were hardly a bunch of grizzled grid warriors. Most felt far more comfortable wielding a pen than a ball, or anything else jock-like. As writers, they were used to putting their brains through fast drills, not their bodies; therefore they winded easily during their lunch time work-outs. Consequently, they created rules for their evolving game of frisbee football that attempted as much as possible to eliminate running. Lines of scrimmage and downs were too redolent of that macho sport of football, so these were replaced with rules that made their new game more flowing and spontaneous. Over time and through much trial and error, a set of rules for playing their evolving new pastime were agreed on by consensus. (But alas, they never were able to eliminate the running. As a matter of fact, today's Ultimate game is a real work out not recommended for the shallow lunged, or tobacco impaired!)

When Joel Silver left *The Columbian* staff for the Student Council, a mock rivalry developed between that body and the scribes. The only way to resolve this, obviously, was to stage a challenge match. In the spring of 1969, this first match, played between two large co-ed teams with the student body as spectators, was won by the Columbian staff by a score of 11-7. The Frisbee used in these early Ultimate games was Wham-O's Master model.

In the summer of 1969, the popularity of this new game was greatly assisted by the installation of a 24 hour a day "playing field," a lighted student parking lot located down the hill from the school. This led, in the summer of 1970, to Buzzy Hellring writing the first version of the rules for the game they had now dubbed "Ultimate Frisbee." These were refined by Joel Silver, Jon Hines and Mark Epstein, then published in the fall. The players also agreed on a team name, "The Columbia High School Varsity Frisbee Squad" (CHSVRS) as they somewhat tongue-in-cheek, named themselves. In fact, in a much reproduced photograph of this frisbee squad, first published in the school newspaper, the school custodian appears as "Head Coach" and the security director fills the role of "General Manager." Plus, the legendary but entirely fictitious director of the International Frisbee Association, Harvey J. Kukuk, was included on the player roster!

This frivolous attitude permeated Columbia High School Ultimate frisbee. In the spirit of the day, Ultimate was meant to be a sport not to be taken too seriously. Instead it provided a refreshing alternative to the muscle flexing, gridiron mentality that infests school spirit. From the start, the intent of Ultimate was to avoid the negative, aggressive elements of other established sports in America.

Reflecting this intent, the sport has from the beginning been played without referees. Self-officiating emphasizing ideal standards of the honor system has for 30 years now been the regulating mechanism of match play. In this gentleperson's game, it is the responsibility of all participants to fairly and equitably work out disputes with players calling their own fouls. Though an admirable system with a long tradition, it's becoming increasingly obvious that as Ultimate grows and expands, this system is no longer adequate to regulate play in this fiercely competitive sport. Too often in recent years, games have been marred by long, drawn out arguments—loss of civility rather than order has been the result. Consequently, increasing numbers of Ultimate players are coming to recognize the need for officiating, and to reluctantly embrace it. The realization is growing that to achieve the prominence it deserves, adding referees, though controversial,

Metal can covers were used to play frisbee tennis in New England. 1950.

will in the long run be looked upon as positive step in this fast paced sport's evolution.

The First Interscholastic Ultimate game was played on November 7, 1970, in which the CHSVFT defeated Millburn High School 43 to 10. The first Intercollegiate Ultimate match, Rutgers versus Princeton, took place on November 6, 1972 on the same field where these same two institutions had met for the first intercollegiate football game 103 years earlier! Rutgers narrowly prevailed, 29 to 27 in front of nearly 1000 spectators. The match was covered by both the *New York Times* and ABC's Wide World of Sports. Ultimate has grown to the point where there are now nearly 1500 teams in 35 countries. The Ultimate Players Association, the ruling body of the sport, now has nearly 10,000 members. (Contact the UPA for more information. See listing in Appendix III.)

Can Cover Tennis

In 1950, this game was played with at least two people on each side of the net on a standard tennis court. As in tennis, the server attempted to throw the disc over the net and into the regular service area. The receiver's job was to catch the disc before it touched the ground. If the disc landed or was dropped inside the lines, the thrower scored a point. The basic idea or "flow of the game" was to catch and throw the disc with the same motion.

Another version of this game was played with 4 people per team on tennis courts where the enclosing fence was constructed with rounded corners instead of square ones. The entire surface of the tennis court was in play, and the disc could be thrown against or along the canvas fence causing it to carry around the corner at the other end of the court. Bringing the rounded corners into play sharpened the thrower's accuracy and made the receiver's job catching the disc that much more difficult.

The International Frizby Championships
Dartmouth College, 1954

In the 1940's and 1950's Dartmouth College in Hanover, New Hampshire was a hot bed of cookie can cover/Frisbie pie pan gamesmanship. During the evening hours and especially on weekends, members of the Omicron Deuteron Charge of the Theta Delta Chi student fraternity would meet at the "open air Frizby pit" to play a game they had invented known as "Frizby." (No doubt the name was a derivative of "Frisbie" as in Frisbie's Pies!)

It should be noted that many of these pioneering Dartmouth Frizby players had attended Kimball Union Academy (KUA) located in nearby Meriden, VT, a boarding school that sent many of its students on to Dartmouth. Students at Kimball were playing their own version of the cookie

Mr. Frederic Hawkins was the "Chancellor of the Match" for the "International Frizby Championships." (To right) The Dartmouth Blossom Brothers get ready with a pre-game huddle. 1954. Photo by: David Oberlander

The Dartmouth Blossom Brothers ham it up for the camera before winning the International Frizby Championships. Nov. 7, 1954. Players from left: Harry Ambrose, John Demas, Colin Hunt, Ralph Destino. Standing left: E. Swift Lawrence and Gordon Nichols. Photo by : David Oberlander

can cover game. Bill Robes, the school's ski instructor, taking note of the tin tossing, was motivated to invent the Space Saucer in 1953, a plastic disc very close in form to the tin covers the students tossed. (See Chapter III)

It's not surprising that the evolution of "frisbee culture" spawned by can cover or pie tin play would at some point lead to an organized championship among college students. That is exactly what happened at Dartmouth College on November 7, 1954. This contest was played between the Dartmouth Blossom Brothers of the afore mentioned Theta Delta Chi fraternity, and a visiting All Star rugby team (from the Westmount Rugby Football Club of Montreal Canada), who were dubbed the "Montreal Tweedy Free Throwers."

Using a 5 inch metal cookie can cover called a "unit," the opposing teams of five members each stood 10 meters apart facing each other across the "Frizby Pit." Team members had to stand an arm's length from each other.

The player with the "unit" would then make a throw called a "thrust" to the opposing team. The thrust had to fly within grasping range of any member of the receiving team. The receiving player could only take one step in any direction in an attempt to catch or "grasp" the unit with one hand. No body traps were allowed. The player who made the catch was required to make the return thrust with a continuous motion. If the same player made two consecutive catches it was then his duty to hand the unit with a bow to a teammate. (Etiquette counted for a lot in this game. Coats and ties were a requirement!) A throw that scored a point was called a "capital thrust." Points were only scored when someone dropped a thrust, or when the thrust was uncatchable.

Dartmouth Frizby very much a "gentleman's game." All participants competed under a "code of conduct," with the spirit of the game held in constant high regard. If there was a disputed call, or a transgression, the player involved was expected to make the correct call. Though light hearted and to quite an extent tongue in cheek, the game was meant to be played with grace, vitality, etiquette, mixed liberally with athletic showmanship

The Montreal Tweedy Free-Throwers conduct a pre-game "Round of Snaps." Note: The third player from the left is holding the 5" metal cookie can cover (unit) that was used during the Frizby Championships. (Fourth from left is Bob Woodberry, Host Coach). 1954. Photo by: David Oberlander

and not a little beer.

Since the thin shell metal can cover "unit" was easily dented, it had to be handled with care during play. A player was not permitted to damage or dent the unit in any way. "Thrusting" players would try to make a variety of different throws, such as a right or left curve, hover throw, dip shot, or attempt to sail the unit a few inches off the ground. But the object of this game was not to throw as hard as possible, unlike today's guts frisbee. Again, style and comportment counted as much as scoring a point.

When a particularly good capital thrust was made, teams would stop play for a "round of snaps." This consisted of all players gathering together and snapping their fingers in appreciation. Not surprisingly, a goodly amount of imbibing was an important aspect of this first Frizby Championship. One of the sacred duties of the game's "Chancellor" was to call frequent "time outs" for friendly rounds of refreshments. Players kept their drinks on the ground next to their feet. If an incoming unit knocked a drink over during play, this "spilling of spirits" was a serious matter. In such cases, the receiving team scored an automatic point regardless of whether the thrust was grasped or not.

More than 150 spectators witnessed this "International Frizby Championship." The Blossom Brothers won the three hour event 21 to 16. It was a well placed "left handed reverse-cut thrust" that won the game. But obviously it was fun and comradery that truly prevailed!

Guts Frisbee Game

The game of "Guts" is the chief occupant of the testosterone department of frisbee play. Basically, the idea is to fling the disc as hard as possible at an opposing player or team so the disc can't be taught. Then the disc is spun back at you with the same malevolent intent. Today's professional Guts player can hurl 108 grams of pure polyethylene over 100 miles per hour. Only one hand catches are allowed. The Guts game has evolved from contrived contests in many different places— one up man ship seems to be its inspiration. At a certain point a student tossing a pie pan or tin lid back and forth decides, "enough of this kid stuff, I'm going to burn one!" The no doubt startled receiver will then "return to sender" in like fashion. Tit for tat, and there you have it— a new game is born! Suddenly, a gentle throw and catch game becomes a contest of speed, power, determination and "pure guts."

John Gorman gets ready to launch a metal cookie can cover at the opposing team. Note the well used Chi Phi Fraternity frizby court. Dartmouth College 1955. Photo by: Kenneth W. Lundstrom

It's clear the Guts game developed anywhere soft tossing suddenly turned hard (which was no doubt just about everywhere flying discs were thrown). But all this really was, and is, is a friendly form of frisbee rough-housing. It wasn't designed to hurt anyone. Guts originated as one of those rites of passage challenges— "Bet you can't catch this," says the thrower to his partner as he gives the metal tin a wicked toss. However, over time, the game of guts did become more organized with a set of rules to govern competition.*

Guts had its gentler antecedents too. One such game was when two players stood approximately 10 meters apart, the object being to make an accurate throw to the opposing player. The receiving player needed to be able to catch the tin or pie pan with one hand without having to move

But before this occurred there are early accounts of students at Princeton (1955) and Ohio State at Miami (1957) playing a guts-like game with a circular saw blade! Yes, they still retained marginally enough grey matter to know enough to wear gloves. But their motivation nonetheless remains a mystery...

World Frisbee Championships at the Rose Bowl, Pasadena, CA. Guts Frisbee Demonstration. Library Bar vs. The Berkeley Frisbee Group. 1974. Credit: Wham-O Inc.

more than one step in any direction. An out of reach throw meant a point was awarded to the receiver. But if the receiver fumbled or was unable to make a clean, one handed catch, a point went to the thrower. Opponents would increase the distance by taking one step back after each point was scored. Games were played until one player scored 11 or 21 points. Another popular version had teams of 5 players each standing abreast and defending their court, a game quite similar to today's established Guts game.

Reportedly, the International Frisbee (Guts) Tournament (IFT) started at Eagle Harbor, MI in 1958. The original event of 1958 was a Sunday afternoon picnic for members of the Healy family and their friends who lived in the area. The Healy brothers, Bob, John, Tim, and Peter formed a team called North Central. They are credited with winning the first nine IFT's. However, there is no record or documented evidence that I could find to support the claim that this event was a formal affair during these years with other teams invited to participate. The first "real" IFT probably did not occur until 1966. I conducted an extensive search of many newspapers, historical societies, as well as contacted knowledgeable, old time guts people from Michigan.

The earliest account I came across of team competition was from a newspaper article in the July 11, 1967 *Detroit Free Press*, entitled, "Our Frisbee Team Is Great," by Judy Wax. This described how a Detroit frisbee team, the "Foul Five" defeated the "North Central" team. But even if as seems likely, the IFT was for some years no more than a family picnic, it still does rank as the longest running frisbee tournament in the world. To this day it is held annually over the 4th of July weekend in Michigan. (Contact the Guts Frisbee Association for more information).

Today's Guts frisbee game is played with two, three, or five person teams who face each other across a 15 meter "battle zone." (Both men's and women's teams compete). Team members must stand at arms length behind their respective lines. The basic game is simple. A member of the

The famed Berkeley Frisbee Group. Golden Gate Park, San Francisco, CA. 1970. Members: Back Row: (L-R) Kate May, Bob May, John "Z" Weyand, Chuck Schultz, Cole Marie Fulwider, Victor Malafronte, Chuck Pitt, Rob Kalnitsky. Front Row: (L-R) Steve Gottlieb with friend, Steve Sewell with friend, Ines Sam. Not in photo: Jay Shelton, Dave Book, Monika Lou, Anne Hodgkinson, Rev. Gregory (Che) Quicksilver, Tom McRann, Hal Erickson, Tom Boda, Bill Schneider, Mike Schneider, Neal Hoellwarth, Dave Zouzounis, Teresa Gaman, Dudley Gaman, Ray Muller, Ron Weir, Roger Barrett, Don Peirce. Photo by: Brock de Lappe

throwing team lets loose (usually accompanied by a bull like roar) and tries to throw the frisbee right through the receiving team. Only a clean, one handed catch of the disc is allowed. The person making a successful catch must then return the throw (another bull like roar, or at the very least, a Monica Seles grunt). Wide or bad throws count against the throwing team. Today's top Guts players can hurl a plastic disc at speeds up to 100 mph! But few players wear gloves. That would not be very guts-like.

I would venture to say that this game like so many other frisbee games, had its roots in the northeastern United States. It's quite similar to games that were being played by New England area college students in the 1950's or even as early as the 1940's, a notable example being the already described "Dartmouth Frizby Championship" of 1954.

Sky Golf

One of the first written sets of rules for playing golf with a disc was introduced by the Copar Electronics Company of Chicago, IL in 1959. The game set came with an instruction booklet on "How the Play Sky Golf." 6 Sky Saucers, and 6 two foot wide metal hoops were used as targets. Each player had to traverse a 6 hole course, the object to throw the disc through the hoop and complete the round in the fewest number of throws or strokes. Players chose one of six planet names before the start of the game. Throwing from the "Launch Pad," the object of the game was to land in the "Space Station."

Modern Day Frisbee Golf

The direct antecedent to today's disc golf game made its debut in the mind of Californian, George Sappenfield, a recreation major, following a round of conventional "ball golf." It dawned on Sappenfield how nicely the frisbee could be utilized to play disc golf with the kids he worked with at his local playground. In 1968, now the Parks and Recreation Supervisor for the Conejo, California Valley Community Park, he set up a standardized disc golf course. Some of his target "holes" were plywood cut-outs of animals where the player had to throw through the arms or between the legs.

Grasping that the game would attract serious as well as recreational players, George introduced frisbee golf at the 1969 "All Comers Meet" held at Brookside Park in Pasadena, California. Many of the most enthusiastic and accomplished players of the day who attended including, Jay Shelton,

Steve Sewell, Dave Book, Bob May and Chuck Pitt, marveled at the concept. These players brought the game back to the U.C. Berkeley where it quickly became a favorite daily activity enjoyed by the members of the Berkeley Frisbee Group. The BFG established a standard par 68 frisbee golf course on the U.C. Berkeley campus in 1970.

In the meantime, on the east coast, Jim Palmeri of Rochester, New York, took frisbee golf one step further. In 1974 he organized "The American Flying Disc Open" held at John Hopkins University in Rochester, NY, and introduced the first standardized frisbee golf targets. (Shallow wooden boxes placed on the ground were used as targets or pins.) Jim even went so far as to offer a brand new Datsun sedan as first prize!

It was "Steady Ed" Headrick, the great Wham-O disc innovator, and his son Ken, who made the greatest impact on this new game, which continues to this day. In 1976 they invented and patented a standardized frisbee catcher called a "Disc Pole Hole." With this invention, they established the first permanent 18 hole disc golf course at Oak Grove Park in the city of La Canada, CA. During its first year of operation, nearly 5,000 people per week came out to play this new version of the game. Today, disc golf is probably the most popular and widespread of organized frisbee activities with over 700 disc golf courses located in 15 countries. Substantial prize money is offered at a number of tournaments—one event dangled a purse of $50,000 dollars! Specialized golf discs, including drivers, approach discs, and putters have for some years now, been marketed and sold by several flying disc manufacturers.

From spontaneous beginnings in a number of places with diverse sets of rules and targets, disc golf has evolved today to be probably the most widespread and unifying activity of organized frisbee sports. There's no better or cheaper way to enjoy the idyllic surroundings of nature, and at the same time be involved in an activity that truly challenges both mind and body to work together, than to "hole out" that disc with the fewest number of throws. The music of the polehole target chains receiving a successful putt will become pleasantly fixed in memory. Then on to the next hole, and the next, and...Try it— this is a sweetly addictive sport.

Williams College student tossing a plastic can cover with style. 1958. Photo by: Bill Tague. Courtesy: Williams College Archives and Special Collections.

English Professor George "Frisbie" Whicher. Students at Amherst College (circa 1949) are calling the game of a throw and catch with a metal can cover or pie tin "Frisbie". The game was named after the much admired Prof. Whicher. Born: 1889. Died: 1954. Credit: Amherst College Archives

"Frisbee Tournament on the Third Floor." 1959. Amherst College Archives

Three students at Amherst College enjoy the frisbie game with a small metal cookie can cover. 1939. Credit: Amherst College Archives

Joe Richardson get ready to launch another perfect throw. 1958. Credit: Amherst College Archives

Cole Elbert gets ready to catch the pie pan thrown by his partner, Paul Ericksson. They were part of the 1939 Middlebury College Delta Upsilon (Frisbie pie tin) trip to Lincoln, Nebraska. Frisbee dog statue entitled "Frisbee" by sculptor Patrick Farrow. Photo by: Erik Borg ©1989.

Senior Multi-World Frisbee Champion Ralph Williamson cataloging his Frisbie pie pan collection. 1995. Photo by: Bob Giles. Ralph's Frisbee Museum is the back cover photo for this book.

Frisbee's first touring professional player, Bill Schneider, aka "Professor of Frisbee" gets ready for another national TV show in Hamburg, Germany. 1972. Photo by: Hans Ernst Muller

FRISBEE IN JAPAN

Sam Ferrans, former World Disc Golf Champion gets ready to launch another 400 foot drive. Showa National Government Park in Tachikawa, Japan. 1995. Credit: Hero Nobo.

Ken Climo, World Disc Golf Champion, wins first place prize money at the Japan Open Disc Golf Tournament. 1995. Credit: Hero Kobo

While on their second national frisbee to tour of Japan, Overall World Frisbee Champion and star professional performer, Monika Lou and her partner Victor Malafronte (the author) ham it up for the Japanese media. 1976. Credit: Chunichi Shimbun

Japan's first frisbee clinic. Nearly 200 school children enjoy "Frisbee Day in the Park" in Nagoya, Japan. 1975.

The 1996 Japan Open Disc Golf Championships competitors and families. Frisbee play has become very popular in Japan. Many frisbee golf courses and Ultimate teams have been established nationwide. Credit: Hero Kobo.

Chapter III

POETRY IN PLASTIC:
THE FRISBEE FINDS ITS FINEST FORM

The Story of Warren Francioni and Walter (Fred) Morrison: The Flyin Saucer Brothers

Walter (Fred) Morrison is well known as having been inventor of the first plastic flying discs. But almost no one, including those close to the sport, realizes that Morrison had a partner! The circumstances surrounding the origin and history of the first plastic flying disc and its inventors have long been unclear, with contrasting stories and theories both of its creation and that of the American Trends Pluto Platter Flying Saucer which followed. Some people with direct knowledge of "what happened" have been all too vague and conveniently forgetful about dates, places and people involved, leaving a blurred composite for these essential events of the dawning of discdom.

What has been well publicized is Fred Morrison invented the plastic disc. But what's been conspicuously absent in previous accounts is the fact that he had a partner in his early efforts by the name of Warren Franscioni who deserves every bit as much as credit as Fred! Here for the first time is some of the lost history of the invention of the "Flyin Saucer" revealed by two who were close to the source, Warren Franscioni's daughters, Coszette and Alona.

The process of setting the story straight began with a phone call placed by Coszette Eneix to Ralph Williamson, one of the foremost frisbee collectors in the world. Ralph in turn contacted me with the realization that this book would be the perfect forum for the Franscioni family to at long last ensure proper recognition and rightful credit for their dad's contributions to frisbee playing. Dr. Stancil E.D. Johnson, frisbee historian and author of *"FRISBEE" A practitioner's manual and definitive treatise* (1975), was first to reveal that Fred had a partner. However, the good doctor never had the opportunity to see the extensive files and correspondences the late Warren Franscioni left behind. By courtesy of the Franscioni family, I now have!

A careful review of these 400+ documents has been revealing. Now, at long last, production dates for the 1948 Flyin Saucer with "raised letters," the "retooled" 1950 LI'L Abner's Flyin Saucer, and the 1953 "soft poly" Flyin Saucer have been firmly established. These documents have also aided in deciphering and explaining the origin of Fred Morrison's American Trends Pluto Platter. Much other historically invaluable production data is also contained in these long awaited documents which has helped us piece together the history of the first plastic flying disc.

The Vision

The plastic flying disc revolved out of the vision of two former World War II Army Air Force pilots, Warren Franscioni and Walter (Fred) Morrison who saw the need to create a flying disc that wouldn't cut up hands during play. Aside from eliminating the mayhem factor, they perceived this disc also needed to be easier to control than a metal cake tin or pie pan. These insights led to years of playful experimentation...

Many of the discoveries that have defined the second half of the twentieth century came out dire necessity brought about by World War II, that monstrous mother of invention. Plastic is the one that has perhaps impacted our daily lives the most. Right after the war in 1946, Warren and Fred saw the potential of this new material and decided to use it to invent a much more air worthy, user friendly "flying saucer." In the basement of Warren's San Luis Obispo home, they experimented by placing sheets of plastic over a water heater and hand-forming these into crude flying disc shapes. They can rightfully be called the Wright brothers of frisbee sports, as they experimented with these first crude prototypes that would lead to a new age of recreational flight.

In 1946, Fred made a drawing of a prototype flying disc he dubbed, "The Whirlo Way." From this design emerged the world's first plastic flying disc, only the name was changed to "Flyin Saucer." Now, Fred and Warren decided to form a company called "Pipco" which stood for "Partners in Plastic," to sell the Flyin Saucer across the country. They knew it was a ripe moment for such a venture; just then, the whole country was captivated by the great Roswell UFO flap—what better time to add another saucer to the mix?

To perfect their new product Fred and Warren conducted indoor tests for various flight characteristics for prototypes they were producing. These included comparing launching thrust, forward speed, accuracy, and crashability. Finally, the partners decided to produce seven different model prototypes, then test these for lift, gyroscopic balance, stability of flight and comfortable gripping. Test models ranged from 12 inches in diameter to under

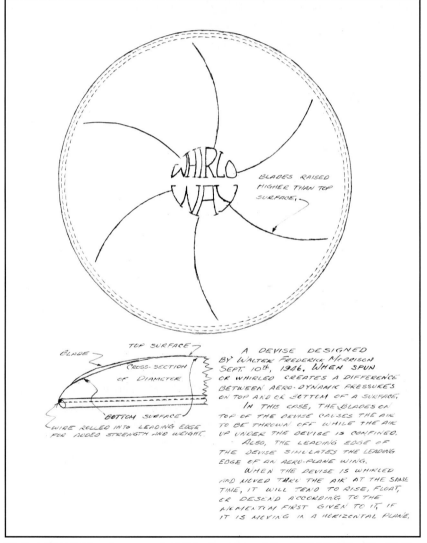

Walter (Fred) Morrison created this drawing of the "Whirlo Way" in 1946. The design went on to become the first plastic flying disc.
Courtesy: Coszette Eneix

Co-inventor Warren Franscioni.
Photo by: Frank Franscioni

7 inches, and weighed from 9 1/4 ounces to under three ounces. When all the results were evaluated, the 9 inch-5 ounce test model proved to be the best overall flyer. After a bit more fine tuning, they decided to produce a 9 inch flying disc. It is a tribute to their designing savvy that even today, most flying discs are manufactured in this size.

In the spring of 1948, the first prototype flying disc was machine formed (not created by hand as other accounts have stated) from a solid block of "Tennessee Eastman's Tennite." This early cellulose plastic material was very stiff and brittle—the sort of stuff that threatens to fall apart if you look at it wrong! Warren and Fred were fortunate to be able to complete a number of successful test flights before their "Tennite Flyin Saucer" struck the ground and shattered into pieces. One month later, a contract was signed with Southern California Plastics, of Glendale, CA, to manufacture and sell the Flyin Saucer for the Pipco Company. Fortunately, the partners by now had found more durable stuff for the injection molding of these first period Flyin Saucers, a plastic material known as "Butyrate."

In the meantime, these two disc pioneers spent a lot of time demonstrating their new toy and game at the Pomona County Fair in southern California. As they were performing their demonstration, a spectator could be heard to comment, "I'll bet those guys fly that thing by wires!" Fred and Warren with the improvisational flair found in so many inventors, were quick to incorporate this into their sales pitch— "The Saucer Is Free, But The Invisible Wire Cost 10 Cents Per Foot—and It Only Comes In 10 Foot Lengths!" As they flung back and forth along their "invisible wires," Fred and Warren billed themselves the "World's Champion Flyin Saucer Pilots."

One of the first major department stores to feature the Flyin Saucer was Woolworth's in Glendale, CA. But disc sales were very low as potential customers didn't really understand what to do with this new toy. To correct this woeful ignorance, Fred and Warren offered to perform a demonstration right in the store. Woolworth's management okayed the idea, but only if Fred and Warren would perform in a wire cage to protect the customers! These original Flyin Saucers were made of rock hard plastic and weighed nearly 6 ounces.

The introduction of the new, softer polyethylene plastic in 1953, finally made the Flyin Saucer "user friendly." Still, Fred and Warren on their sales rounds would at times encounter store owners who though interested in their product, expressed concerns about either safety or durability. One of the partners would then quell all doubts by throwing a "soft poly" Flyin Saucer hard against the store window— no harm resulting to either. Most proprietors, though no doubt a little taken aback, would quickly place an order with the dynamic duo.

But with sales tepid at best, despite all their promotional efforts, the partners realized they needed to link their new fangled flyer with a well known product. They thought they'd made the ideal connection when in April, 1950,

Coszette Eneix, (right) the daughter of Warren Franscioni, who co-invented the first plastic frisbee and playmate take a frisbee break. "It was probably safer to just hold on to the rock hard and heavy disc so no one could get hurt trying to catch it!"1952. Credit: Coszette Eneix

they signed an advertising agreement with Al Capp, the creator of the widely popular comic strip "Little Abner," that would allow them to link the promotion of the Flyin Saucer with the LI'L Abner characters. On April 15, 1950, as part of this promotion. Al Capp began featuring a UFO flying saucer in his strip. However, apparently the partners went beyond the stipulations of their agreement with Al Capp by featuring a label and inserts from the comic strip in the Flyin Saucer they marketed. This resulted in cancellation of the contract and Al Capp threatening to sue if the partners did not pay him $5,000 for damages, quite a chunk of change in that era. But before all this occurred, hundreds of Flyin Saucers with Li'L Abner labels and cartoon inserts were produced.

This unfortunate conclusion to what seemed such a promising breakthrough evidently marked the beginning of the end both of Pipco and the Morrison/Franscioni partnership. Already burdened by the investments they had made in getting Pipco off the ground, the Al Capp fiasco was too much for Pipco to absorb. This along with other financial set backs resulted in Franscioni reapplying to be called back to active duty in the Air Force in 1951, and with the Korean Conflict underway, he was readily accepted. Thereafter, though Franscioni never lost interest in the Flyin Saucer, his military duties and all the relocations that go along with that life, took precedent, and he was never again able to seriously pursue marketing his and Fred's invention.

Fred Morrison, also greatly affected by the misfortunes of Pipco, moved to Los Angeles where he became a building inspector for the city. But he continued to put plenty of time and energy into marketing and promoting the plastic flying disc.

In 1956 when Franscioni tried to apply for a patent on a design for "An Aerial Sounding Toy Or Similar Article," (U.S. Ser. No. D-42,045) he was unable to get the signature of his co-inventor on the application and gave up on these efforts. Was this "Aerial Sounding Toy" similar to the Pluto Platter design which just a year or so later was to become the first trademarked Frisbee? We may never know. Responding to my inquiry, the patent office could not locate the application file! Cozzette, Franscioni's daughter, was then too young to remember any such detail. And, Warren Franscioni himself can never shed light on the issue, for he died of a heart attack in 1974, a frisbee pioneer without portfolio.

To this day, Franscioni's daughter, Coszette Eneix remains bitter that her father has been given no credit as co-inventor of the plastic flying disc. Interviewed in 1997 by the *San Luis Obispo New Times*, she stated, "When you read about the history of the frisbee you always hear Fred Morrison. Fred Morrison did this. Fred Morrison did that. Bullshit. Excuse my language. Bullshit. It was a partnership. I think they should have equal billing."

The reluctance of Fred Morrison to co-sign the 1956 patent application with his estranged partner may in part have had to do with Morrison being hard at work developing his own flying disc, the Pluto Platter, destined to become the first trademarked Frisbee. One of the reasons it was to make such an indelible mark on our culture was due to continued advances in plastic technology. In 1953, Fred began selling the soft-poly version of the Flyin Saucer under the company name of American Trends. It was probably a short time later that he created the Pluto Platter Flying Saucer, the flying disc that would introduce this new sport to the masses.

Fred Morrison and the Wham-O Mfg. Co.

Morrison's Pluto Platter Flying Saucer was a redesign of his and Warren's Flyin Saucer into the basic flying disc form that is most commonly used to this day. It had a thinner flight plate, a rounded profile, and a turned under rim that was very comfortable to grip during play. Time would prove it the perfect design for flying discs used in toss games. Fred Morrison applied for a U.S Design Patent on July 22, 1957, and was awarded Des. Pat. #183,626 on September 30, 1958 for his "Flying Toy."

In the meantime, in a historical move that has impacted frisbee sports to this day, in 1956 Fred Morrison teamed up with Spud Melin and Rich Knerr, co-founders of Wham-O Mfg. Co. of San Gabriel, CA. This was a fortunate joining of forces because Knerr and Melin had the kind of marketing savvy that Morrison and Franscioni had lacked. Jointly they planned the nationwide introduction of the first mass produced plastic flying disc toy, setting the stage for the beginning of modern day frisbee sports. On January 13, 1957, with much of North America in its deep winter sleep, the first of over 300 million plastic discs began to fly off the Wham-O production line.

Ernest C. (Bill) Robes and His Space Saucer

Morrison and Franscioni were not the only early experimenters shaping plastic into flying discs. The east coast can claim its own innovator of early disc technology in the person of Ernest C. (Bill) Robes. Robes was already a legend in his own right as one of the true pioneers of the sport of skiing. His astounding ability to perform somersaults on skis and fly through the air for great distances got him an invitation to demonstrate his daring talents at the 1935 Winter Sports Exposition held at the Boston Garden. A *Boston Globe* writer was inspired to call him "The Sky Comet Who Takes Your Breath Away." Bill would eventually be inducted into the National Ski Hall of Fame in 1987.

Being the skier he was, in 1943, Robes appropriately found employment in cold and snowy New Hampshire as ski

SPACE SAUCER IS A NEW FASCINATING GAME DESIGNED FOR ALL AGES. A GAME WHICH TEACHES AND DEVELOPS COORDINATION, SKILL, JUDGMENT AND GOOD SPORTSMANSHIP. $1.00

EXCLUSIVELY

AT THE

DARTMOUTH CO-OP

Advertisement in "The Dartmouth" for Bill Robes Space Saucer. Sold by the Dartmouth Co-op. 1955. Credit: Dartmouth Co-operative Society, Inc.

director at the Kimball Union Academy prep school, an institution which sent many of its graduates on to matriculation at nearby Dartmouth College. Robes was director of the school's outing club as well as coach of the ski team. Bill, like Fred Morrison, whose father had invented the sealed beam headlight, came from an inventive background. (Robes' father developed the two party telephone line). This inventive streak in Bill was stimulated by the sight of KUA students playing toss and catch games with metal can covers. Evidently, various kinds of covers and pie pans have been flying around the KUA campus since the late nineteen thirties.

Having inherited his dad's fondness with tinkering, the younger Robes created useful handmade tools and gadgets. As he observed the various forms of tin being flown about Kimball Union Academy Robes couldn't help but notice how the metal bruised and dented all too easily during play. Students were banging up their hands and even cutting themselves

Two boys enjoy playing throw and catch with Bill Robes' Space Saucers at the 1955 Dartmouth faculty picnic. Credit: Dartmouth College Archives

in some cases.*

Bill Robes' response to the metal mayhem factor was to design a plastic flying disc close in form to the tin covers he had observed flying about, which he dubbed the "Space Saucer." He produced the first of these in 1953.

Robes began work on his plastic prototype Space Saucer in a log cabin that he had built, heating up a sheet of plastic known as "Bolteron" in an oven and then shaping it in a mold made from a washing machine agitator! The disks were then trimmed to size and "hand stamped" with the Space Saucer name.

In 1954, his patience likely wrung with washing machine technology, Bill invested in an injection mold to mass produce his new flying toy. A small sales force comprised of mostly KUA and Dartmouth students now began marketing and selling Space Saucers to earn a little extra money. By 1956, the Dartmouth and Yale Co-op's were selling thousands of saucers which spread from New Hampshire to southern California. Being sold in these official campus stores guaranteed good exposure for Robes' saucers. As the student body dispersed to the far corners of America during semester breaks and summer vacations, so did many a Space Saucer.

Included with Bill's patent application and packaging for the Space Saucer was a drawing and description of the "Space Saucer Game." This game was very similar to the basic throw and catch games (cover can tennis) that were being played at many other schools located in the northeastern United States. When played with 4 or more players, each team had to rotate its positions on the playing field as in the game of Volleyball. Bill received patent number 2,822,176 in 1958 for his "Aerial Disk" game.

Although I've been unable to verify my suspicions, I do believe that the Space Saucer game and disc was more than a little instrumental in inspiring Empire Plastics to produce its Zolar and Mystery Y Frisbee models in the late 1950's. The description of a game on Empire's disc and packaging is almost exactly the same as Bill Robes' 1955 Space Saucer game— I believe this is not coincidence!

*I have received accounts of students in various locations having made something of a blood sport challenge out metal tins' tendencies to cut and shred. Luckily the kinder, gentler plastic disc came along before such "games" could bleed their way prominently into the record!

Pete Wheeler and his date enjoy tossing the Space Saucer for fun at the 1955 Sigma Phi Epsilon's "Green Key" weekend picnic party. Dartmouth College. Photo by: Richard T. Gardner Jr.

Bill's Space Saucer was conceived and created independently of the 1948 west coast Flyin Saucer. Robes had never seen another plastic flying disc. By 1962, he had created eleven different (collectible) periods of his Space Saucer, and sold nearly 65,000 saucers. When he quit the business, 1,440 Space Saucers (mostly Second Generation-Fifth Period) remained stored in his log cabin. Thanks to some great investigative work by East coast disc sleuth extraodinaire, Jim Palmeri, these are now in the hands of collectors everywhere.

"Steady Ed" Headrick, Father of Modern Day Frisbee Sports

Throughout history, men of vision, creativeness and conviction have stepped forward to give the world new avenues of self-expression as well as unique new ways to just plain have fun. For the frisbee, Ed Headrick was truly the sauce that made the mix merry! This visionary is probably more responsible than anyone else for starting the modern day era of frisbee sports.

When Wham-O introduced Fred Morrison's Pluto Platter in 1957, it ne-

United States Patent [19]

Headrick et al.

[11] 4,039,189

[45] Aug. 2, 1977

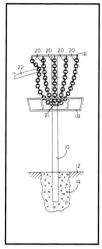

[54] FLYING DISC ENTRAPMENT DEVICE

[76] Inventors: Edward E. Headrick; Kenneth A. Headrick, both of 4900 Crown Ave., La Canada, Calif. 91011

[21] Appl. No.: 678,125

[22] Filed: Apr. 19, 1976

[51] Int. Cl.² A63B 67/06
[52] U.S. Cl. .... 273/105 R
[58] Field of Search .... 273/105, 102.4, 102 R, 273/102 S, 127 R

[56] References Cited

U.S. PATENT DOCUMENTS

868,950	4/1907	Vasey	273/105 R
1,169,966	11/1915	Kenstowicz	273/102 R
2,126,245	8/1938	Darby	273/105 R
2,321,835	6/1943	Marlow	273/102 R
2,811,358	10/1957	Ruth	273/102 R
3,338,579	8/1967	McKain	273/127 R
3,421,764	1/1969	Smith et al.	273/105 R
3,455,554	7/1969	Rademacher	273/102.4
3,540,734	11/1970	Temple	273/105 R

FOREIGN PATENT DOCUMENTS

1,142,043	1957	France	273/105 R
2,152,251	1973	Germany	273/29 A
223,425	1924	United Kingdom	273/95 R

Primary Examiner—Richard C. Pinkham
Assistant Examiner—Lawrence E. Anderson
Attorney, Agent, or Firm—Keith D. Beecher

[57]   ABSTRACT

An entrapment device is provided for use in a flying disc golf game, or the like, and which provides a structure for absorbing the kinetic energy of flying discs thrown at the device to arrest the forward motion of the discs, and to cause the discs to be caught by the device. The device in one of its embodiments constitutes a post mounted in the ground, a basket mounted on the post, and energy absorbing structure mounted on the post above the basket. When the flying disc is thrown in the direction of the post, so as to strike the energy absorption structure, the energy absorption structure acts as a cushion for the disc thereby arresting its forward motion, and it causes the disc to drop into the basket.

3 Claims, 4 Drawing Figures

U.S. patent for the original Frisbee Golf Catcher invented by "Steady Ed" Headrick and his son, Ken.

ver reached higher status than just another Northeast college fad, about on par with goldfish swallowing and Volkswagen stuffing. It wasn't until after "Steady Ed" was hired by Wham-O in 1964 as Vice President of Sales and General Manager, that the Pluto Platter really took off!

"Steady Ed" saw the potential for both athletic achievement and personal artistry in this little plastic toy. He was already an accomplished player who therefore understood the complex nature and potential of the flying disc. Evaluating the Pluto Platter, and its various spinoffs, Headrick correctly envisioned these had not nearly reached the top rung of disc evolution. Ideas for major improvements in the Pluto Platter's flight characteristics began running through his head.

Quickly, with all the mass disc producing capacities of Wham-O at his beck and call, "Steady Ed" put his ideas into practice, and in 1964 created and patented the Professional model Frisbee Disc. His invention included the incorporation of "flight rings" or "the Lines of Headrick." These concentric raised grooves were located around the shoulder surface of the Pro model. They created a "spoiler" effect that increased the "laminar" flow of air across the top surface of the disc. This novel feature gave the disc better stability during flight—now it would more likely end up where the thrower intended it to go.

Headrick also increased the depth of the rim and added more overall weight to his new pro model which, as its name implies, was intended for the serious player. The Pro was the first "sporting goods store" variety of the Frisbee, and for the next 30 years, would remain the standard form of Wham-O's entire Frisbee line of 25 different models.

"Steady Ed" is a man of many firsts. In 1965, he was the first frisbee player to appear on the Johnny Carson Show. In 1967, Ed founded the International Frisbee Association which eventually claimed 112,000 members, and, that same year, established the Junior Frisbee Championships. Nearly 10 million youngsters have participated in this annual event. In 1974, Headrick established and organized the World Frisbee Championships held annually at the Rose Bowl until 1981. This was the biggest and most prestigious frisbee event of its kind. It and similar events sponsored by Wham-O were responsible for propelling frisbee play as sport into the minds of millions.

The father of modern day frisbee playing, "Steady Ed" Headrick.

Dan (Stork) Roddick performing one of his famous "con-stork-ion" free-style moves. Is he catching the frisbee or getting ready to throw it?! Photo by: Harvey Y. Brandt. Courtesy: Wham-O Inc.

In 1975, "Steady Ed" left Wham-O and went to work independently, inventing and patenting standardized equipment for the game of disc golf, as well as establishing the Disc Golf Association. In 1979, he organized a $50,000 Frisbee Disc Golf Tournament, a landmark event for the sport. Today, there are over 700 disc golf courses located in 13 countries, and 12,000 Professional Disc Golf Association (PDGA) members. "Steady Ed" is truly the inventive force behind disc golf, the most popular of organized frisbee games, and his influence remains immense to this day. His vision over the years has guided more people to more fun than can possibly be calculated! And now, this frisbee pioneer has donated his registered trademark "Disc Golf" to the public domain, for all of us to use freely. "Steady Ed" once said, "frisbee will change your life." He was right!

The Variable Flying Disc

Though over the years Wham-O has far and away dominated the flying disc market, many another whimsical device has flown out of the minds of inventors and into the marketplace. Some have been inflatable, others have come with parachutes, LED lights, whistles, noise makers, air baffles and chambers. At least one has come attached with a string, belying the freedom of flight, while others have been gas propelled.

Altogether since 1948, several thousand different plastic flying discs have been created and marketed by nearly 100 companies around the world. Most of these have been flash in the pan companies producing only novelty items that have soon found themselves in the surplus bin. But significant advances in disc technology have taken place in response to the popularity of frisbee golf and the special needs of the sport. With fairways often well over 300 feet long, weighted, beveled edged, high tech specialty flying discs have been designed specifically for championship play. They penetrate far and deep down field, but have none of the friendly hover and glide of the graceful frisbee. In other words, these are not designed for a game of catch! But the long wiry arms of championship distance throwers have bested 600 feet with them.

With every passing year, despite at best lackluster promotion, more and more flying discs are sold, more countries are introduced to the game, more disc golf courses are installed, more Ultimate teams formed, more people become regular aficionados, and some become world champions. Slowly has spread the realization that frisbee activities provide an inexpensive, wholesome ticket to joy on whatever level one wishes to pursue them.

Frisbee is one of those childhood games that can be enjoyed with more seriousness, vigor and style as an adult, and still offer that child-like glee every time you play. Unlike the fads that catch on like pet rocks and fall with a thud, frisbee games are a growing worldwide phenomenon in new age sports and alternative recreation. There's a lot of talk these days about establishing a bridge to the 21st century. Toss a disc and you will have established one!

More Highlights of Today's Frisbee Pastime

- Nearly 300 million frisbees have been sold.

- Ten million youngsters have participated in the Junior Frisbee Disc Championships.

- The game of Ultimate is played at nearly 600 colleges and in 32 foreign countries. The UPA has 8,000 members.

- The 1997 PDGA (Frisbee Golf) World Championships featured 350 qualified participants and $50,000.00 in prize money.

- Thousands of frisbee contests and tournaments are held worldwide each year.

- There are 700 frisbee golf courses in 15 countries.

- The latest Gallup Poll states that 15 million people in the U.S. enjoy frisbee activities every year.

- All this started with a plastic disc that was designed to fly to a distance of 100 feet!

Professional Disc Golf Champion Geoff Lissaman "putting out" at the 1996 PDGA World Championships, South Bend, IN. In background, second to left, is Scott Stokely, world distance record holder with a throw of 211.32 meters, longer than two football fields!
Credit: Disc Golf Journal

Chapter IV

FRISBEE COLLECTING!

Frisbee Collecting: A History

Serious frisbee collecting began, as have any number of other serious movements, in the city of Berkeley in northern California in 1968. There, members of the Berkeley Frisbee Group, a diverse group of students and local players united by a love of games involving flight, began to collect certain Wham-O Professional model Frisbees because they admired their superior flight characteristics. Then, when one player traded two Pro models for a particular one he coveted, when two or three discs were first displayed on someone's wall, and most especially, when one B.F.G. member, Roger Barrett with that combination of vision and fanaticism that gets movements going, became overwhelmed by the need to collect every kind of flying disc he could get his hands on, collecting became almost as big a pastime as tossing. With big dreams and small transactions, the hobby of frisbee collecting was off and running!

Roger and I, working together, would always try to buy two discs of every model, mold and color produced. On our competitive excursions we worked flea markets, retail stores, and pestered manufacturers, as well as friends and family. Gradually, we unearthed evidence of a rich history of flying discs in the many antique artifacts we found. In the complex trading wars and negotiations over our new found treasures which followed, we would find ourselves, in less combative moments, pondering the historical significance of these flying toys. The discussions/bartering could last for hours and often involved 20 to 30 previously unknown discs.

The first major discovery that heightened our collective curiosity was the Pluto Platter. During one of our frequent flea market junkets, Roger spied an unknown disc with strange, antique looking engravings laying on a blanket. Before the seller could blink, he'd plunked down his quarter and made off with it. Examining this "Rosetta Stone" of an artifact, we noticed that it was engraved with the names of all the planets of the Solar System. Also, the company name, "Wham-O" appeared on the disc three times, plus "Pluto Platter," and "Frisbee" with a circle R signifying trademark registration.

Then, one week later, as luck would have it, I stumbled across another Pluto Platter languishing in a store's discount bin. This version of the Pluto Platter cost me twice Roger's investment, but was justified in every sense of the word! This was a conspicuously different version of the Pluto Platter with "Wham-O" inscribed but once. The "Pluto Platter" insignia was included, but the "Frisbee" inscription was entirely absent! That was when Roger and I realized that there were different "periods" or production runs for the Pluto Platter. My treasured find turned out to be a "first period" Pluto Platter; Roger's disc with all the extra inscriptions was a subsequent, fourth period model. Now, collectors have pieced together that there were 7 different periods of Pluto Platters. Which piece of this early disc history might you have passed over during one of your flea market adventures!

In the early 1970's not long after the Berkeley Frisbee Group pioneered disc collecting, the frisbee phenomenon accelerated from a casual pastime to a full scale flap! Suddenly, with the introduction of organized tournaments that attracted players from all over, players who had been developing their skills in isolated groups all across the country met each other for the first time. Naturally, they shared technical information on different throws and catches. At the same time, it was the flying disc itself that became a major point of discussion and intrigue. (At this early stage it was the Wham-O Frisbee that was almost universally used in competition, due simply to its easy availability and superior design and flight characteristics as opposed to other flying discs). Members of the Berkeley Frisbee Group, by now veteran "flight testers," could point out to their new friends many subtle differences in frisbee performance.

These could be determined simply by observing the mold number on the bottom of each disc. Different mold numbers meant different performance capabilities for the disc. For instance, a Pro Frisbee with a #10 or #15 mold number stamped on the bottom, was on the light side and didn't skip very well, whereas the #1 or split digit 1-4 mold disc was thicker and heavier and could be counted on to perform high speed skip shots exactly where you wanted them to go! Because of the nature of manufacturing and production runs, certain molds such as the heavier ones just referred to, were only on the market for a short period of time. As a result, such "limited production" frisbees were soon sought after by both serious collectors and players alike.

Over time, increasing numbers of players found collecting frisbees to be an interesting and worthwhile hobby. People began bringing boxes of frisbees to tournaments to trade and sell. Collectors from all over the world would compete on the field by day, and be involved in serious disc wheeling and dealing by night. Disc auctions were held with certain collector items even at this early stage, going for over $400.00!*

Frisbee Collecting Today

Worldwide, since 1948, nearly 300 million flying discs have been produced and taken flight. Nearly 25,000 variations of these are considered collectible. These represent many different classifications and manufacturers. As a result, if you are just starting out as a collector, you may find this hobby to be complex and confusing. This is also one of its attractions— there is so much to learn, and for that matter so much unrevealed about history and chronology awaiting discovery, that you may just find yourself making an essential contribution!

But in the meantime, a pop quiz! Do you know what a Speedy is? Can you identify a Mystery Y, Twirl-A-Boom, or a Mars Platter? Can you find the esker on any given disc or diagnose one with Wellishes Disease? Would you find eating a Sky Pie to be a taste sensation? Give up? Don't. Instead, read on— you'll find the answers to these questions and many others in this book. My best advice for anyone starting a disc collection is to learn as much as you can from the wealth of information herein so you can make wise and educated decisions on which discs or disc classifications to pursue. (There are also plenty of helpful collectors around to advise you— see listing, Appendix III.)

The more knowledge you gain about flying discs, their historical significance and value, the more likely it is that you'll be able to share in the excitement of a rare find. For instance, you may be walking through a park one day, and a rare disc may go sailing past your face like an elusive

*The Master's World Flying Disc Championships has held annual disc auctions for the "Save the Children's Foundation" for the past 20 years. Thousands of dollars have been donated. At the same time, much information of historical and technical nature was unearthed and shared. Eventually, due to overwhelming demand, tournament directors had to schedule time devoted to collector activities. "Fly Marts" continue to this day to be an important part of frisbee events.

bird of paradise. If so, you can follow it back to the hand that flipped it and begin to bargain. (Some of our "old time" collectors can peg a disc, even on a spinning trajectory, from 100 feet away!)

Several hundred frisbee collectors are active around the world. Together, we have assembled a vast amount of information concerning nearly 25,000 collectible flying discs. To help facilitate the reader's smooth transition into this plastic galaxy of collectibles, this book contains nearly 400 photographs as well as a price guide for the most popular flying discs. Also included is an extensive glossary of terms. (There are many colorful ones associated with frisbee play for the reader to become acquainted with!) Twenty classifications of disc types and specialties are also to be found herein.

In addition, there are listings of the many flying disc retail merchandisers, as well as recognized organizations and publications that govern frisbee sports. Also, the reader who gets caught up in the excitement of it all and decides to take a stab at collecting would do well to consult the extensive list herein of many of the top frisbee collectors and dealers around the country. Introduce yourself to one in your area!

Whatever category of disc collecting inspires you, whether it be antiques, golf discs, novelties, super pros, or perhaps those eccentric sensory discs that make noise or glow in the dark, there is a whole new world waiting for you. Maybe I'll see you at the next frisbee tournament, national toy show, or at your local flea market. I'll be the guy trying to look casual as I zone in on yet another plastic gem, or on one of those old Frisbie pie tins that inspired it all!

Where to Find Collectible Flying Discs

There are a number of avenues open to the enterprising seeker of antique frisbees:

1.   Contact any of the frisbee collectors or dealers listed in this book for particular classifications of collectible discs you may be interested in tracking down. Also placing personal classified ads in flying disc magazines is advisable. (Refer to Appendix III for a complete, up to date listing of these publications.)

2.   Flea markets. Flea markets are well named. Just like the hardy lit-

tle creatures that astound with their jumping ability, a flea market is an endlessly dynamic place with bargains that alight for a moment, but soon as said, are sprung out of there in the possession of knowledgeable, canny buyers. But the great thing about flea markets is if you missed something last visit, there's probably a new treasure to take its place this time around. Haunting flea markets, and even more importantly, establishing a relationship with dealers, or "pickers" as they are often referred to, will reap dividends for the frisbee collector. These professionals, once you establish a relationship, will keep an eye out for whatever it is you are looking for—it's good business for them.

Remember, a flea market is a central gathering point for newly surfaced treasures (and more junk than you can ever imagine) from all over your local area, and sometimes from much farther afield. One collector, for example, found a very rare advertising sign for the Frisbie Pie Company at a flea market in Wisconsin, almost half a continent distant from the New England/New York area the company served. And in 1995 four Frisbie pie pans were purchased at a Seattle, Washington flea market for $1.00. You just never know! Antique flying disc items you may come across at flea markets include Frisbee Horseshoe Games, Flying Saucers, Pluto Platters, Wham-O Professional Model Frisbees, and sometimes rare, even unknown discs may crop up.

3.   Thrift stores. Second hand stores such as Salvation Army outlets, Goodwill Industries, St. Vincent de Paul, and the like provide often fruitful hunting grounds for the collector. Check your local yellow pages for locations.

4.   Toy shops as well as some sporting goods stores that sell second-hand merchandise are worth checking. Any discs in stock will likely be stored in a barrel or box. Check your yellow pages for listings.

5,   Church and charity fund raisers. Such events will be listed in your local newspaper, and might reward a visit.

6.   Garage sales, yard sales, tag sales, estate sales, moving sales...they all mean one thing: One man's junk is...! These sales dot the landscape like dandelions on any nice weekend day in season. Since many a yard saler neglects to bring out old frisbees to add to the pickings, I always make it a point to ask— such queries have often resulted in rich finds!

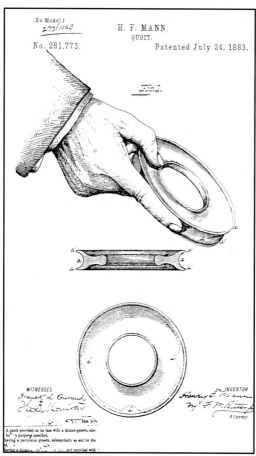

(No Model.)
273/1063
No. 281,773.

H. F. MANN.
QUOIT.

Patented July 24, 1883.

WITNESSES
Frederick L. Durand

INVENTOR
Henry F. Mann
by F. W. Ritter
Attorney

A quoit provided on its face with a thumb-groove, substantially specified.
having a peripheral groove, substantially as and for the
.....
having a thumb .... and provided with

1883 patent for a new quoit throwing disc.

7, Hover about your local park like a sharp eyed hawk. You may well find a collectible being tossed casually back and forth. Because the interruption of their game may not be worth the $5.00 you offer, be sure to have a disc along to sweeten the deal so the seller can both profit and continue play!

8. Toy show dealers, antique stores (get on their "wish list") and collectible toy magazines may feature a few old or rare frisbees. Most of these will probably be, in their original packaging. Prices should be very reasonable ($20-$40) unless of course the sellers have gotten wind of all the information herein!

9. Disc events: Many major frisbee tournaments schedule one evening just for a "fly mart." These feature a wide variety of frisbees available for trade or sale. For a schedule of the varied flying disc competitions, and world championship competitions taking place in your region, contact the respective organizations listed in Appendix III.

10. Check out any local general retail store with a toy department section. Many flying discs (such as novelties) are seasonal, and in many cases will be on the open market for only the year they are issued. If they are unusual or appealing enough, these discs can probably be counted on to become collectible within a few years.

Also, especially in the case of small, independently owned toy or sporting goods stores, unsold inventory from years past may still be present. Such languishing goods may include collectible frisbees— if they've been laying around long enough, you're liable to find them deeply discounted!

The Search for Color and Variations

All colors and mold numbers listed for each flying disc presented in this collector's guide are known to exist. However, there could very well be additional colors for certain items (i.e. antiques) that were unknown to collectors at the time of publication. My determination of disc color rarity, where this information is otherwise unknown, is based on what established collectors have on hand in their collections. If the reader becomes aware of additional information on discs and colors, please submit this to the author for inclusion in a future update of this price guide.

Where possible, quantities produced of flying discs have been listed as well. However, as is the case with colors, production listings for most discs have been difficult to determine, mainly due to the fact that most manufacturers were notoriously lax with production records.

On one hand, these uncertainties regarding disc production history are frustrating. But on the other hand, you, the collector, might just rectify some of these unknowns with your own finds! Therefore, always be sure to closely examine any collectible disc that you obtain. It just might be a rare variation that until now has gone unnoticed, or has slipped by the sharp scrutiny of other collectors.

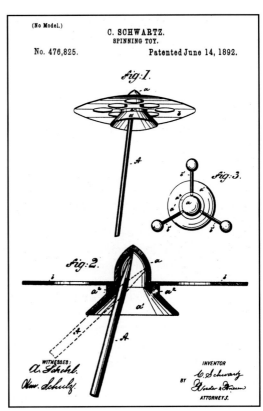

"Has anyone seen this 1892 flying toy?"

Anomalies to keep a lookout for could be anything from unusual mold numbers, such as those on discs not issued to the general public, an undetected esker, (What's an esker? Check Appendix II) or a different label used for decoration. Perhaps you might even come across a previously unknown disc! Keep your eyes open and always inform other collectors about your new discovery (See Appendix III for a listing of collectors in your area).

Storage

As with any collection, there are certain procedures that are necessary to follow in order to protect your frisbee finds. Common sense will play an important role in keeping your collectibles in prime condition. Here are a few procedures to follow to safeguard your valuable items:

•   Do not stack your discs one on top of the other. This will cause warpage and scratches, especially for discs that have any kind of decoration, such a foil hot stamp or a paper label. In addition, always try to store each disc in a plastic bag. If they are to be stored in a cardboard box, circular tube, or on a rack, pack them loosely and keep them in a vertical position.

•   For antique discs that are still in their original packaging, you might want to consider placing them individually into an unused pizza box type container. This will protect your most valuable discs and packaging from sunlight and further damage.

•   After a few months of direct sunlight, the color pigment in your discs and the packaging may start to fade. For long term storage try to store your collectibles in a cool, dry place. Collections that are displayed on the wall or in a showcase etc., will do fine if they are not directly exposed to sunlight. Very cold temperatures can cause certain antique discs to crack, especially if they are tightly packed.

Taking Care of Your Collection

Any collection that is displayed on a wall, showcase, or in any open area will collect dust and other particles produced by smoking or airborne materials. Therefore, it is always a good practice to dust each disc with a soft, dry cloth once a month. Remember that you are dealing with shiny, smooth plastic that can develop fine scratches if handled improperly. Any decoration such as a foil hot stamp or paper label can lose some of its luster or sharpness if it is subjected to repeated physical abuse.

If you have just purchased a disc at a flea market or garage sale, chances are that it will be necessary to wash it. Always use a mild detergent, warm water and a soft non-abrasive cloth or sponge. Be extra careful not to get water or any other potentially damaging substance on a paper or foil label. Wash around the label. There is nothing that you can do to improve the look, value, or condition of a paper or foil label. Chances are, anything you try will only damage the label, so leave it alone. The hot stamped foil decoration can also be damaged by abusive handling.

All of your most valuable collector items should be left in their original condition. There is nothing that can be done to improve the value or look of an antique or favorite disc. Antique discs are popular and valuable, in part, because they look old. It is highly unlikely that you will find a 45 year old mint condition plastic disc in its original mint package. Signs of age, therefore, are as respectable on your disc as they are on a venerable grandparent.

There are a few counterfeit discs out there to be aware of, so always look closely at anything in mint condition that someone wants you to pay a small fortune for. For instance, bootlegged discs have been found that ape Wham-O's 1958 Flying Saucer. There are also antiques that have been reissued where the original mold was used to produce new versions or parts. These discs are listed in the price guide in chapter V. (The Giant Mystery Y, Sailing Satellite, Whiz-EEE, and Sky Pie, are other examples of antique discs that have been reissued.)

Also, be careful when showing your collection to others. Even mildly inquisitive fingers can be as threatening to one of your antique discs as a grizzly's paws. Fingernails can leave scratches and sometimes deep little grooves on the underside of the disc. Always proceed with caution and a friendly warning, when handing one of your highly prized collectibles over to the scrutiny of an admirer.

I remember an incident that happened many years ago at the home of Dan "Stork" Roddick, former long time Sports Promotion Director for (Wham-O/IFA). He was showing a prized item to the king of all disc collectors, John Kirkland. The item was a blue prototype Wham-O disc that mysteriously glowed in the dark, even though it wasn't supposed to. Stork called it the "Blue Moon," and he was almost infatuated enough to spoon with it! As John was inspecting this rare disc, he gave it a little squeeze (to get a "feel" for it) and the "Blue Moon" cracked, quickly turning into two half moons!

I think I last saw John running through the woods in New Jersey somewhere, with Stork closing in on him. After this incident, most collectors could be heard muttering a version of the Charmin mantra, "Please don't squeeze the disc!"

Displaying Your Collection

There are numerous ways in which a disc collection can be displayed. Take a look at the photographs in this book. All you need is a little imagination and some wall space. There even are specialized, plastic "frisbee hangers" the dedicated collector can purchase.

Frisbees come in a wide assortment of colors and sizes. One of the smallest is a Mini measuring only 3 3/4 inches in diameter. At the other end of the scale is the nearly two feet wide, CPI Saucer Tosser which is almost large enough to start a U.F.O. flap! There are many different patterns or combinations of display that you can create with the range of sizes and colors you may find have landed in your collection.

Some collectors display all their glow in the dark discs on one wall. Then when the lights are turned off, these discs go on displaying themselves in a ghostly manner, creating a very unusual effect. Another impressive display is a wall full of hot stamp foil discs which will reflect the light in the room. The combination of using small discs and gradually larger discs in concentric circles, or by alternating different sizes is another effective design. Displaying a solid wall of discs is also pleasant to look at. If you can amass a collection like that of Ralph Williamson's, you will have a true museum. (See back cover).

One popular technique with antique discs is to display them chronologically, by the year that they were first manufactured. This makes a nice linear history of these important discs. Another technique is to create a "disc sculpture" of a geometric shape or object. Anything is possible. The most important thing is to just have fun with your collection.

Availability

When starting a frisbee collection, it is important to evaluate the category or categories of collectibles that you may wish to pursue. There are dozens of areas to choose from; going by your emotional response may be the best way to decide on a specialty. Thus, how the item looks, feels or what it represents may all factor in to what attracts the eye of the beholder. There are many discs that represent all sorts of things— popular product names, professional athletes, folk heroes and the very popular "space related toy" collectibles.

In addition, there are many collectible plastic flying discs which are now nearly 50 years old, and some Frisbie pie pans have been around for 125 years. Despite such venerability, the chances of finding a particular disc in near mint condition is both realistic and achievable. Most of the discs listed in this book are in the hands of collectors. Many will certainly be available for sale or trade. Also, it's more than likely that there are still quite a number of 1948 Flyin Saucers and American Trends Pluto Platters stored away in attics and garages. Plus, the dedicated searcher will still come across Frisbie pie tins in the New England area. Hopefully, the international exposure generated by this "first time" price guide will put more of these important and popular discs in the hands of collectors.

Aside from the personal value and pleasure of owning these important projectiles of our leisure time culture, there is good money to be made in frisbee collecting. Though I personally believe that it is much more fun and worthwhile to trade a disc for a disc, the escalation of disc values over the years has been impressive.

Assigning Value to Collectible Discs

Since 1948, nearly 300 million plastic flying discs have been produced and sold throughout the world. That's a lot to sort out! Assigning value to these is often tricky and subjective. Just because a given disc is nice to look at, can be thrown very far, only 2 were made, or it has a unique design, doesn't necessarily qualify it as being "collectible." What does? As with other collectibles, there is no single factor or "golden rule" governing the value of flying discs. The complicated/not so complicated bottom line is that somebody's got to want it! Such desirability is a combination of factors mostly guided by personal appeal and interest. For the most part, a disc or classification of discs should be considered collectible due to one or more of the following factors: condition, age, historical significance, rarity, novelty, aesthetic value, uniqueness, and/or popularity. In addition, serious players eagerly seek certain discs for their flight characteristics alone.

Once you focus on a certain disc classification, it will quickly become clear to you which discs are desirable and why. The collector who specializes in Wham-O Pro Models will likely value a "flamed black ring bandmold number 1 Pro" far more highly than a collector of golf discs. It's all in the (trained) eye of the beholder.

Grading Collectible Flying Discs

"Time wears" is a truism that applies to all things. It follows therefore, that finding collectible discs in absolute mint condition won't happen very often, even though it's a worthy goal of the collector. But by the time a disc travels through the manufacturing process en route to a temporarily secure shelf life, there will already have been numerous opportunities for the "wear and tear" of existence to affect its overall condition.

Plastic discs may come right off the mold flawed, yet in perfectly saleable condition. The discs are made first by melting the plastic by heating it to nearly 400 degrees, then pressing it into the mold. It is this wrenching process of heating and cooling the plastic that usually creates the flow marks "flaws" found on the surface of many flying discs. Some exacting collectors may find such marks to be detracting, but these can also be celebrated as unique "beauty marks" such as those which often enhance a person's face.

In addition to a flawless plastic skin, a disc to be designated "mint" must also make the grade in its baubly extras. Decorations applied by hot stamp foil, ink silk screening, or consisting of a paper/foil adhesive label, must be in flawless shape. In many cases, it is but a small particle of dust, dirt, or a tiny air bubble that leaves a blind spot or telltale "fish eye" flaw in the decoration.

Also, to technically pass muster, the lines of the decoration must be sharp, clear and continuous. Each of these factors must be taken into consideration when grading any disc that is claimed to be in mint condition. As this price guide notes, any disc found in a such rare state of flawlessness is worth considerably more than one with even the slightest of imperfections. But seeking perfection has its flaws too. Many flying discs in good to excellent condition await out there, to be treasured by lucky finders who won't part with them for the world!

The highly sought after Frisbie pie pan is also not likely to arrive in your hand in mint shape. After all, most will have experienced the delicious fate of having pies baked in them, so coming across one in its virginal tin sheen would be quite a coup. But Frisbie tins do exist that are shiny enough to see your reflection in them, and it's quite possible one or more of these may land in your collection.

Here, in descending order, are descriptions of the various grades of discs one may encounter:

MINT CONDITION: The disc should look as if a white glove service has handled it from the manufacturing process right on up to its ending up in your hands. In other words, there should be no marks, scuffs, scratches, or even imperfections in the plastic such as flow marks, specks of pigment, or the slightest warpage of any kind. The disc and package should be perfect! Of course, these conditions are most likely to be met for a disc that has never been removed from the original package it was sealed in. In such a case, the package must be perfect along with the disc it contains. *Add 35% to the mint price for a collectible disc in its original unopened package.

NEAR MINT CONDITION: This is a realistic and achievable grade that can be accurately assigned to many collectible flying discs (plastic or metal, etc.) During the molding, packaging and shipping process, such a disc could be slightly scuffed or marked simply by the handling of it from one procedure to another. If there is only a very slight scratch, nick, scuff mark, or slight imperfection in the disc or decoration, then the disc is in near mint condition. Its color and luster should not have faded or lightened in any way. (Note: Just because a disc is still in its original package doesn't necessarily mean that it is in mint or near mint condition. Any collector should give a disc a rigorous examination under a good light. Under such "hot seat" scrutiny, you may discover that there is some scuffing, nicks, or even scratching, despite the packaging.)

Also, check for possible warpage. (Table test: Lay the disc on a flat surface— its rim should be in complete contact) Of course, a Catch 22 problem that frequently arises is that one cannot completely examine a disc unless it is taken out of the package, in which case it will lose some of its special value. In such instances the actual condition of the disc will likely remain hidden forever.

For near mint designation, the packaging a disc may be found in must be unopened, and still be in sharp, crisp condition. If there is cardboard backing, the corners and edges should not be bent, creased, torn, or price marked with an ink pen. There can be only the slightest evidence of wear and tear. Add 35 percent of the near mint price to all collectible discs still in their original packaging. *Discs in near mint condition will command 85% of the mint price.

EXCELLENT CONDITION: A disc in excellent condition will appear as if it's been played with a bit, but not experienced a very active life. It will lack the scuff marks of hard contact, appearing to have only encountered grassy surfaces. Its color and luster will not have been affected— it will have spent minimal time in the sun. Only a few scuff or scratch marks will be present on the entire surface (top and bottom). Fortunately, most such blemishes will be found on the less prominent underside of a disc because the thrower's fingernails as he/she grips the disc are the main source of these. But, be sure there are no "delay" marks on the underside of the disc. These are the result of players balancing a spinning disc at the end of their finger— dedicated "freestylers" even go so far to attach fake nails both for practice and competition. Fine for the freestyler, but this practice results in "digs" in the underside of the disc that subtract from its value as a collector's item.

Also, for a disc to be in excellent condition, its decoration should be complete. Keep in mind that a hot stamped foil decoration will develop scratch marks more easily than one made by ink silk screen process. In either event, the lines of the decoration should be sharp, clear and continuous. *A disc in excellent condition will command 70 percent of the mint price.

VERY GOOD CONDITION: To be so rated, a disc will show the usual light surface scratches, minor scuffing, and wear and tear around the rim. Its color will not have faded; its original luster will still be prominent. There should be no deep chips or cuts within the plastic. Decoration, if any, should be intact and show only minor wear and tear. A disc in this condition will also lack the scruffy wear marks that come from contact with concrete and other abrasive surfaces. *Discs in very good condition will command only 50 percent of the mint price.

GOOD CONDITION: In this state the entire disc, especially around the rim will show moderate signs of wear and tear. Many obvious scratches, cuts, and delay marks may be present; however, there can be no cracks, or tooth marks signifying dog abuse. The disc will seem to have had at most only fleeting contact with abrasive surfaces. *Discs in good condition will command only 30 percent of the mint price.

FAIR/POOR CONDITION: Now we're getting into the ratty territory of pronounced wear and tear. Deep scratches, gouges, cracks, the toothy reminders of undue dog attention, and warpage will be evident. The decoration will likely be in tatters, or missing altogether. Unless a disc in this condition is rare or an antique, set it free, and pray it won't come back. *A fair/poor disc you might find worth keeping will only command 5 percent of the mint price.

General Notice

This is the first ever international frisbee price guide distributed to the general public. Readers not familiar with the collectability of frisbees may be quite surprised at some of the prices listed here for these. I have been fortunate to have been able to work with the most knowledgeable frisbee collectors from all over North America, and the prices listed herein are the result of consulting with these experts.

As for any collectibles, the prices you actually encounter may vary widely from those listed here. But this price guide gives the collector a good, solid sense of what any particular item might be worth on the open market. It will enable the buyer to avoid inflated prices that may on occasion be encountered. Prices are also based on my awareness of most major collectors' inventories so buyers are relatively assured against unexpected "flooding" of the market!

Note on Established Prices: a Disclaimer

One of the main purposes of this book is to provide the reader with a general introduction to frisbee collecting. The values or prices listed herein for collectible Frisbie pie tins and flying discs, and all other related items are intended to be used as only a guide. Prices listed are not the only prices or values for collectible flying discs and related items. These can and do vary from one part of the country to another. Auction prices will vary greatly for popular items. From one dealer to another, prices will vary depending on popularity, rarity, condition and demand. The author, publisher and printer of this book cannot assume responsibility or liability from any person, either directly or indirectly for any loss or misinformation that might occur as a result of referring to or depending upon this guide.

Major Collectible Flying Disc Classifications

Millions of flying discs have been produced over the years for almost countless purposes. Perhaps a majority of those produced have been for the purpose of selling a vast array of products. But more than a few have been manufactured for various odd chores, such as the durable one with a raised plastic bone in the center that your dog can happily gnaw on all day without leaving a mark. Of course, such a delectable menu of flying disc production is very inviting to the collector who likes to specialize.

Therefore, to give you an idea of some of the major classifications, here are 20 specialty areas for disc collecting, one or more of which may attract your interest. (Note: A particular disc can be classified in a number of categories. For instance, a disc made for a frisbee tournament in Sweden can be dubbed a club disc, a foreign disc, and if it was used for competition, can be also described as a throwing stock/playing disc. In this country, its main classification would be as a foreign disc. But in Sweden, it would be best described as a tournament disc! Disc classification, therefore, can be quite subjective, and in many cases is up to the collector to decide. A collection of Wham-O Pros, for instance, can cross over into 7 different classifications, including glo-discs, tournament, premiums, foreign, uni-color, Olympic and antique discs. But nonetheless, both for educational and organizational purposes, disc classification has its uses!)

1.   ANTIQUES: All flying discs in this class must be at least 25 years old. They can be made of metal, wood, plastic, paper, foam, or fabric. These antiques represent and chronicle the early history of frisbee sports. They are the most popular, hence the most valuable and collectible of all the flying discs. Examples of these include the Flyin Saucer, the Exhibition Device, Frisbie pie pans, the Sky Pie, Space Saucer, Magic Saucer, Jupiter 11, "It Came

From Outer Space," Pluto Platter, Speedy, Sailing Satellite, Sky Saucer, Olympic Pro Model, Zolar, and the Mystery Y. (Other antique models related to flying disc type objects could include the early game apparatus for quoits, discus throwing, clay/metal pigeons used in trap shooting, and throwing rings.)

2.   CLUB DISCS: There are many items to collect in this classification. These discs over the years have been produced and sold by frisbee clubs or other organizations around the world. They cover a wide spectrum of classifications, such as golf discs, World Class Gram-Series, Fastbacks and tournament discs. Some of these club discs are graced with high quality artwork and have garnered the "Disc Of The Year" award, which annually recognizes the most outstanding artistry to appear on a disc.

3.   FASTBACKS OR PREMIUM DISCS: This classification contains a few thousand different toy flying discs. Premium discs are low cost promotional vehicles produced to advertise companies, special interest groups, organizations, disc clubs and even individuals. These are usually designed in the shape of the Wham-O Fastback. They are approximately 9" in diameter with sloping shoulders and a 4-6" diameter flat imprint area in the center of the flight plate. The vast majority of these premiums are not valuable or collectible. However, premiums which commemorate a major championship, a celebrity, product name, or throwing disc, (i.e. for the event of maximum time aloft), or are of exceptional aesthetic quality, are collectible. Mass produced by manufacturers around the world, these poorly designed throwing discs are by far the largest of all the groups of flying discs.

4.   FLYING RINGS: These include any disc where the diameter of the hole is larger than the shoulder of the ring plate. Early examples of flying rings were made of metal, rubber, rope, leather and fabric. They were produced from the 1800s to the early 1900s. Most of the early metal rings weighed about 3 pounds. A lighter weight ring made of fabric in the 1800's was used in probably the first non-spheroid throw and catch game. The modern day "Aerobie" flying ring has been thrown farther than any other object; 1,257 feet. The vast majority of modern toy flying rings are made of plastic.

5.   FOREIGN DISCS: Any disc which was manufactured outside the U.S.A. comprises this class. The vast majority of foreign discs will have the country of origin displayed or engraved on the underside or topside of

the disc or on the packaging. There are nearly two dozen foreign countries to collect from. Most of these foreign manufacturers have produced more than one model. Some received a license from Wham-O to reproduce its line of Frisbee products.

6.   FRISBIE PIE PANS: There are at least 40 different Frisbie pie pans to collect. Some variations include lettering type, DEP or 5c DEP., hand stamped deposits, vent hole size and pattern, round or square shoulder, and raised or sunken letters (See Chapter VI for a listing of all known different styles of Frisbie pie pans).

7.   GLOW IN THE DARK: Flying discs in this class are made with a phosphorescent material, and indeed do glow at night with occasional coaxings from a flashlight to recharge luminosity. Most of these discs are dull or pale green or yellow though they have been created in other colors too. Glow in the dark discs have been produced by many manufacturers. One of the most popular of these among collectors is the Night Flyer, the first to be designed specifically for use in disc golf.

8.   GOLF DISCS: This is the newest classification, and a very popular one for collectors. Since 1976, over 100 different models of golf discs have been produced. In addition to stock models, hundreds of custom designs and artwork have made collecting golf discs very desirable. Most of these comparatively heavy weight discs have a beveled edge, and are designed for use on 18-27 hole championship frisbee golf courses, and for distance competitions. Golf discs that are heavy weights and do not have an imprint (blank) are highly collectible.

Manufacturers to collect include: Innova Champion Discs, Disc Golf Association, Brand X Mfg. Co., Lightning Discs, Discraft Products, Wham-O Mfg. Co., Destiny Discs, AMF Voit, Drastech Discs, Dynamic Discs and Ben Wal. (See the listing of disc merchandisers for golf discs and equipment in Appendix III, or visit your local disc golf course for more information. Careful— it's a great game and you may get hooked!)

9.   MANUFACTURER ONLY: This specialty area includes flying discs produced by one specific manufacturer, for instance, Wham-O, the leader in world wide disc production, and Innova Champion Discs a leader in golf disc sales. Or, for this specialty, a collector may seek one disc from every manufacturer, or one disc of every mold or retooling from all manufacturers.

10.   MINI FLYING DISCS: These are small (under 5" in diameter) miniature copies of disc companies' full sized models. Wham-O pioneered producing these and created many versions, based on the company's Master model. The original Wham-O mini, first produced in 1968, is a favorite item with many collectors. These first period minis have a small puddle or bubble of plastic located on the underside center of the disc. Mold numbers located on the underside near this "puddle" are A, B, G, E, etc. Many professional frisbee players have contracted for personalized mini disc business or greeting cards. Starting in 1970, Wham-O produced minis without the bubble protrusion. These are also collectible, as well as easier to find than their puddled predecessors. Other minis are made by Innova and Lightning Discs. Wham-O Pocket Pros and Midnight Flyers made by the Disc Golf Association are highly collectible.

11.   NOVELTY DISCS/GENERAL RETAIL: There are four basic categories within this class. First there are those engineered novelties which wear their welcome with unusual effects such as a whistling or twirling sound, battery powered illumination, LED action, attached streamers, and designs for spinning on a stick or finger, etc. Next, there is the general retail, a catch-all category for a wide variety of discs sold in retail stores. The third group of these is the mimetic. These discs are designed to resemble objects, i.e., cookies (There's a very tasty looking Oreo disc out there to be hauled in!), pizza with pepperoni, flying bottle caps. There are even flying sombreros, automobile tires, and pancakes, that one enterprising soul or another has put out. Finally, there are two-piece discs that are made from two or more separate parts that are joined together to form one complete disc. Novelties are the most fun discs to collect. Historically, these unusual flying discs have "bloomed" on the market for only short periods of time, say from April to September of any given year). But with the first frown of Fall these discs usually disappear from the marketplace, never to be seen again (except maybe at a flea market or garage sale!).

12.   OLYMPIC DISCS: This class includes any flying disc which has the official Olympic logo or any words referring to the Olympics games on the disc or decoration.

13.   "PRO" PROFESSIONAL FRISBEE DISC: These early Wham-O Pro models represent the beginning of "modern day" frisbee sports. They were the first frisbees to be nationally sold in sporting goods stores. In 1964, the first Pro models were designed with the official Olympic logo

on the label (Three interlocking rings on top and two on the bottom), making these also the first Olympic theme discs produced. In 1965, the Olympic logo was discontinued in favor of the FRISBEE Label. They are both highly collectible and a favorite with many collectors. Wham-O Pros were produced in a variety of colors with the following mold numbers: 1, 4, 10, 14, 15, 16, 17 and Split Digit 1-4 and 1-6. Mold numbers are located on the underside near the center of the disc. Tournament discs and collectible premiums were also produced with this model.

14.   PROTOTYPE DISCS: These are flying discs from the first test run of a new or retooled mold meant to evaluate performance and marketability before mass production, and are usually produced in quantities of less than 1000. Some prototype production runs are as low as 50-100 discs or even fewer. These discs are difficult to find on the open market. It is collectors with "inside" information who can sometimes secure a few such discs before they disappear. There are several conditions of manufacture that qualify a disc as a true prototype. One example is discs discontinued after the initial test run; another is when the first run is made from a different material than the original test run. When an original mold for mass produced, marketed discs is retooled, the first, but only the first run of resulting product, is considered to be a prototype. A first run product from such a retooled mold is at the same time considered to be a new model on the open market. Prototypes, if you can get a hold of them, are highly desirable. The best means for the new collector obtain these is to contact some of the collectors listed in Appendix III.

15.   SUPER PRO/CLASSIC SUPER PRO: The first Super Pro, a slightly larger disc than the Pro, was introduced by Wham-O in 1972. They were mass produced in two basic colors, (blue and orange) and in two mold numbers, 50 and 51, located on the underside near the center. There are many collectible items within this popular classification. Rare test market colors, tournament and premium discs were produced. Some Super Pros were hot stamped with an eagle design, while others had a larger paper label of an eagle covering the original eagle hot stamp. These items were sold in stores for a short period of time. The "Classic Super Pro" has a 4" label depicting the zodiac and was produced in a wide variety of color combinations. These were never sold in stores, which helps make them highly collectible items.

16.   THROWING STOCK OR PLAYING DISCS: Most serious disc players will collect particular kinds of flying discs which they use only

during certain competitions. Each event has preferred discs best suited for that particular competition. For example, avid disc golfers (and there are thousands of them) will probably own 50-300 specialty golf discs from various manufacturers. If a certain popular disc is discontinued for whatever reason, remaining throwing stock can become instantly sought after, either to be put aside for a collection, or saved for use in key tournaments.

17.   TOURNAMENT DISCS: This area is devoted to flying discs produced to commemorate or advertise world, national, and state/local tournaments and championships. There are many creative and beautifully designed discs in this classification. They include the North American Series, Signature Series, World Frisbee Championships, World Class-Gram Series, Pros, Super Pros, club discs, golf discs and Fastbacks. This is a popular class among collectors.

18.   UNI-COLOR GROUP ONLY: In this category the collector seeks discs of one particular color; red, green, blue, glow in the dark, etc. Uni-color collections can represent a wide cross reference of many different classifications.

19.   UNPIGMENTED (CLEAR) DISCS: These discs were produced without any pigment in the plastic. They are either transparent or translucent. They may have a colored decoration, such as a label or hot stamp attached to the top of the disc. They also can represent many different classifications.

20.   WORLD CLASS-GRAM SERIES: In 1975, Wham-0 introduced this new design for high performance sport discs. They were produced in six different weights: 86 grams, 97 grams, 119 grams, 133 grams, 141 grams and 165 grams. These discs were used to commemorate the North American Series, which were major national championships held throughout the country from the mid 1970's to the early 1980's. They were also used for the Signature Series in which World frisbee champions for each particular year had their facsimile signatures hot stamped on these discs, sold nationally in sporting goods stores. Signatories received a small percentage of the royalties. World Class discs also commemorate the World Frisbee Championships which were held annually at the Rose Bowl in Pasadena, CA from 1974 to 1981. Finally, there was the HDX Series version of this disc, a nearly unbreakable high performance Frisbee.

There are many high quality artwork designs in these series to collect and appreciate, including some which received "Disc of the Year" awards, which were in recognition of the artistic merit of their decorations. All Series discs come in a variety of colors. Their mold numbers 40, 41, 42, 50, 51, 80, 81, 81C etc. are located on the topside, or underneath near the shoulder or center of the disc. There are many different World Class hot stamped combinations and quantities that were issued for the WFC and National and North American Championship series. Also to be found are collectible art work samples that had very limited runs and therefore are scarce. Any of these added to one's collection will give it a very unique flavor. For this guide, I have tried to list models that were the first issue of these varieties.

Chapter V

COLLECTIBLE FRISBEES

Introduction

Thanks to the first class consideration by my many old time frisbee collecting buddies, I was able to review and evaluate nearly 25,000 flying discs for this price guide. Most of the collectible discs that were cut from the "starting lineup" could be featured in another book.

My plan was to feature a cross section of as many categories of flying discs as possible. Of course, antiques received special attention, as they are the mainstay of any collection. Nearly 95 percent of all known varieties of antique flying discs are pictured in the following pages. Most of them feature the popular "outer space" theme. As for the other classifications, discs were selected based on criteria of history, aesthetics and popularity. For example, there are probably 1000 different minis to collect. Of those, I was able justify picturing but a few of these spheroid Lilliputians even though minis have easily enough popularity and value to justify a book solely devoted to them. Likewise, I had to make tough decisions in every category as for what to include or omit. What's here is the tastiest of samplers I could put together. Many of you whose appetites are whet in these pages can further indulge by contacting one or more of the many knowledgeable disc collectors listed in the appendix. You'll likely find at least one who specializes in a category you find intriguing. But for now, enjoy the plethora of plasticus discus laid out here— it's our first Frisbee Thanksgiving!

• For this guide: I have listed all known manufacturers, dates of first issue, colors, mold numbers and most variations for each disc listed herein.

• In some cases, one color might be listed for a particular disc. This does not necessarily mean it's the only color available.

• The larger disc of the same type and design will usually command more value. (40/50 mold.)

• A complete set of any class or type of disc (ie, antiques, Night Flyers, WFC, HDX, Space Saucers, Frisbie pie pans) will command more value.

• Many of the designs that won the Disc of The Year award became very popular, and were reissued with other disc and imprint color combinations. This award was presented to the original/first run of the winning design. "First runs" (50-200 discs) could have been made of clear or unpigmented plastic.

• There could exist other variations of flying discs that were unknown to collectors at the time of publication. If you have one, please contact a collector near you who specializes in that particular classification.

• Prices for discs in a poly bag package include the header card as shown in AT-25. If a disc is photographed in the package, then the price listed is for that particular disc with its entire package. (Header card/poly bag.)

• Do not store batteries inside electronic and illuminating discs.

THE FIRST OFFICIAL COMPLETE BOOK OF FRISBEE PRICE GUIDE

Antiques

EXHIBITION DEVICE
A metal pie pan with two whistles, a color wheel and illuminating light. Only a few of these hand crafted "discs" where produced. Made by the Ball Can Co.
Extremely Rare. (Illustration)
AT-01 Walter Heekin 1933
Mint:$1995. Very Good:$998.

BUCK ROGERS FLYING SAUCER
This is probably the first "throw and catch disc" to be marketed in the United States. Constructed of two inverted "paper plates" and a styrofoam type core center that is fastened together with a metal ring.
Colors: White disc "plates" with Red, Black lithograph.
AT-02 S.P. Co. 1937
Mint:$625. Very Good:$313.

SA-LO
An original Sa-Lo from Camp Longhorn, Burnet, TX. A metal can cover used at summer camp for organized Sa-Lo flying disc games. Rare.
AT-03 Tex Robertson 1940's
Mint:$500. Very Good:$250.

FLYIN SAUCER
The first "plastic" flying disc. Injection molded of Butyrate plastic. Only 54,000 made. Raised Letters. Colors: Red, Yellow, Blue, Amber, Green, Black, Pink, Ivory, Maroon. Variegated. Very Rare.
AT-04 Pipco Products 1948
Mint:$895. Very Good:$448.

FLYIN SAUCER
AT-04A Close-up: Flyin Saucer Lettering.
(PAT. APPLD. FOR)

SKY PIE
The Sky Pie was sold with a triangular shaped wire catching device. The original Sky Pie was made of a softer and more flexible plastic and does not shine like the stiffer reissued samples. 1979 Reissue Bright Orange. Mint:$40.
Colors: Red, Orange, Maroon.
AT-05 Hall Mfg. Co. 1949
Mint:$525. Very Good:$263.

SKY PIE
Disc in package with wire catcher.
AT-05A Hall Mfg. Co. 1949
Mint:$795. Very Good:$398.

LI'L ABNER'S FLYIN SAUCER
Second Period Flyin Saucer-Hard Plastic. The "first premium" disc made from the original 1948 Flyin Saucer mold. "Pat. Appld. For" appears on the top center. Only 5000 made. Many found.
Colors: Red, Blue, Yellow.
Mint:$275. Very Good:$138.
Colors: White, Green, Black, Pink, Variegated. Very Rare.
AT-06 Pipco Products 1950
Mint:$695. Very Good:$348.

LI'L ABNER'S FLYIN SAUCER
AT-06A Second Period. Paper insert.

LI'L ABNER'S FLYIN SAUCER
AT-06B Second Period. Close-up of script PAT. APPLD. FOR under label.

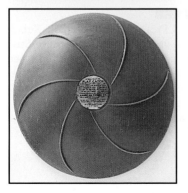

AMERICAN TRENDS FLYIN SAUCER
Third Period Flyin Saucer-Soft Poly. Only 2000 were reportedly sold via mail order at La Puente, CA with an American Trends "New Way To Play Catch" label. Not all packaged discs had labels. Label in photo is a black & white copy of the original. Difficult to detect an original 1953 issue without the label. Off-color disc could be an original sample.
Colors: Red, Yellow, Orange, Blue, Brown, Variegated. Very Rare.
AT-07 American Trends 1953
Mint: $795. Very Good:$398.

AMERICAN TRENDS FLYIN SAUCER

Third Period. Close-up of script: Flyin Saucer. Pat Pend.(under the label). Hundreds of Flyin Saucers were sold without a label during the 1950's.
AT-07A Pipco 1950's

AMERICAN TRENDS FLYIN SAUCER

Third Period. Flyin Saucer in package (without label). Header card not shown.
AT-08 Pipco 1953
MInt: $610. Very Good: $305.

FLYIN SAUCER DISNEYLAND PACKAGE

Same as the "soft poly" only in this style Disney package. Hundreds of Flyin Saucers without labels were sold at Disneyland and elsewhere.
Colors: Various. No label. Rare.
Header card not shown.
AT-09 Pipco 1953
Mint:$495. Very Good:$248.

SPACE SAUCER

First Generation Prototype. Ernest (Bill) Robes hand formed the first of five different Space Saucers in his log cabin by compressing a heated sheet of plastic into a die made from a washing machine agitator. They were trimmed and stamped by hand. Lettering is larger and more spaced apart.
Colors: Red. Rare.
AT-10 Bill Robes 1953
Mint:$450. Very Good:$225.

SPACE SAUCER
Prototype. Lettering is slight
ly smaller and closer to-
gether. Colors: Red. Rare.
AT-11 Bill Robes 1953
Mint:$450.VeryGood:$225.

SPACE SAUCER
Prototype. Lettering includes:
"Trade Mark Reg."
Colors: Red. Rare.
AT-12 Bill Robes 1954
Mint:$450.Very Good:$225.

SPACE SAUCER
AT-12A Close-up: "Trade
Mark Reg."

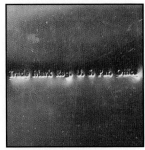

SPACE SAUCER
Prototype. Space Saucer let-
tering is spaced apart. Trade
Mark Reg. U.S. Pat. Office.
Colors: Red. Rare.
AT-13 Bill Robes 1954
Mint:$450.Very Good:$225.

SPACE SAUCER
AT-13A Close-up: "Trade
Mark Reg. U.S. Pat. Office".

SPACE SAUCER
Prototype. Script is closer
together. Mfg. by E.C Robes
Etna, N.H. Trade Mark Reg.
Colors: Red. Rare.
AT-14 Bill Robes 1954
Mint:$550.Very Good:$275.

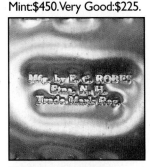

SPACE SAUCER
AT-14A Close-up: "Mfg. by
E.C. Robes Etna, N.H. Trade
Mark Reg."

SPACE SAUCER
Second Generation.
First Period. This generation
was injection molded of

stiff plastic. Ribs located on
the underside taper off
near the rim. REG. US PAT.
OFF. is engraved on the
topside under the word
"Space." Rare.
Colors: Red, Blue, Yellow,
Green, Turquoise,
Marbleized.
AT-15 Bill Robes 1955
Mint:$345.Very Good:$173.

SPACE SAUCER
AT-15A Detail of ribs found on the bottom of the Second Generation. First Period. Ribs taper off at the end.

SPACE SAUCER
Second Generation.
Second Period.
Bottom ribs do not taper off. They are thicker at the end. Rare.
Colors: Red, Blue, Yellow, Green, Turquoise, Marbleized.
AT-16 Bill Robes 1955
Mint:$345. Very Good:$173.

SPACE SAUCER
Second Generation.
Third Period. Bottom ribs extend into the triangular section. Rare.
Colors: Various, especially variegated.
AT-17 Bill Robes 1956
Mint:$345. Very Good:$173.

SPACE SAUCER
Second Generation.
Fourth Period. Bottom rib design same as third period. Rare. PAT. APLD. FOR added above the word Space Saucer.
AT-18 Bill Robes 1955-6
Mint:$345. Very Good:$173.

SPACE SAUCER
AT-18A Fourth Period.
Close-up: PAT. APLD. FOR.

SPACE SAUCER
Second Generation.
Fifth Period. Topside engraving same as fourth period. No ribs underneath, only triangle shapes near rim. New script states, "Caution Do Not Throw Aginst (sic) Hard Surfaces." (Common Period – Many Found).
Colors: Various.
AT-19 Bill Robes 1957-9
Mint:$175. Very Good:$88.

SPACE SAUCER
Second Generation.
Fifth Period.
AT-19A Closeup: Misspelled "Aginst".

SPACE SAUCER
Second Generation. Sixth Period."Soft Poly" Space Saucer with the word Frisbee on packaging. No engraving on bottom of disc. Header card not shown. Colors: Yellow, Green. Rare.
AT-20 Bill Robes 1959-60
Mint:$565.Very Good:$283.

IT CAME FROM OUTER SPACE FLYING SAUCER
This disc has a very shallow rim and measures under 7 3/4 inches in diameter. It resembles a UFO spaceship with 6 circles and 6 shallow arcuate veins engraved on the top surface. Colors: Red, Green, Blue. Rare.
AT-21 C&W Plastics 1955
Mint:$425.Very Good:$213.

AMERICAN TRENDS PLUTO PLATTER FLYING SAUCER
This was the first true modern frisbee design. They were only sold via mail order by Fred Morrison in La Puente, CA. Planet names around shoulder. Play Catch – Invent Games & American Trends Co. is engraved on the underside. Note: The words Wham-O or Frisbee do not appear on the disc or packaging.
Very Rare. Price includes disc with label.
AT-22 (Left) Fred Morrison 1955-6
Colors: Red, Yellow, Blue.
Mint:$795.Very Good:$398.
Colors: Black, Green, Brown. Extremely Rare.
Mint:$1250.Very Good:$625.

AT-22A Close-up: American Trends Script. (Center)
AT-22B Close-up: American Trends Company label underneath disc. (Right)

WHAM-O PLUTO PLATTER FLYING SAUCER

First Period. The First Period Pluto Platter will only have the word Wham-O inscribed once. An esker located on the underside covers the original American Trends script and the name Wham-O is added with Pat. Pend., plus a Wham-O (Wam-O) sticker. The word Frisbee does not appear on the disc or packaging. The center dome will have ribs. Frisbee was added to packaging, header card and disc after June 17, 1957.

Colors: Red, Yellow, Blue, Green, Apricot, White.
AT-23 (Left) Wham-O E1957
Mint:$495. Very Good:$248.
Colors: White. Rare. (No Photo).
Mint:$595. Very Good:$298.

AT-23A Close-up: Center dome with rib design.(Center)
AT-23B Close-up: Wham-O/Wam-o sticker. (Right)

WHAM-O PLUTO PLATTER FLYING SAUCER

First Period disc in First Period package without the word Frisbee.
(Header card not shown).
(First produced E1957).
Rare.
AT-24
Mint:$895. Very Good:$448.

WHAM-O PLUTO PLATTER FLYING SAUCER

First Period disc in Second Period package with header card and the word Frisbee.
(First produced after June 17, 1957.)
AT-25
Mint:$669. Very Good:$335.

PLUTO PLATTER

Second Period. The second period will have the word Wham-O inscribed three times and Frisbee once. No circle R after Frisbee. An esker with the Wham-O name and Pat. Pend. appear on the underside. Ribs on the center dome.
Colors: Red, Blue, Green, Brown, Apricot, Yellow.
AT-26 Wham-O 1958-9
Mint:$275. Very Good:$138.

PLUTO PLATTER
Third Period design will have no ribs on dome. Close-up: Dome with no ribs.
Colors: Red, Blue, Green, Brown, Apricot, Yellow
AT-27 Wham-O 1959-60
Mint:$250. Very Good:$125.

PLUTO PLATTER
Fourth Period with the addition of trademark symbol circle R after Frisbee. No ribs on dome. Rare. Close-up of circle R trademark symbol.
Colors: Red, Blue, Yellow, Apricot.
AT-28 Wham-O E1960's
Mint:$450. Very Good:$225.

PLUTO PLATTER
Sixth Period with no eskers and the inscription Des. Pat. 183626. Rare.
Colors: Red.
AT-29 Wham-O E1960's
Mint:$450. Very Good:$225.

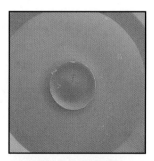

PLUTO PLATTER
Seventh Period with the addition of a backwards number one mold. Rare.
Colors: Red, Blue, Apricot.
AT-30 Wham-O E1960's
Mint:$325. Very Good:$163.

— No Photo —
Fifth Period.
Two eskers. Rare.
Colors: Red.
AT-31 Wham-O E1960's
Mint:$450. Very Good:$225.

WHAM-O PLUTO PLATTER FLYING SAUCER HORSESHOE GAME
The first Horseshoe game issued by Wham-O was called a "Pluto Platter" Flying Saucer Horseshoe Game, and was packaged with four First Period Pluto Platters, two lengths of cord (not shown) and two wooden stakes. Wooden stakes and discs will have

the "Wam-O" stickers.
Colors: Red, Blue, Yellow, Green. Very Rare.
AT-32 Wham-O 1957
Mint:$2995.
Very Good:$1498.
After 1957 - 60, this Wham-O "Pluto Platter" game could have been packaged with a combination of Pluto Platters, Speedys or Flying Saucer models.

Wham-O Pluto Platter Flying Saucer Horseshoe Game. Packaged with (four) Second Period Pluto Platters. (Early/Late).
Very Rare. (No Photo)
AT-32A Wham-O 1958
Mint:$2250. Very Good:$1125.

SAILING SATELLITE
Second Period.
Colors: Red, Yellow, Blue,
Apricot.
(Frisbee does not appear on
disc or packaging)
AT-33 Wham-O 1957
Mint: $450. Very Good: $225.
First Period.
Color: Silver. (No photo)
Mint:$550. Very Good:$275.

SAILING SATELLITE
Second Period in package.
AT-34 Wham-O 1957
Mint:$608. Very Good:$304.
(Reissued in White 1979.
Mint: $45.)

MARS PLATTER
This disc is a "knock off" of
the Morrison/Wham-O Plu-
to Platter. The original Mars
Platter will have the planets
Venus and Mars (in that or-
der) directly above the word
Mars located in the center of
the disc. "Play Catch" script
is located on the underside.
Colors: Sky Blue, Dark Blue,
Green, Brown.
AT-35 Premier Products 1958
Mint:$425. Very Good:$213.

MARS PLATTER
With the word Frisbee on
underside. Rare.
Colors: Various.
AT-36 Premier Products
1961-2
Mint:$450. Very Good:$225.

MARS PLATTER
This item probably is an
illegal copy of the original
Premier knock-off of the
Morrison/Wham-O Pluto
Platter. The words Mars and
Venus (reverse order)
appear directly above the
word Mars. (Esker) Premier
Products Co.
Colors: Powder Blue.
AT-37 Premier Products
L1950's
Mint:$375. Very Good:$188.

MARS PLATTER
AT-37A Close-up: (Esker)
Premier Products. (Knock-
off.)

ZOLAR FLYING SAUCER

This is the first disc to feature a hot stamp decoration. Knock-off of Morrison/ Wham-O Design Patent. The packaging does have the words "Play Frisbee." Colors: Red, Blue, Silver, Turquoise.
HS: White. Rare.
AT-38 Empire Plastics 1958
Mint:$425.Very Good:$213.

SPEEDY-FLYING SAUCER

This disc will have the word Speedy only on the packaging.
Colors: White.
AT-39 Wham-O 1958-66
Mint:$225.Very Good:$113.
Colors: Apricot, Green. Rare.
Mint:$450.Very Good:$225.

FLYING SAUCER

Many variations and dates of production. Discs were made with or without names of planets, ridges, small or large circle R and different mold numbers. (Disc with Pat. Pend., Mold 2 and no planets names are priced at Mint: $425.)
Colors: Red. Yellow, Blue, Apricot.
AT-40 Wham-O 1958-64
Mint:$175.Very Good:$88.

FRISBEE JR.

Fastback design small size disc four per package. Frisbee trademark name on package. (Frisbee golf type game on back of header card).
Very Rare.
Colors: Green, Blue, Yellow, Orange.
(Price includes package.)
AT-41 Transgram Co. 1958
Mint:$513.Very Good:$257.

MYSTERY Y FRISBEE

There is the letter Y on one of the player's T-shirts, and a description of a frisbee game on the underside. Two models made, Junior Frisbee and Super/ Giant Frisbee both are identical in design.
Colors: (Junior) Red, Blue, Yellow.
AT-42 Empire Plastics 1959-60
Mint:$395.Very Good:$198.

MYSTERY Y FRISBEE

Box Set. "Super and Jr. FRISBEES". Very Rare.
AT-44 Empire Plastics E1960's
Mint:$1375.Very Good:$688.
—No Photo—
Super/Giant.
Colors: Red, Blue, Yellow. Rare.
AT-43 Empire Plastics 1959-60
Mint:$495.Very Good:$248.

MYSTERY Y FRISBEE

Back of Box Set.
AT-44A Empire Plastics
1959-60.

MYSTERY Y FRISBEE

The Giant model was reissued in 1979 by Wham-O in Yellow.
Close up: There are four small nicks or lines located on the shoulder of the Cupola of the reissued models.
AT-45 Wham-O 1979
Mint:$45. Very Good:$23.

WHIZ-EEE GIANT JET FLYING SAUCER

Large disc with small center dome and four cones on top. Rare.
Reissued by the Brumberger Co. in 1977.
Colors: Various.
AT-46 Moncarch L1950's
Mint$:535. Very Good:$268.

SKY SAUCER

This disc was sold general retail and inside the Sky Croquet Game (Sky Golf).
Colors: Red, White, Blue, Yellow, Orange, Green.
AT-47 Copar 1959
Mint:$295. Very Good:$148.

SKY CROQUET GAME

Sold with six Sky Saucers, six yellow wire hoops with forks and instructions (booklet) for playing the game of Sky Golf. White box with Red, Blue lettering. Very Rare.
Colors: Red, White, Yellow, Blue, Orange, Green.
AT-48 Copar 1959
Mint $2590. Very Good:$1295.

ORIGINAL WHIRLEY WHIRLER

Sold with a catching stick.
Colors: Various.
AT-49 Whirley Corp. L1950's
Mint:$175. Very Good:$88.

KNICKERBOCKER'S OFFICIAL TWIRLING SAUCERS
Colors: Red.
Could have been sold with a catching stick.
AT-50 Knickerbocker 1958
Mint:$145. Very Good:$73.

WHIRL IT
Spinning Disc.
Disc is designed to spin on a catching stick.
Colors: Red
AT-51 Unknown L1950's
Mint:$125. Very Good:$63.

FLING-A-SAUCER
This large disc is almost identical to Empire's Giant Mystery Y Frisbee model. There is no "Y" on the player's T-shirt.
Made in Australia.
Colors: Apricot.
Very Rare.
AT-52 Unknown E1960's
Mint:$595. Very Good:$298.

MAGIC SAUCER
A "back to back" disc made of "ping pong ball" material.
Colors: Yellow, Red, Blue, Green.
Decals: Black, White, Brown.
AT-53 Liflik Products
E1960's
Mint:$195. Very Good:$98.

U1 SAUCER
A large disc made of "ping pong ball" material. Space theme paper decoration.
Colors: Red, Blue, Yellow.
AT-54 Eureka E1960's
Mint:$225. Very Good:$113.

U1 SAUCER
Standard model in package with decals.
Colors: Yellow.
AT-55 Eureka E1960's
Mint:$129. Very Good:$65.

PFI FLYING SAUCER

A dome disc with protruding outer ring rim. Ridges are located on the underside.
Colors: Various.
AT-56 Plastic Pipe Fittings E1960's.
Mint:$275. Very Good:$138

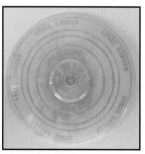

TWIRL-A-BOOM

Made of flexible and fine quality plastic. Disc has a dome center for catching on the finger or stick.
Colors: Green, Blue, Violet.
AT-57 Unknown E1960's
Mint:$275. Very Good:$138.

JUPITER II

A "back to back" disc made of "ping pong ball" material with Star of David on underside.
Colors: White.
AT-58 Abel Enterprises E1960's
Mint:$150. Very Good:$75.

HOLY TOLEDO

Aka-Atlantis.
Paper label: White, Black, Green.
Colors: Green, Blue, Red.
AT-59 Auburn Rubber Co. 1964
Mint:$175. Very Good:$88.

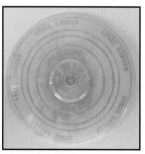

GEMINI INTERSTELLAR SPACE CRAFT

Space theme disc.
Colors: Tan.
AT-60 Unknown 1960's
Mint:$250. Very Good:$125.

INVENTED BY CAMP LONGHORN

The game of Sa-Lo has been played at Camp Longhorn since 1939.
Mold 1 & 2.
Colors: Orange.
HS: White.
AT-61 Colt & Dumont 1960's – Present.
Mint:$75. Very Good:$38.

GIANT FRIZZY

Reissue of the WHIZ-EEE. Disc has a small dome in the center. Giant Frizzy name on package only. Reissue discs are usually warped. Colors: Various.
AT-62 Brumberger 1977
Mint:$75. Very Good:$38.
Junior Frizzy.
Mint:$40. Very Good:$20.

WHAM-O MYSTERY Y

Wham-O took possession of Empire's molds. The Junior model was retooled with Wham-O Frisbee and ridges. Test run.
Mold 6 & 7.
Colors: Red, Yellow.
AT-63 Wham-O L1970's
Mint:$95. Very Good:$48.

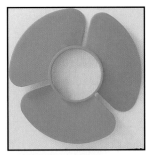

AERIAL KOIT

Disc resembles a boat propeller. Air Koit games were played with stakes and hoops. Only 1200 made. Colors: Red, Orange. Blue. Yellow, Green.
AT-64 Cleveland Plastics 1969
Mint:$75. Very Good:$38.

WHAM-O'S FRISBEE HORSESHOE GAME

Sold with four retooled Speedys with ridges and the words Flying Saucer, two wire hoops and two wooden stakes.
(1970 date on box).
AT-65 Wham-O 1970
Mint:$195. Very Good:$98.
Irwin Toy Frisbee Horseshoe Game. Mars Platters.
Colors: 2 Red, 2 Yellow.
Mint:$120. Very Good: $60.

CLASSIC SUPER PRO FRISBEE MODEL

50 Mold made in various disc and hot stamped color variations with an astrological paper label.
AT-66 Wham-O 1973
Mint:$135. Very Good:$68.

SUPER PRO FRISBEE MODEL

50 Mold (sold in stores). Hot stamped eagle is under oversize paper label. Colors: Blue. HS: Gold.
AT-67 Wham-O 1973
Mint:$100. Very Good:$50.

Club Discs

Frisbees produced in limited quantities by clubs throughout the world.

FLYING CIRCUS BERKELEY ULTIMATE
81C Mold.
Colors: White. HS: Black.
CD-01 Wham-O L1970's
Mint: $75. Very Good: $38.

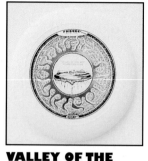

VALLEY OF THE SUN FRISBEE DISC CLUB
81C Mold.
Colors: White. HS: Black.
CD-02 Wham-O L1970's
Mint: $95. Very Good: $48.

OAK GROVE GOPHERS FRISBEE DISC TEAM
81 Mold.
Colors: White. HS: Black, Red.
CD-03 Wham-O 1979
Mint: $125. Very Good: $63.

MINNESOTA FRISBEE ASSOCIATION
40 Mold.
Colors: Yellow. HS: Black.
CD-04 Wham-O M1970's
Mint: $75. Very Good: $38.

JPL PHLYERS FRISBEE DISC TEAM
80C Mold.
Colors: Orange.
HS: Gold, Blue.
CD-05 Wham-O E1980's
Mint: $95. Very Good: $48.

HIGHER FLYERS
81 Mold.
Colors: White. HS: Black, Gold.
CD-06 Wham-O E1980's
Mint: $95. Very Good: $48.

HEART ULTIMATE
81C Mold.
Colors: White. HS: Black, Gold.
CD-07 Wham-O E1980's
Mint: $115. Very Good: $58.

ULTIMATE!
40X Mold. Colors: Glo.
SS: Brown, Dark Brown.
CD-08 Brand X 1981
Mint: $95. Very Good: $48.

Foreign Discs

Foreign discs can now be found from nearly two dozen countries. Many are of original design.

DISCO FLY-MOD CAMPEAO
Colors: Red. Paper label: Red, White, Blue.
FN-01 Novel 1970's Brazil
Mint:$40. Very Good:$20.

MOON SAUCER
Colors: Purple. Paper label: Blue, Gold, White.
FN-02 Reliable Toy Co. 1970's Canada
Mint:$55. Very Good:$28.

BATIOVNI
Colors: Green.
FN-03 Costa Rica 1970's
Mint:$40. Very Good:$20.

ROYAL WEDDING '81 LADY DIANA
50 Mold. Colors: White. HS: Black, Red.
FN-04 England 1981
Mint:$125. Very Good:$63.

ARIEL SKY SURFER
Colors: Red, Blue.
Paper label: Black, Silver.
FN-05 England 1970's
Mint:$70. Very Good:$35.

PROFESSIONAL FRISBEE DISC
Pro Mold.
Colors: Orange.
Paper label: Black, Gold.
FN-06 England 1970's
Mint:$30. Very Good:$15.

UNITED KINGDOM FRISBEE ASSOCIATION
Colors: Blue.
Paper label: White, Black.
FN-07 England 1970's
Mint:$60. Very Good:$30.

PAPILLON
Colors: Pink. SS: Black.
FN-08 Ethiopia 1970's
Mint:$40. Very Good:$20.

KITTA SCHUHE UFO
Colors: Brown.
Paper label:
Gold, Black.
FN-09 Germany 1970's
Mint:$65. Very Good:$33.

FLY BEE MASTER TOURNAMENT
Colors: Yellow.
Paper label: White, Black.
FN-10 India 1970's
Mint:$40. Very Good:$20.

CALIFORNIA 72 SUPER PRO
Colors: Black, Yellow. HS:Gold.
Paper label: Gold, White.
FN-11 Italy 1978
Mint:$75. Very Good:$38.

VOLA VOLA IL DISCO VOLANTE
Colors: Red. HS: Black.
Paper label: Gold, White.
FN-12 Italy 1972
Mint:$70. Very Good:$35.

GOLDDRAKE ATLAS UFO ROBOT
Colors: Blue.
Paper label: Multi-color.
FN-13 Italy 1970's
Mint:$125. Very Good:$63.

FREEZLY FREESTYLE
Collector's Series Pope
John Paul. Colors: White.
HS: Blue, Gold, Red.
FN-14 Italy 1979
Mint:$65. Very Good:$33.

SKY-LAB FRISBEE
Colors: Blue.
Paper label: Silver, Black.
FN-15 Italy 1970's
Mint:$60. Very Good:$30.

PROFESSIONAL DISC ROYANTE
Colors: Black. HS: Gold.
Paper label: Multi-color.
FN-16 Italy 1970's
Mint: $35. Very Good: $18

INVASOR
Colors: Red. HS:Silver.
FN-17 Mexico 1970's
Mint:$40. Very Good:$20.

WELCO
Colors: Orange.
Paper label: Gold, Black.
FN-18 Mexico 1970's
Mint:$40. Very Good:$20.

VIVA ASTRO DISC PROFESSIONAL
Colors: Blue.
Paper label: Multi-color.
FN-19 Panama 1970's
Mint:$35. Very Good:$18.

CNOPT TAPENKA
Colors: Blue.
FN-20 Russia 1980's
Mint:$50. Very Good:$25.

HAMMER & SICKLE
Colors: Yellow. Paper label:
Blue, Yellow, Black.
FN-21 Russia 1970's
Mint:$150. Very Good:$75.

DISC-VOLLEY MOD.DINAO
Colors: Yellow.
FN-22 Spain 1970's
Mint:$40. Very Good:$20.

UFO JUNIOR
Colors: White. Paper label:
White, Yellow, Blue.
FN-23 Sweden 1970's
Mint:$40. Very Good:$20.

APOLLO PILOT
Colors: Black. Paper label:
Gold, Red, Black.
FN-24 Sweden 1970's
Mint:$40. Very Good:$20.

EXTRA FRISBEE SPORTKORONG
Colors: Orange. HS: Gold.
FN-25 Sweden 1980's
Mint:$25. Very Good:$13.

DISCO PROFESSIONAL 250
Colors: Orange. HS: Gold.
FN-26 Venezuela 1990's
Mint:$30. Very Good:$15.

Golf Discs

A special Frisbee Golf Price Guide featuring 130+ collectible discs should be published this year!

NIGHT FLYER
The First Golf Disc. (Set numbered 1-8). 40 Mold.
Colors: Glo. HS: Black.
GD-01 DGA 1978
Mint: $125. Very Good: $63.
Set 1-8: $1250.

GOLF DISC
World Record Holder Master's Distance 1981.
40X Mold.
Colors: Glo. SS: Black.
GD-02 Brand X1981
Mint:$95. Very Good:$48.

WDCS 1983
Eagle Model.
Colors: Orange, Yellow, Pink. HS: Blue, White, Gold, Blue.
GD-03Innova-Champion1983
Mint:$125. Very Good:$63.

AERO
(Pat. Pend)
Colors: White, Orange, Green, Blue, Red, Purple.
HS: Silver, Gold, Black.
GD-04 Innova-Champion 1983
Mint:$95.Very Good:$48.

THE BULLET
Generic Stamp.
Colors: Black HS: White.
GD-05 Destiny 1983
Mint:$50. Very Good:$25.

FRISBEE BRAND
Golf Disc 150G.100 Mold.
Colors: Glo HS: Brown
GD-06 Wham-O 1981
Mint:$95.Very Good:$48.

AMF VOIT SPORT
Disc-Golf 21CM
Colors: White. HS: Pink.
GD-07 AMF 1982
Mint:$85. Very Good:$43.

GOLF SHOT 2
40X Mold #1-4
Colors: Glo SS: Black.
GD-08 Disc Wares 1981.
Mint:$75. Very Good:$38.

Minis

Miniature copies of full size models are popular with many collectors.

WHAM-O MINI FRISBEE OLYMPIC RINGS
Olympic label: 3 Rings Over 2. Puddle. A/B Mold.
Colors: Black, White.
HS: Gold. Rare.
MI-01 Wham-O 1967
Mint:$145. Very Good:$73.

WHAM-O MINI
Package (2).
3 Over 2 Olympic label.
Rare.
Colors: Black, White.
MI-02 Wham-O 1967
Mint:$392. Very Good:$196.

WHAM-O MINI FRISBEE OLYMPIC RINGS
(Pat Pend). Olympic label: 2 Rings Over 3. Puddle.
C Mold. Rare.
Colors: Black, White.
HS: Gold. Raised Letters.
MI-03 Wham-O 1967
Mint:$135. Very Good:$68.

WHAM-O MINI FRISBEE OLYMPIC RINGS
Olympic label: 3 Rings Over 2. Puddle. E/F Mold.
Colors: White, Black.
HS: Black, Gold.
MI-04 Irwin Toy 1967
Toronto label.
Mint:$75. Very Good:$38.

WHAM-O MOONLIGHTER MINI FRISBEE
Colors: Glo. Raised Letters.
Puddle. G Mold. Rare.
MI-05 Wham-O 1968
Mint:$150. Very Good:$75.

MOONLIGHTER MINI FRISBEE
In the package (3).
Very Rare.
MI-06 Wham-O 1968
Mint:$608.Very Good:$304.

WHAM-O MINI
Raised Letters. Puddle.
D Mold.
Colors: Red, Yellow, Blue.
MI-07 Wham-O 1968
Mint:$65.Very Good:$33.

WHAM-O MINI (3)
MI-08 Wham-O 1968
Mint:$264.Very Good:$132.

ED HEADRICK IFA #001
Colors: White. Puddle.
C/D Mold. HS: Gold, Black.
MI-09 Wham-O E1970's
Mint:$75.Very Good:$38.

RAGGEDY ANN
Colors: White. Paper label:
Red, Blue, Black.
C/D Mold. Puddle.
MI-10 Wham-O 1974
Mint: $100.Very Good:$50.

BRITISH OLYMPIC
Colors: White.
HS: Red, Blue. Puddle.
Oly Logo. H Mold.
MI-11 Wham-O 1970's
Mint:$75.Very Good:$38.

1976 WFC
Colors: Gold.
HS: Gold, Orange.
"Reserved Seating."
C Mold.
MI-12 Wham-O 1976
Mint:$75.Very Good:$38.

TOM McRANN
Frisbee Business Card.
Colors: White.
HS: Black, Silver.
MI-13 Wham-O 1976
Mint:$15.Very Good:$8.

INDIAN SUMMER '78 UFOS
Colors: White.
HS: Gold, Blue.
D Mold.
MI-14 Wham-O 1978
Mint:$100.Very Good:$50.

STARSHIP 1979
Colors: White.
Paper label: White, Red.
C Mold.
MI-15 Wham-O 1979
Mint: $125. Very Good: $63.

LITTLE BIG WHEEL FLYING SAUCER
Colors: Blue.
Raised Engraving.
MI-16 Unknown 1970's
Mint: $40. Very Good: $20.

PRESIDENT CARTER
5c Per Hour.
Colors: White.
HS: Green. D Mold.
MI-17 Wham-O 1980
Mint: $50. Very Good: $25.

MIDNIGHT FLYER
Colors: Glo. HS: Dark
Green. Numbered 1–8.
30 D Mold.
MI-18 Wham-O 1980's
Mint: $35. Very Good: $18.

LARGE LUNCH PAIL
Colors: Yellow. Paper label.
MI-19 Japan 1980's
Mint: $10. Very Good: $5.

THE GORBEE FLYER
Colors: White, Yellow.
HS: Metallic Green,
Rainbow logo.
MI-20 Flight Center 1990's
Mint: $20. Very Good: $10.

BABY FRISBEE
Non-Wham-O Issue
Frisbee knock-off.
2 Minis with Launcher.
Paper label.
MI-21 Japan 1990's
Mint: $65. Very Good: $33.

MIGHTY MORPHIN POWER RANGERS
5 Mini discs with Launcher.
Paper label.
MI-22 Gordy Toy 1994
Mint: $12. Very Good: $6.

FRISBEE MINI SUNSCREEN OIL
Level 6. 4 oz. bottle.
Colors: White, Brown.
Paper label: Multi-color.
MI-23 Wham-O 1980's
Mint: $75. Very Good: $38.

Misc. Accessories

A wide variety of books, magazines, posters, T-shirts, buttons, toys and frisbee jewelry.

WORLD FRISBEE CHAMPIONSHIPS
Metal buckle given to competitors at the 1976 WFC.
MA-01 Wham-O 1976
Mint:$75.Very Good:$38.

WORLD FRISBEE CHAMPIONSHIPS
Wood buckle given to competitors at the1977 WFC.
MA-02 Wham-O 1977
Mint:$55.Very Good:$28.

IFT 16
Button pin back.
MA-03 Jon Davis 1973
Mint:$35.Very Good:$18.

17th IFT JULY 6&7 PEQUAMING
Button pin back.
MA-04 Jon Davis 1974
Mint:$25.Very Good:$13.

DENIM FRISBEE BAG
Given to competitors at the 1976 WFC.
MA-05 Wham-O 1976
Mint:$60.Very Good:$30.

WORLD FRISBEE CHAMPIONSHIPS ROSE BOWL 1980
Given to competitors at the 1980 WFC.
MA-06 Wham-O 1980
Mint:$75.Very Good:$38.

$50,000 FRISBEE DISC GOLF BAG
Given to competitors at the invitational event.
MA-07 Wham-O 1979
Mint:$75.Very Good:$38.

1979 NORTH AMERICAN SERIES IF PIN
(Jo Cahow) Jewelry.
MA-08 Wham-O 1979
Mint:$50.Very Good:$25.

IFA PIN
Jewelry.
MA-09 Wham-O 1979
Mint:$20. Very Good:$10.

JOE COOL FRISBEE PIN "SNOOPY"
Jewelry.
MA-10 1979
Mint:$50. Very Good:$25.

1974 WORLD FRISBEE CHAMPIONSHIPS
Poster. Rose Bowl.
MA-11 Wham-O 1974
Mint:$50. Very Good:$25.

1974 WORLD FRISBEE CHAMPIONSHIPS
Poster. Rose Bowl.
MA-12 Wham-O 1975
Mint:$40. Very Good:$20.

FRISBEE JAPANESE INSTRUCTIONAL POSTER
MA-13 Iwamoto Trading Co. 1975
Mint:$30. Very Good:$15.

WHAM-O $50,000 FRISBEE DISC GOLF TOURNAMENT
Poster.
MA-14 DGA 1979
Mint:$35. Very Good:$18.

WORLD DISC CHAMPIONSHIPS SANTA CRUZ
Poster.
MA-15 Tom Schot 1984
Mint:$50. Very Good:$25.

ISLE ROYALE FRISBEE SOCIETY
The first Frisbee shirt.
MA-16 1968.
Mint:$100. Very Good:$50.

1974 WORLD FRISBEE CHAMPIONSHIPS
T-shirt. Colors: Red, Blue.
MA-17 Wham-O 1974
Mint:$75. Very Good:$38.
White T-shirt. Mint: $45.

1975 WORLD FRISBEE CHAMPIONSHIPS ROSE BOWL

T-shirt.
Given to competitors.
MA-18 Wham-O 1975
Mint:$75.Very Good:$38.

1981 FLYING DISC WORLD CHAMPIONSHIPS

T-shirt.
MA-19 Tom Schot 1981
Mint:$50.Very Good:$25.

FRISBEE WORLD

Magazine.
Volume 1. Number 1.
MA-20 Wham-O 1976
Mint:$50.Very Good:$25.

THE DALLAS DISCONNECTION

Magazine.
Volume 1. Number 1.
MA-21 John The Printer 1979
Mint:$50.Very Good:$25.

FLYING DISC MAGAZINE

MA-22 Palmeri/Guernsey 1980
Any issue. (3)
Mint:$50.Very Good:$25.

JAPANESE FRISBEE SONGS

Record.
Masato Shimon "Guts Frisbee" song.
MA-23 1975
Mint:$75.Very Good:$38.

JAPANESE UFO TIN SPACE TOY

Will launch space robot and two mini discs.
MA-24 Japan 1975
Mint:$150.Very Good:$75.

JAPANESE UFO TOY

Will launch a single mini disc.
MA-25 Japan 1975
Mint:$100.Very Good:$50.

THE OFFICIAL FRISBEE HANDBOOK

MA-26 Goldy Norton 1972
Mint:$75.Very Good:$38.

FRISBEE A PRACTITIONER'S MANUAL AND DEFINITIVE TREATISE

MA-27 Dr. Stancil E.D. Johnson 1975
Mint:$60.Very Good:$30.

FRISBEE BY THE MASTERS

MA-28 Charles Tips 1977
Mint:$40.Very Good:$20.

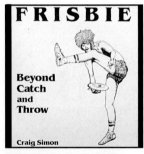

FRISBIE BEYOND THROW AND CATCH

MA-29 Craig Simon 1982
Mint:$50.Very Good:$25.

Novelty-Engineered Discs

These are collectibles designed to produce an unusual effect such as whistling, battery powered lights and electronic sounds.

UNITED STATES EXPLORER II
Hard plastic disc with two men sitting at control panel. Battery operated lights turn on when disc is rotating.
Colors: Yellow.
HS: Black.
"Glo in the Dark" light covers.
NED-01 COX 1974
Mint:$245. Very Good:$123.

SST SONIC SPACE TOSSER WHISTLE DISC
Attached whistles make noise when disk is rotating.
Colors: Yellow.
Whistles: Brown.
NED-02 1974
Mint:$95. Very Good:$48.

I.F.O. THE WHISTLING DISC
Designed to whistle when rotating.
Colors: Blue.
Foil paper label: Silver, Blue
NED-03 M1970's
Mint:$65. Very Good:$33.

WHISTLE-DISC
Designed to whistle when rotating.
Colors: White.
Paper label: Light & Dark Brown.
NED-04 Joyful Toy Co. 1970's
Mint:$55. Very Good:$28.

MI-FLIP
Battery operated disc will light up.
Colors: Various.
Battery covers "Glo in the Dark".
NED-05 Mi-La In E1970's
Mint:$95. Very Good:$48.

LFS-200 FRISBEAM
Frisbee trademark knock-off. Battery operated disc will light up.
Colors: Clear. HS: Gold.
NED-06 Diodart E1970's
Mint:$150. Very Good:$75.

FUTURE FLIGHT
Battery operated disc will light up.
Colors: White. Paper label: Black, White, Brown.
NED-07 Polaris Mfg. Co. L1970's
Mint:$60. Very Good:$30.

U.F.O LIGHT UP FLYING SAUCER
Disc will light up. Battery operated.
Colors: Clear. Paper label: Multi-color.
NED-08 CAP L1970's
Mint:$115. Very Good:$58.

UNIVERSAL LEO 7 SOUND-FLASH-UFO
Disc will light up and make noise. Battery operated.
Colors: White.
Decal: Black, Blue, Purple.
NED-09 M1980's
Mint:$85. Very Good:$43.

SUPERSTAR'S STARFLYER 118G
Disc will light up. Wayne Gretzky signature model.
Colors: Red. HS: Silver.
NED-10 Istari 1980's
Mint:$60. Very Good:$30.

FANTON 4
Battery-powered fan blades.
Colors: White.
Foil labels: Blue, Black, Red.
NED-11 1981
Mint:$45. Very Good:$23.

BUCK ROGERS INVADER

Gas engine powered flying saucer disc.
NED-12 COX E1980's
Mint:$175. Very Good:$88.

SKY SCREAMER FLYING SAUCER

Sound source when tail of disc is turning.
Colors: Various.
NED-13 1980's
Mint:$95. Very Good:$48.

TRICK SPIN

Center dome designed with ball bearings. Dome will rotate when spinning on finger.
Colors: Raspberry.
NED-14 Ultra Sports Inc. 1987
Mint:$65. Very Good:$33.

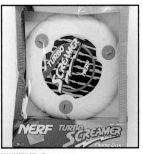

TURBO SCREAMER FLYING DISK

Soft disc with whistle built-in as a sound source.
Colors: Yellow.
Paper label: Multi-color.
NED-15 NERF E1990's
Mint:$35. Very Good:$18.

UFO SONIC SAUCER

Disc will light up and make noise. Center dome will flare open when in flight.
Colors: Red.
HS: Multi-color.
NED-16 Ku Chang E1990's
Mint:$60. Very Good:$30.

ELECTRONIC SOUND FLYING DISC-RAP RAP

Disc will play rap music.
Colors: Black.
Paper label.
NED-17 Chase Toys M1990's
Mint:$75. Very Good:$38.

Novelty-General Retail

A wide variety of space theme collectibles, etc. can be found in this catch all category.

WHAM-O FRISBEE
Regular model.
Raised letters. Various colors, mold numbers.
NGR-01 Wham-O 1966
Mint:$20. Very Good:$10

WHAM-O MASTER
Colors: Black.
HS:Gold,White. Double label with serial number.
NGR-02 Wham-O 1967
Mint:$60. Very Good:$30.

WHAM-O MASTER
NGR-03 Close-up:
Numbered label. Lower numbers have more value.

HASBRO-GLOWS IN THE DARK
Colors: Glo. Paper label:
Black, Orange, White.
NGR-04 Hasbro 1968
Mint:$95. Very Good:$48.

ALL AMERICAN FRISBEE MODEL
White. HS: Blue, Red.
Paper label.
NGR-05 Wham-O 1971
Mint:$25. Very Good:$13.

CPI ALL STAR
Single Band. Raised Letters.
Colors:Various. HS: Black.
Paper label: Gold, Black.
NGR-06 Continental
Promotions 1972
Mint:$65. Very Good:$33.

CPI GIANT SAUCER TOSSER
Largest retail disc.
Colors:Various.
NGR-07 Continental
Promotions 1972
Mint:$75. Very Good:$38

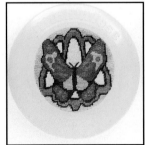

STITCH 'N TOSS
Two-piece disc with cloth center. Sold with yarn.
Colors:Yellow.
NGR-08 Slantzi Craft
1970's
Mint:$75. Very Good:$38.

KEDS SPACE SHIP
Promotional item given
away by Keds.
Colors: Various.
NGR-09 Keds E1970's
Mint:$30. Very Good:$15.

FLAPJACK
Rubbery disc used for flap-
jack guts game. Raised let-
ters. Colors: Orange.
NGR-10 Funstuf 1974
Mint:$40. Very Good:$20.

MASK RIDER
Japanese inflatable disc.
Colors: White.
NGR-11 1975
Mint:$50. Very Good:$25.

BATMAN & ROBIN
Colors: Green.
Paper label: Multi-color.
NGR-12 Azrak-Hamway
1973
Mint:$75. Very Good:$38.

SUPERMAN
Colors: Green.
Paper label: Multi-color.
NGR-13 Azrak-Hamway
1973
Mint:$75. Very Good:$38.

SPIDER-MAN
Colors: Green.
Paper label: Multi-color.
NGR-14 Azrak-Hamway
1973
Mint:$75. Very Good:$38.

FLASH GORDON
Colors: Various.
Paper label: Yellow, White,
Blue, Red.
NGR-15 1970's
Mint:$25. Very Good:$13.

WALT DISNEY
WORLD-DISNEYLAND
Colors: Orange.
Paper label.
NGR-16 Disney 1970's
Mint:$50. Very Good:$25

TEE BIRD
Colors: Red. SS: White.
NGR-17 Allentown Scien-
tific M1970's. Large Size.
Mint: $50. Very Good:$25.
Small size.
Mint:$30. Very Good:$15.

PUFF FLYING SPACE SAUCER
Soft foam with UFO packaging.
NGR-18 RBC Bros. E1970's
Mint:$88. Very Good:$44.

MICKEY MOUSE
Colors: Yellow. Paper label: Black, Tan, Red, Orange.
NGR-19 Azrak-Hamway M1970's
Mint:$85. Very Good:$43.

SKYRO
Original long distance flying ring.
NGR-20 Parker Bros. 1970's
Mint:$65. Very Good:$33.

MOHAWK
Flying disc made from carpet material.
Colors: Whitish Gray.
NGR-21 Grand Barron 1970's
Mint:$55. Very Good:$28

PYRA-DISC
Spin on your finger.
Colors: Various.
NGR-22 Positive Pyramids L 1970's
Mint:$25. Very Good:$13.

HDX 100
Mold #100.
Colors: Blue.
HS: Silver. First Run.
NGR-23 Wham-O 1978
Mint:$110. Very Good:$55.

NOODLE THE WONDER DOG
Foam disc.
Colors: Turquoise.
HS: Brown.
NGR-24 Nerf 1970's
Mint:$25. Very Good:$13.

GRATEFUL DEAD DISC
Floater model.
Colors: Blue.
SS: Red, Black.
NGR-25 Destiny E1980's
Mint:$85. Very Good:$43

HUMPHREY FLYER
Endorsed by Bob May, Distance Champ.
Colors: White.
HS: Red, Blue, Brown.
NGR-26 H. Flyer 1976
Mint:$85. Very Good:$43.

FLATBALL AMF
Floater model. Ball design.
Colors: White.
Imprint: Black.
NGR-27 AMF Voit 1981
Mint:$70. Very Good:$35

AMF VECTOR
Floater model.
Colors: Glo. Paper label.
NGR-28 Destiny 1981
Mint:$100. Very Good:$50.

ADJUSTABLE DISC
Sold with rubber weights
under the disc.
Colors: Dark Orange, Green.
NGR-29 M1980's
Mint:$95. Very Good:$48.

FRISBEE DOG WITH DISC AND FRISBEE CLOTHES
NGR-30 Japan 1980's
Mint:$100. Very Good:$50.

SUPER FRISBEE 14G
World's smallest Frisbee.
NGR-31 Wham-O 1980's
Mint:$10. Very Good:$5.

THRO-YO FLYING YO YO
Disc ring on a string with
wrist band.
NGR-32 Kidpower 1990's
Mint:$40. Very Good:$20.

TEENAGE MUTANT NINJA TURTLES
NGR-33 1980's
Mint:$60. Very Good:$30.

DISNEY'S THE LITTLE MERMAID
NGR-34 Spectra Star
M1990's
Mint:$50. Very Good:$25.

DONALD DUCK TWO PIECE DISC
NGR-35 Spectra Star
L1990's
Mint:$40. Very Good:$20.

MICHAEL JORDAN
Colors: Turquoise.
Paper label: Multi-color.
NGR-36 Mac D's L1990's
Mint:$35. Very Good:$18.

WF SUPERSTARS
ULTIMATE WARRIOR
NGR-37 Spectra Star 1990
Mint:$40. Very Good:$20

STAR WARS
NGR-38 Spectra Star 1994
Mint:$45. Very Good:$23.

Novelty-Mimetic

Frisbee "mimics" are designed to resemble objects such as a flying sombrero, a cookie or a pizza pie.

GOODYEAR
POLYGLASS TIRE
Colors: Black.
NM-01 E1970's
Mint:$50. Very Good:$25.

OREO COOKIE
Colors: Black.
NM-02 E1970's
Mint:$60. Very Good:$30.

DEUTSCHE MARK
COIN
Colors: Silver.
NM-03 1970's
Mint:$50. Very Good:$25

CALIFORNIA GOLD
KNEW RADIO 91
RECORD
Colors: Black.
NM-04 M1970's
Mint:$75. Very Good:$38.

COCA-COLA FLYIN
BOTTLE TOP
Colors: Silver.
NM-05 1980's
Mint:$50. Very Good:$25.

Novelty-Two-Piece Construction

These collectibles are made from two separate parts that are joined together to form one complete disc.

CONNECTION X-175

Two-piece disc partly hand crafted. Salesman sample.
Colors: Red Top,
Black Rim. HS: Silver.
NTP-01 Brand X 1981
Mint:$90. Very Good:$45.

VECTOR HYPER-FOIL

Two-piece disc. Limited run in a few retail stores. Made by Brand X for AMF.
Colors: Smoke Brown top, Silver Gray rim. HS: Silver.
NTP-02 AMF Voit 1982
Mint:$75. Very Good:$38.

SPACE SHUTTLE COLUMBIA

AMF Sport Disc.
Two-piece disc.
Colors: Blue Top,
Black Rim. HS: Silver.
NTP-03 AMF Voit 1982
Mint:$95. Very Good:$48.

MAGNA HDR

Two-piece disc.
Colors: Red Top, Red Rim.
HS: Gold, Blue.
NTP-04 Wham-O 1984
Mint:$60. Very Good:$30.

SPECTRA 137G MODEL

Three designs.
Two-piece disc.
Colors: Blue Rim.
HS: Multi-color.
NTP-05 Wham-O 1983
Mint:$45. Very Good:$23.
112G Model.
Mint:$40. Very Good:$20.

Olympic Discs

A disc representing the Olympic Games, Special Olympics or just incorporating the Olympic logo.

MONTREAL 1976
Colors: White. Paper label: Red, White, Blue.
OLY-01 IGC 1976
Mint:$125. Very Good:$63.

MONTREAL 1976 OLYMPIC SAUCER
Colors: White.
SS: Red, Blue.
OLY-2 Brand X 1976
Mint:$75. Very Good:$38.

GIORDANI DISKY
Colors: Orange, Green, Blue.
Paper label: Red, White, Blue.
OLY-03 Italy L1970's
Mint:$60. Very Good:$30.

MOSCOW OLYMPICS XXII 1980
Colors: Green. HS: Gold.
OLY-04 Russia 1980
Mint:$150. Very Good:$75.

MISHA
Colors: White.
SS: Black, Gold, Red, Blue.
OLY-05 Premium Co 1980
Mint:$60. Very Good:$30.

DANMARKS OLYMPISKE KOMITE
100D Mold.
Colors: White. HS: Red, Gold.
OLY-06 Denmark 1980
Mint:$40. Very Good: $20.

OLYMPIC MOMENTS JESSE OWENS-7/11
FB #7.
Colors: White.
HS: Red, Blue.
OLY-07 Wham-O 1980
Mint:$40. Very Good:$20.

OFFICIAL OLYMPIC FLYER LAKE PLACID
Colors: White. SS: Green Blue, Black, Red, Yellow.
OLY-08 Brand X 1980
Mint:$50. Very Good:$25.

1980 OLYMPIC GAMES MOSCOW
Colors: White. SS: Black, Red.
OLY-09 Premium Manufacturing Co. 1980
Mint: $60. Very Good: $30.

CALGARY OLYMPIC
Colors: Green.
HS: White.
Gold. Paper label: Oly Logo.
OLY-10 Inter. Insignia Ltd. 1988.
Mint: $40. Very Good: $20.

CALGARY OLYMPIC
DISK-175 GRAMS Howdy & Heidi Mascots.
Colors: Black. HS: Gold.
OLY-11 Inter. Insignia Ltd. 1988
Mint: $40. Very Good: $20.

OFFICIAL OLYMPIC FLIER
Colors: White. SS: 5 colors.
OLY-12 Brand X 1980
Mint: $60. Very Good: $30.

1984 OLYMPIC LOS ANGELES
90 Mold. Colors: Red.
HS: Blue, Red, Gold.
OLY-13 Wham-O 1984
Mint: $75. Very Good: $38.

SPECIAL OLYMPICS
Canada. Pro Model.
Colors: White. HS: Red.
Paper label: Red, White.
OLY-14 Irwin Toy 1980's
Mint: $50. Very Good: $25.

GO FOR THE GOLD!

Congratulations to all our Olympic Athletes!

BARCELONA 1992
Birdie model.
Colors: White.
HS: Red, Blue.
OLY-15 InnovaChamp 1992
Mint: $25. Very Good: $13.

USA (OLYMPIC) TEAM USA 1996
Imprinting over entire disc.
OLY-16 Wham-O 1996
Mint: $15. Very Good: $8.

Premium Discs

Promotional flyers designed to advertise cartoon characters, sport heros, celebrities or company products and special events.

EVEL KNIEVEL FLING-A-MA-BOB
Colors: White.
Label: Red, White, Blue.
PM-01 Ideal 1975
Mint:$30. Very Good:$15.

STAR TREK
Sold with a light stick. (not shown).
Colors: White. SS: Blue.
PM-02 Brand X E1970's
Mint:$75. Very Good:$38.

THE CISCO KID
Regular model.
Colors: Gold with Black label.
PM-03 Wham-O M1970's
Mint:$50. Very Good:$25.

OFFICIAL SNOOPY TOSSERINO
Colors: White.
HS: Black.
PM-04 Aviva 1970's
Mint:$35. Very Good:$18.

HARLEM GLOBETROTTERS WORLD FRISBEE CHAMPIONS
Premium test run with signatures of touring professional World Frisbee Champions, Victor Malafronte & John R. Kirkland. Fastback #1.
Colors: Orange.
Decal: Blue, Yellow.
PM-05 Wham-O 1974
Mint:$75. Very Good:$38.

HANGING GARDENS PASADENA, CA
Throwing disc for MTA/TRC with collapsed rim. Fastback #3.
Colors: Green. HS: Gold.
PM-06 Wham-O 1976
Mint:$50. Very Good:$25.

TOURNAMENT OF ROSES 1976 UCLA/OHIO
Colors: Red. HS: Gold.
PM-07 1976
Mint:$25. Very Good:$13.

ELVIS
The King of Rock' n Roll
Colors: Orange.
HS: Blue
PM-08 Brand X 1981
Mint:$95. Very Good:$48.

STAR WARS
Collector series.
Seven different designs.
Colors: Silver. HS: Black.
PM-09 20th Century Fox 1977
Mint:$40. Very Good:$20.

MARTHA BRINGS 'EM BACK (GUINNESS BOOK)
No slip grip.
Colors: Orange. SS: Black.
PM-10 Brand X 1980
Mint:$45. Very Good:$23.

PLAY SAUCER GOLF AT SOFT TOUCH
Colors: Blue. SS: White.
PM-11 Colt & Dumont 1970's
Mint:$60. Very Good:$30.

AMERICA ON PARADE DISNEY
Colors: White.
SS: 5 colors.
PM-12 Brand X 1970's
Mint: $40. Very Good: $20.

STAR TREK FRISBEE
Fastback #1.
Colors: Glo. HS: Black.
PM-13 Wham-O M1970's
Mint: $125. Very Good: $63.

CAPTAIN GRAPEFRUIT OUTSPAN FLYER
Colors: Yellow.
Paper label.
PM-14 England 1970's
Mint: $50. Very Good: $25.

RONALD McDONALD FUN FLING
Colors: White.
SS: Multi-color.
PM-15 Brand-X 1980's
Mint: $35. Very Good: $18.

AMF VOIT SAILOR
Floater model.
Colors: Clear.
HS: Blue. Paper label.
PM-16 Destiny 1983
Mint: $65. Very Good: $33.

LEASAT HUGHES SHUTTLE MISSION 41D
First Frisbee launch, June 1984. Rumored to be on board this flight. FB#19.
Colors: Black.
HS: Blue, Green, Silver.
PM-17 Wham-O 1984
Mint: $50. Very Good: $25.

Pro Model Frisbees

The original national sporting goods store Frisbee models. Pros represent the start of modern day frisbee sports.

PROFESSIONAL FRISBEE FLAMED PRO

Original prototype has a spray painted black ring band. Band has a dull finish. Raised letter script. Olympic rings logo 108 grams label. Mold #1. DES. PAT.
Colors: White only.
PRO-01 Wham-O 1964.
Rare.
Mint:$245. Very Good:$123.

PROFESSIONAL FRISBEE FLAMED PRO

PRO-01A Close up: Spray painted, flamed ring band. Edges are not sharp.

PRO MODEL

Fourth Period with patent number 186,626. Hot stamped black ring band with a shiny finish and edges are sharp.
Mold # 1.
Colors: White, Maroon, Turquoise, Purple, Chartreuse.
HS: Black. Paper label with Olympic logo Black, Gold. 108 Grams.
PRO-02 Wham-O 1967.
Mint:$130. Very Good:$65.

PRO MODEL MOONLIGHTER

Raised Letters. Split Digit 1-4 Mold.
Colors: Glo.
HS: Gold.
Paper Frisbee label: 120 Grams Black, Gold.
PRO-03 Wham-O 1969
Mint:$145. Very Good:$73.

PRO MODEL

Raised Letters. 108 Gram Paper FRISBEE label.
Mold numbers: 10,14,15.
Colors: White, Purple, Maroon, Chartreuse, Glo, Turquoise, Fire Orange.
HS: Black, Gold.
Paper Frisbee label:
Black, Gold.
PRO-04 Wham-O 1967-70
Mint:$75. Very Good:$38.
Glo. Mint:$100.

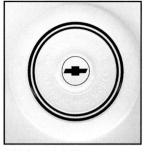

PRO MODEL
Canadian.
Double Black Band.
No Mold #.
Colors: Orange. HS:
Black. Paper Olympic
Logo label: Black, Silver.
PRO-05 Irwin Toy E1970's
Mint:$60. Very Good:$30.

PRO MODEL
Hex Label Double Gold
Band Raised Letters.
Mold #17.
Colors: Fire, Orange, Glo.
HS: Gold.
Paper Frisbee label: Gold,
Black.
PRO-06 Wham-O 1972
Mint:$45. Very Good:$23.

PRO MODEL
Premium.
Chevy logo label.
Mold #10.
Colors: White.
Double Black band.
Paper label: White, Black.
PRO-07 Wham-O 1969
Mint:$125. Very Good:$63.

**CAPTAIN JET
FRISBEE**
Premium.
No Mold #.
Colors: Glo. HS: Blue,
Red. Paper label: Yellow,
Red, White, Black.
PRO-08 Wham-O 1974
Mint:$135. Very Good:$68.

**START SOMETHING
WITH
WOLFSCHMIDT**
Premium.
Mold #14.
Colors: Green. HS: Gold.
Paper label: Gold, Red.
PRO-09 Wham-O 1974
Mint:$125. Very Good:$63.

CHUM 1050
Premium.
Canadian radio station.
Mold #16.
Colors: White. HS: Black,
Red.
PRO-10 Irwin Toy M1970's
Mint:$85. Very Good:$43.

Tournament Discs

These discs are devoted to commemorating world, national, state and local tournaments or championships.

1972 CANADIAN NATIONAL EXHIBITION TORONTO

CNE Irwin Frisbee Competition.
Pro Mold #16.
Colors: White.
HS: Red, Black.
TR-01 Wham-O 1972
Mint: $145. Very Good: $73.

1974 WORLD FRISBEE CHAMPIONSHIPS ROSE BOWL

The first World Frisbee Championships.
Fastback #1.
Colors: White.
HS: Red, Blue.
TR-02 Wham-O 1974.
Mint: $75. Very Good: $38.

1974 WFC PRO MODEL

Mold #14/15.
Colors: White, Yellow, Red.
TR-03 Wham-O 1974
Mint: $195. Very Good: $98.
Price is only for 1974 WFC discs with mold numbers marked with a felt pen on the Wham-O "Not For Resale" label.

1974 WFC PRO MODEL

TR-03A Close-up: "Not For Resale" label with mold number written with a particular marking pen.
14/15 Mold.

1974 WFC SUPER PRO

Mold #50. With "Not for Resale" label.
Colors: Orange, Blue. HS: Gold.
TR-04 Wham-O 1974
Mint: $150. Very Good: $75.
Single label (top) discs are collectible. Mint: $100.
Master model. (no photo)
Colors: White, Black with both labels.
Mint: $125. Very Good: $63.

NOTICE: 1974 WFC DISCS

There are green, glo, pink Pros with the 1974 WFC label. These discs may not have been part of the original issue. Red, White, Yellow Pros with both labels and no marking pen are collectible. Mint: $100.

OCTAD FLYING DISC CHAMPIONSHIPS

Held at Rutgers University. Retooled Super Pro model. Mold 50/51. Colors: Orange. HS: Blue, Gold. TR-05 Wham-O 1974 Mint:$100. Very Good:$50.

INTERNATIONAL FRISBEE TOURNAMENT IFT

Tournament used only label on underside. Pro Mold #15. Colors: Yellow. HS: Red. Paper label: Gold, Red. TR-06 Wham-O 1975 Mint:$75. Very Good:$38. Super Pro Yellow 50 Mold. (No Photo). Mint:$125. Very Good:$75.

1975 WORLD FRISBEE CHAMPIONSHIPS ROSE BOWL

40 Mold. Colors: White. HS: Red, White, Blue. Mint:$90. Very Good:$45. TR-07 Wham-O 1975 50 Mold. Colors: White. Mint:$100. Very Good:$50.

1975 WORLD FRISBEE CHAMPIONS SIGNATURE DISC

(MonikaLou/Bruce Koger/ Jo Cahow/Dave Johnson) Colors: Yellow, Turquoise, Chartreuse, Brown. HS: Gold. TR-08 Wham-O 1975 119G. Mint:$65. Very Good:$33. 141G. Mint:$75. Very Good:$38.

RUTGERS ULTIMATE FRISBEE

Fastback #1 Mold. Colors: Red. HS: Black. TR-09 Wham-O 1975 Mint:$75. Very Good:$38.

INTERCOLLEGIATE ULTIMATE FRISBEE CHAMPIONSHIPS

(Yale University)
Master model.
Colors: White. HS: Gold,
Black.
TR-10 Wham-O 1975
Mint:$150. Very Good:$75.

76' NATIONAL CHAMPIONSHIP SERIES

First Run.
Mold# 40.
Colors: Yellow. HS: Black,
Silver, Blue.
TR-11 Wham-O 1976
Mint:$80. Very Good:$40.

1976 WFC ROSE BOWL

Fastback # 5/6.
Colors: White, Gold.
HS: Red, Silver, Orange.
TR-12 Wham-O 1976
Mint:$55. VeryGood:$28.
40 Mold.
Colors: White.
Mint:$75. Very Good:$38.
50 Mold.
Colors: White.
Mint:$85. Very Good:$43.

1976 WFC

(MonikaLou/Peter Bloeme)
Colors for 119G and 141G
include: Yellow, Brown,
Chartreuse, Turquoise.
HS: Gold
97G, 141G.
Mint: $40. Very Good:$20.
141G
Mint: $50. Very Good:$25.
165G
Colors: Red, White,
Mint: $60. Very Good:$30.
TR-13 Wham-O 1976

WHIZBO A SPORT RENAISSANCE

40 Mold.
Colors: Yellow.
HS: Gold.
TR-14 Wham-O 1976
Mint:$50. Very Good:$25.

1976 NATIONAL ULTIMATE FRISBEE CHAMPIONSHIPS

(Amherst, Mass.)
Master model.
Colors: White.
HS: Gold, Black.
TR-15 Wham-O 1976
Mint:$100. Very Good:$50.

1977 WESTERN ULTIMATE FRISBEE CHAMPIONSHIPS

(Irvine, CA)
80 Mold.
Colors: White. HS: Black.
TR-16 Wham-O 1977
Mint: $75. Very Good: $38.

ASHLEY WHIPPET WORLD K-9 FRISBEE DISC CHAMPION

41 Mold.
Colors: Yellow. HS: Black.
TR-17 Wham-O 1977
Mint: $60. Very Good: $30.

77' NATIONAL CHAMPIONSHIPS

(John Bird)
HS: Gold, Blue.
TR-18 Wham-0 1977
40 Mold.
Colors: Clear.
Mint: $40. Very Good: $20.
50 Mold.
Mint: $50. Very Good: $25.
80 Mold.
Mint: $60. Very Good: $30.

1977 WFC ROSE BOWL

FB #17/18
TR-19 Wham-O 1977
Colors: White. HS: Blue, Gold.
Mint: $40. Very Good: $20.
40 Mold.
Colors: Clear. HS: Green, Silver, Blue.
Mint: $60. Very Good: $30.
50 Mold.
Colors: Clear. HS: Green, Silver, Blue.
Mint: $70. Very Good: $35.

1977 WFC SIGNATURE DISC

(John Kirkland)
(Monika Lou did not sign)
Colors: Red, White. HS: Red, Gold.
TR-20 Wham-O 1977
119G.
Mint: $40. Very Good: $20.
141G.
Mint: $50. Very Good: $25.
165G.
Mint: $60. Very Good: $30.

1977 CANADIAN SERIES CHAMPIONSHIPS

(Gail McColl)
40 Mold.
Colors: White. HS: Black.
Paper label.
TR-21 Irwin Toy 1977
Mint: $45. Very Good: $23.

20TH INTERNATIONAL FRISBEE TOURNAMENT (IFT)
Pro model.
Mold 14.
Colors: Fire Orange.
HS: White.
TR-22 Wham-O 1977
Mint:$50. Very Good:$25.

SMITHSONIAN FRISBEE FESTIVAL
40 Mold.
Colors: White.
HS: Blue.
TR-23 Wham-O 1977
Mint:$75. Very Good:$38.

1978 NORTH AMERICAN SERIES (IFA)
(Dave Marini)
TR-24 Wham-O 1978
Colors: Clear.
HS: Gold, Red.
40 Mold.
Mint:$40. Very Good:$20.
50 Mold.
Mint:$50. Very Good:$25.
80 Mold.
Mint:$60. Very Good:$30.

1978 WORLD FRISBEE CHAMPIONSHIPS ROSE BOWL
TR-25 Wham-O 1978
Colors: Clear.
HS: Red, Gold, Blue.
40 Mold.
Mint:$60. Very Good:$30.
50 Mold.
Mint:$70. Very Good:$35.
80 Mold.
Mint:$80. Very Good:$40.

1978 WORLD FRISBEE CHAMPIONS SIGNATURE DISC
(Krea VanSickle/Laura Engel)
Colors: Red, White.
HS: Gold.
TR-26 Wham-O 1978
119G.
Mint:$40. Very Good:$20.
141G.
Mint:$50. Very Good:$25.
165G.
Mint:$60. Very Good:$30.

1978 SANTA CRUZ FLYING DISC CLASSIC
(Ken Westerfield)
Colors: Yellow, White.
Decal: Brown.
TR-27 Disc Technology 1978
Mint:$75. Very Good:$38.

WORLD ULTIMATE CHAMPIONS
Santa Barbara Condors.
Disc Of The Year award.
TR-28 Wham-O 1978
80 Mold. White.
HS: Black.
Mint:$85. Very Good:$43.
80 Mold. White.
HS: Gold, Black.
Mint:$100. Very Good:$50.
80 Mold. Clear.
HS: Gold, Black
Mint:$145. Very Good:$73.

GUTS PLAYERS ASSOCIATION
Pro Mold #15.
Colors: Fire Orange.
HS: Black.
Paper label: Gold, Black.
TR-29 Wham-O 1978
Mint:$50. Very Good:$25.

AUSTRALIAN FRISBEE CHAMPIONSHIPS
Pro model.
Colors: Glo.
HS: Purple.
Moonlighter label.
TR-30 Wham-O 1978
Mint:$65. Very Good:$33.

1979 NORTH AMERICAN SERIES (IF)
(Jo Cahow)
TR-31 Wham-O 1979
Colors: White.
HS: Gold, Black.
40 Mold.
Mint:$40. Very Good:$20.
50 Mold.
Mint:$50. Very Good:$25.
80 Mold.
Mint:$60. Very Good:$30.

1979 CALIFORNIA STATE ULTIMATE FRIZBEE CHAMPIONSHIP
(Reach)
Disky model.
Colors: Raspberry.
HS: Black.
TR-32 Brand X 1979
Mint:$35. Very Good:$18.

1979 SOUTHWESTERN NATIONALS VALLEY OF THE SUN
Disc Of The Year award.
Many other discs and
HS combinations.
TR-33 Wham-O 1979
80 Mold. White.
HS: Black.
Mint:$80. Very Good:$40.
80 Mold. Clear.
HS: Black.
Mint:$100. Very Good:$50.

1979 UNITED STATES FLYING DISC CHAMPIONSHIPS
(Cripple Creek, CO)
81 Mold.
Colors: White.
HS: Gold, Blue.
TR-34 Wham-O 1979
Mint:$75. Very Good:$38.

CENTRAL STATES NATIONAL SERIES FRISBEE DISC TOUR
(Kansas City)
80 Mold.
Colors: Orange. HS: Gold, White.
TR-35 Wham-O 1979
Mint:$75. Very Good:$38.

1979 FLYING DISC WORLD CHAMPIONSHIPS SANTA CRUZ
(Jeff Soto)
Santa Cruz Mold.
Colors: White.
HS: Green.
TR-36 Disc Technology 1979
Mint:$65. Very Good:$33.

1979 WORLD FRISBEE DISC CHAMPIONSHIPS ROSE BOWL
Colors: Red, White.
HS: Red, Gold.
TR-37 Wham-O 1979
40 Mold.
Mint:$60. Very Good:$30.
50 Mold.
Mint:$70. Very Good:$35.
80 Mold.
Mint:$80. Very Good:$40.

1979 WORLD FRISBEE CHAMPIONS SIGNATURE DISC
(Scott Zimmerman/Teresa Gaman)
Colors: White, Red.
HS: Red, Gold.
TR-38 Wham-O 1979
119G.
Mint:$40. Very Good:$20.
141G.
Mint:$50. Very Good:$25.
165G.
Mint:$60. Very Good:$30.

SWIFRISBEE DISC JATTE-OS
(Sweden) (Jens Valasquez)
80 Mold.
Colors: Clear.
HS: Gold, Black.
TR-39 Wham-O 1979
Mint:$75. Very Good:$38.

FLYING DISC WORLD CHAMPIONSHIPS SANTA CRUZ
(Jane Englehart/Suzanne Strait)
Retooled Santa Cruz Mold.
Colors: Glo.
HS: Black.
TR-40 Brand X 1980
Mint:$75.Very Good:$38.

1980 WORLD FRISBEE DISC CHAMPIONSHIPS ROSE BOWL
50 Mold.
Colors: White
HS: Red, Gold, Blue.
TR-41 Wham-O 1980
Mint:$60.Very Good:$30.

1980 WORLD TOUR FREESTYLE PLAYERS ASSOCIATION
Skystyler model.
Colors: Black.
HS: Gold, Orange.
TR-42 Discraft 1980
Mint:$75.Very Good:$38.

1980 MARYLAND STATE CHAMPIONSHIPS
80C Mold.
Colors: White.
HS: Green, Blue.
TR-43 Wham-O 1980
Mint:$60.Very Good:$30.

FREEDOM FRISBEE DISC TEAM HOSHO FESTIVAL '80
52BE Mold.
Colors: Blue.
HS: Black, Gold.
TR-44 Japan 1980
Mint:$60.Very Good:$30.

FIRST ANNUAL 1980 TOURNAMENT SERIES NEW ZEALAND
Disc Sport Flyer.
Colors: White.
HS: Black, Brown.
TR-45 1980
Mint:$60.Very Good:$30.

1981 WORLD FRISBEE CHAMPIONSHIPS ROSE BOWL
81E Mold.
Colors: White.
HS: Blue, Red, Gold.
TR-46 Wham-O 1981
Mint:$50. Very Good:$25.

1982 SOUTHERN NATIONAL FLYING DISC CHAMPIONSHIP
(Austin, TX)
(Jens Valasquez)
Skystyler model.
Colors: Black.
HS: Blue, Red, Gold.
TR-47 Discraft 1982
Mint:$75. Very Good:$38.

HALL OF FAME DEDICATION DISC
80E Mold.
Colors: White.
HS: Black, Silver.
TR-48 Wham-O 1982
Mint:$125. Very Good:$63.

AMF VOIT VECTOR ULTIMATE 28:70U
Floater model.
Colors: Clear.
HS: Red, Blue, Green.
TR-49 Destiny 1983
Mint:$75. Very Good:$38.

1982 WORLD DISC CHAMPIONSHIPS V SANTA CRUZ
Sportdisc. Two-piece.
Colors: Brown, Black.
HS: Gold
TR-50 AMF Voit 1982
Mint:$125. Very Good:$63.

ULTIMATE AMF VOIT SPORT DISC 28:70U
Floater model.
Colors: White.
SS: Red, Black.
TR-51 Destiny 1982
Mint:$75. Very Good:$38.

1983 WORLD DISC CHAMPIONSHIPS
Sport Disc.
Two-piece. Medium size.
Colors: Blue, Dark Blue.
HS: Red.
TR-52 AMF Voit 1983
Mint:$100. Very Good:$50.

CENTRAL STATES REGION ST LOUIS
Disc Of The Year award.
82E Mold.
Colors: White.
HS: Red, Gold.
TR-53 Wham-O 1981
Mint:$100. Very Good:$50.

LA PEDA ULTIMATE SILVER CITY NEW MEXICO
82E Mold.
Colors: White.
HS: Brown, Black, Silver.
TR-54 Wham-O 1981
Mint:$75. Very Good:$38.

1986 NORTHEAST ULTIMATE REGIONALS PURCHASE, NY
Disc Of The Year award.
80E Mold.
Colors: White.
HS: Copper, Blue.
TR-55 Wham-O 1986
Mint:$85. Very Good:$43.

UPA NATIONAL ULTIMATE CHAMPIONSHIPS SAN DIEGO, CA
82E Mold.
Colors: Yellow.
HS: Purple, Black.
TR-56 Wham-O 1988
Mint:$65. Very Good:$33.

25th ANNIVERSARY WORLD JR. FRISBEE DISC CHAMPIONSHIPS
82E Mold.
Colors: Silver.
HS: Purple, Silver, Black.
TR-57 Wham-O 1993
Mint:$40. Very Good:$20.

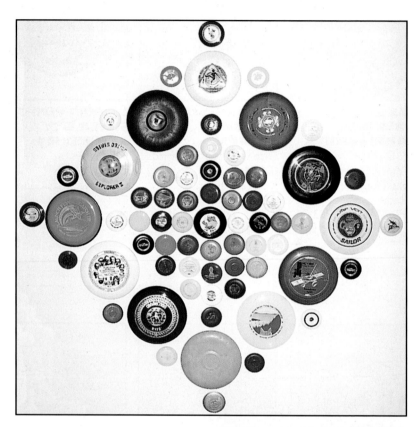

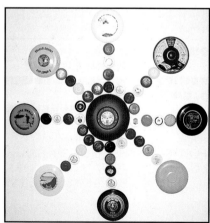 

Frisbee art. Some of the many ways to exhibit your collection. (Above center) Diamond. (Left) Galaxy. (Right) Glo in the dark pyramid.

Frisbee statues located at the Presidential Towers, Chicago, IL. by J. Seward Johnson. Photos by: Robert J. Malafronte

(Above) World Freestyle Champs, Evan David and Corey Basso, perform at the Rose Bowl World Frisbee Championships.
(Below) "Who wants to play?" asks Victor, the Frisbee Champ. Photo by: Iwamoto Trading Co.

This Frisbie pie safe filled with 127 Frisbie pie pans, one for each year since the bakery began in 1871, is the "Holy Grail" for any frisbee collector. (Malafronte collection)

Chapter VI

COLLECTING
THE HISTORICAL FRISBIE PIE PAN

Introduction

Play Catch – Invent Games. These simple words of advice etched in the plastic of every old Frisbee, continue the legacy of the metal disc they're named after— the Frisbie pie pan. Many of these tins, relieved of pie, found themselves soaring through the sky, their hard rims the cutting edge of a new pastime. Today, due to its central role in the history of frisbee sports, the Frisbie pie pan is the most important and popular antique disc to collect, and is the mainstay of any frisbee collection. Thrown for fun by employees of the bakery at breaks and during lunch, the Frisbie pie tin as flying disc became a popular fad for residents and especially Ivy League college students across much of New England, and indeed, the Northeast. This unassuming object gave birth to the "Frisbee," a unique, trademarked name that is recognized by millions of people around the world. A plaque should be commissioned and dedicated at the original site of the famed Frisbie Pie Company in Bridgeport, Connecticut, signifying it as the "Kittyhawk" of frisbee sports!

The Frisbie Pie Company: a Genealogical Introduction

The Frisbie name, in its various spellings, can be traced back through more than 1,000 years of British history, back to before the Norman conquest. In fact, according to the *Frisbee-Frisbie-Frisby Family Genealogy,* the name dates from the Danish occupation (of England) of the ninth and tenth centuries, for the final syllable "by" is a Scandinavian word meaning place or habitation. The family name is listed in the English Doomsday Book as "Frisebi," and is thought to have originated from one of two hamlets located in Leicestershire, England, one called Frisby-on-the-Wreake, the other, Old Frisby. Old Frisby isn't around anymore because its inhabitants, farmer tenants, were kicked off the land in the mid seventeenth

The original horse drawn delivery wagon used by the Frisbie Pie Co. Circa 1871 "W. R. Frisbies Pies." Credit: Historical Collections, Bridgeport Public Library

century during the so called enclosure period when landowners found sheep raising to be more economical and less labor intensive. Therefore, they fenced off the land and evicted the tenant farmer families to go fend as best they could. The other Frisby exists as a small hamlet to this day.

Just what link of the Frisbie family first settled in America is the subject of some debate. The record is clear that in 1644 an Edward Frisbie of England settled in Branford, Connecticut. He was one of the original immigrants to this area, then known as "Totoket." However, Edward's ancestry is less certain. The 1897 *Year Book of the (John) Paul Jones Club* notes that Edward may have been the son of Richard Frisbee, a Huguenot, who became a Puritan, then crossed the Atlantic in 1619 from London to become one of the settlers of Jamestown, Virginia. This yearbook, compiled by club historian, Oliver Libby Frisbee, states that Edward Frisbie was driven out of Virginia in 1643 because he was a Puritan, and settled in Branford, CT where he married Hannah Rose.

Nora Frisbie of Claremont, California, in a preface of the *Frisbie-Frisbee-Frisby Family Genealogy,* also finds that the historical record is not clear enough to positively identify Richard as being the father of Edward Frisbie, though she feels he likely was. There is no birth record for Edward Frisbie in America, probably due to his having been born in the ill fated Jamestown, Virginia settlement where birth records were among those lost or destroyed. It's also possible he was born aboard ship enroute to America. Nora Frisbie describes Richard, Edward's likely father, as having re-crossed the Atlantic to England with his family in 1625, and then as having returned to America with his wife, Margaret, infant daughter, Rose, and Edward in 1634 (another son, Peter, remained behind in England). Either on board ship or shortly after completing the journey, all but Edward are thought to have died as their names disappear from the records. The founder of the Frisbie family in America, therefore, is Edward, likely the sole surviving son of Richard on this side of the Atlantic.

The variety of spellings used in those days has also been a challenge for chroniclers. The original record of this period had Edward's last name spelled Frisbye. (This is the same spelling that was used by Edward in his will). Such misspellings resulted from lack of formal education, and/or carelessness on the part of record keepers who would sometimes record names phonetically. But, Edward Frisbie's name was not recorded in any U.S. document until he applied for a land grant in 1645 just after he, along with 35 others, branched away from Wethersfield, Connecticut to found the town of Branford, near New Haven. Compounding the confusion, his last will and testament was written by a scribe who misspelled his name to read "Frisbeye." "Frizbie" is yet another variation on the family name that has been found. But the end result of all this was "pie" with the Frisbie name attached to it! Nearly eight generations after the Frisbie name was established in Branford, Connecticut, one of Edward's (or Richard's) direct descendants, William Russell Fris-

Joseph P. Frisbie, President of the Frisbie Pie Co. 1903-1940. Credit: Historical Collections, Bridgeport Public Library

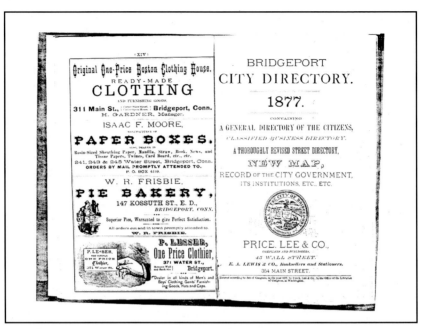

1877 advertisement for the W.R. Frisbie Pie Bakery. Credit: Bridgeport City Records.

The three story bakery built by Joseph P. Frisbie in 1915 on the original site of the family's bakery of 1871. 363 Kossuth Street, Bridgeport, CT. "The Birthplace of Frisbieing." Credit: Historical Collections, Bridgeport Public Library

bie, founded the Frisbie Pie Company. But first it was a Mr. Henry H. Olds, a true baking pioneer who kneaded the dough of Frisbie family destiny. Olds had established his business in New Haven before moving to Bridgeport in 1868, at which time he took on Frisbie as a partner. Obviously, the pie baking business suited William well, because it was only two years later (1871) that he took over Olds' business at 147 Kossuth Street, and renamed it the W.R. Frisbie Pie Bakery. With customers and routes already established, the Frisbie Pie Company from the start was able to produce and sell 300 pies per day.

The second floor of the original building was used as a residence for the Frisbie family. On the first floor was the actual bakery where William's sister Susan and staff made the tasty, increasingly sought after Frisbie's Pies. It must have been quite a location for a growing family, the constant wafting of pie assaulting the senses, and endless temptations for sneaking downstairs for midnight snacks!

During William's tenure the business remained small, with most of its employees family members. The company was content to continue to produce about 300 pies a day. These were distributed by William Frisbie himself who with the able assistance of his long time employee and friend, Charles Eckler, made the rounds of Bridgeport stores in the Frisbie Company pie wagon delivering orders. Eckler once reminisced of some of the challenges encountered by the pair in their years of making deliveries together. Their most notable obstacle, perhaps, was the great and legendary blizzard of March, 1888, the worst to ever hit southern New England. It brought zero degree temperatures and high gales that pushed the blinding snow into drifts of over 20 feet. All this went on for better than three days. But nonetheless, the pies got delivered! Two days after the storm, Eckler and Frisbie with pie laden baskets under their arms, struggled through drifts that their horse and wagon could not begin to challenge. No doubt they were a welcome sight to snowbound Bridgeporters!

The expanding pie domain of Frisbie was all due to the ambitious nature of William's son, Joseph P. When William died in 1903, Joseph P. Frisbie who had been born in 1878 in the family's second floor living quarters above the bakery, became president of the company. Through his father's tenure the company had remained a modest local enterprise, producing and delivering only 300-400 pies per day. But Joseph P. whose first breaths had drawn the scent of pie, obviously had it in his blood. In the early 1900s under the direction of its new president, the Frisbie Pie Company

(Above) Frisbie pies receiving the finishing decoration. Circa 1936. Credit: Nancy and Donald Damtoft. (Below) Frisbie bakery employees working in the apple slicing room. Circa 1936.
Credit: Nancy and Donald Damtoft.

(Above) Frisbie employees sorting blueberries. Circa 1936. Credit: Nancy and Donald Damtoft. (Below) Ford delivery truck used by the Frisbie Pie Co. This same Ford truck was used by the local police department. When arrests were made police could be heard saying, "Call for the pie wagon!" Circa 1930's. Credit: Historical Collections, Bridgeport Public Library.

Looking across the Pequonnock River to the former site of the famed Frisbie Pie Company of Bridgeport, CT. Over 50 years ago, hundreds of Frisbie pie tins were tossed into the river by Frisbie employees.

began to expand its territory. New plants would open, the first in Hartford, CT in 1923. Later, plants were established in Poughkeepsie, NY. and Providence, RI. In the spirit of mass production techniques being pioneered in these early decades of the twentieth century, Joseph Frisbie invented a pie assembly line and installed a machine shop for its manufacture. To run it, Frisbie built his own power plant in the basement. (Power lines hadn't extended to East Bridgeport in 1905, so the ambitious new president decided not to wait!) Also, to speed up the tedious and exacting job of spreading the bottom pie crust in the pans, Frisbie invented a pie making machine that did just that at a rate of 88 per minute! This combination of improvements enabled the company to produce thousands of fresh pies per day.

By 1915, the Frisbie family, its pies increasingly famous, had done well enough to build a three story bakery at the Kossuth Street site. The horse drawn wagon which had originally been used to deliver these freshly baked treasures to consumers was now replaced by a Ford truck. It so happened that the identical model Ford truck was used as a paddy wagon by the local police department. Often when arrests were made, policemen could be heard saying, "Call for the pie wagon!"

But by all accounts, quality was not sacrificed. The Frisbie Pie Company took much pride in using only the best ingredients for its products, taking pains to buy large quantities of fresh fruits when each came into season—strawberries and blueberries in the summer, apples in the autumn. The company's custom was, in Mr. Frisbie's words, "To follow along with the seasons, making various kinds of pies as the fruits were in season." As time went on and refrigeration improved, certain fruits such as blueberries would be incorporated into the pies out of season as well. Widespread acclaim of customers' tastebuds led to daily routes being established throughout most of New England, and much of eastern New York.

Joseph P. Frisbie, though certainly a piebound man, nonetheless had a good sense of humor. In an address to the Kiwanis Club in 1925, he announced tongue in cheek that his middle initial stood for "Pious" and that among the other kings of industry who were Kiwanis members, he had "been crowned with pie." And reminiscing of his childhood spent above the bakery, Frisbie solemnly extolled the "pious" circumstances of his upbringing!

How the Tins Began to be Tossed

Work on a pie production line, or doing pie deliveries, all day, every day, day in and day out, and something's got to give! Though by all accounts, Frisbie company employees were a loyal and well treated crew, they no doubt eagerly anticipated their lunch breaks, and the opportunity for a few short minutes to do anything unrelated to pie production. From repetitive drudgery often arises the fresh air of innovation, and perhaps this was the spirit that launched a craze. In any event, employees of the Frisbie Pie Company in Bridgeport could be seen tossing pie pans to each other in the parking lot and delivery building during their lunch breaks. In a 1979 Bridgeport Post, letter to the editor, Edmound C. Bond, a former employee of the bakery in the 1920's-30's states, "I can verify that (in the 20's/30's) the drivers tossed back and forth to each other demonstrating the various tricks that could be done with them." No doubt thousands of these highly collectible Frisbie pie pans were also flung to rusty oblivion, into the Pequonnock River that runs near the original bakery on Kossuth Street. Indeed, Joseph P. Frisbie lamented that before he began to require deposits, an estimated 10,000 tins per month never found their way back to the plant for reuse!

Pie tin tossing also took place at the Hartford Frisbie plant located at 754

Maple Avenue. Mary Lombardo, who as an eighteen year old girl worked at the Hartford location at the start of the Great Depression, remembers male employees flipping the tins back and forth during lunch breaks and picnics on the company grounds. She also has vivid memories of pie production techniques— how a group of women would stand around a table greasing pie pans with Crisco, then place them on a conveyer belt. Next, the assembly line process took over with first, the bottom crust being added, then the fruit filling, followed by the top crust. Last, each pie would be injected through a hole in its middle with a mix of sugar and water poured from a spout. Finally after baking in the plant's giant, conveyer belt ovens, the pies were ready for packing. Each was now slipped out of its tin (these would be reused) into a cardboard container, then wrapped. Fancy wrapped pies were sent to fashionable West Hartford— the plain wrapped ones went to the common folk. But everyone got the same pies!

After 86 years, nearly 1000 employees, 250 delivery routes and 27 varieties, in 1956, the Frisbie Pie Company was sold to the Wagner Baking Corporation (Table Talk Pies) of Newark, NJ., and two years later in 1958, ceased production forever. Once known for her innovation, it appears "Ma Frisbie" had grown comfortable in her ways over the years. In the meantime, the Warner Corporation's Table Talk pies had begun to take healthy slices of the business away from Frisbie with more up to date production techniques and aggressive marketing. It appears Frisbie held onto the past and didn't modernize to the extent that it could successfully meet these new challenges. Andy Richeleau who worked at the Frisbie plant in Hartford as a mechanic's helper from 1949-51 remembers that some of the trucks dated from the 1920's and though they were lovingly kept up, at least some of the drivers were leery of doing their rounds in the old relics.

One also wonders if the company's ceasing operation may have been spurred by attempts of Frisbie drivers in the mid 1950's to unionize, which resulted in the picketing of Frisbie plants and related pressures. As a company that by all accounts had never lost its family feel, such discontent among employees probably came as something of a shock. Perhaps management saw the attempts to unionize as the death knell for business conducted in the personable, old fashioned way that had long been the Frisbie custom.

In any event, the company's demise occurred at a symbolically significant moment. As if in a passing of the torch, around the time the company

The "Birthplace of Frisbieing." The Frisbie Pie Company loading dock. 1915.

passed into history, Wham-O in California applied for its historic trademark for use of the "Frisbee" name! Now there is no trace of the Frisbie enterprise that for so long was a landmark on the northwest corners of Kossuth and Boroughs Streets in Bridgeport. In 1979, the original building that housed the bakery was torn down— today the location serves as a parking lot for a Jai Alai court, which itself is currently is unoccupied, a reflection of the hard economic times Bridgeport has experienced. However, the Frisbie legend and many a surviving Frisbie tin will live on forever.

The Birthplace of "Frisbieing"

The general public has been very responsive and generous in reply to my request for pre-1960 frisbee playing information. But, I am sure that there are still important individuals or groups who did not have the opportunity to be part of my initial research effort. We still need to hear from you for a future edition of this frisbee history book. Please contact me with any relevant information.

After collecting, reviewing and analyzing all my research material, it's become quite evident that this "just for fun" activity started to become popular around the turn of the 20th century. Of course, there are probably many early examples of "frisbee" playing that originated spontaneously and independently on every continent. Certain areas of North America developed into local "hot beds" of this new throw and catch game. However, it was in the New England area that the "game" first became a popular fad, and where germinated the term "frisbee" by which it will forever be known. And it all began in Bridgeport, Connecticut...

When Joseph P. Frisbie built the three story factory there in 1915, the truck drivers soon discovered that the enclosed loading dock was a good place to play throw and catch. While waiting for their trucks to be loaded, these independent delivery drivers had the perfect frisbie court at their disposal. Year round protection from the weather and a smooth concrete floor enabled employees to sharpen their pie pan flying skills. They no doubt became capable of performing a variety of curve shots that could nearly sail around the dock. The skip shots off the smooth concrete floor they perfected were very tricky to handle and perform. On their delivery routes, throughout much of southern New England and eastern New York, these truck drivers likely became our sport's first ambassadors, introducing pie tin tossing to prep schools, college campuses, military bases and summer camps. The bakery made the fresh pies but it was the drivers who made the Frisbie Pie Company, and most particularly that loading dock in Bridgeport, Connecticut, the Birthplace of FRISBIEING.

One toss led to another, and another... Over time, summer camps, New England prep schools and College students from Yale, Dartmouth, Amherst, Williams, Middlebury, Harvard and Princeton picked up on the fun. All this provided fertile ground for this budding passion to turn into the international pastime it is today!

Miscellaneous Frisbie Pie Company Information

• "W. R. Frisbie Pie Bakery" was the original name for the family owned business of 1871. The name was changed to the Frisbie Pie Company in 1905.

• Although the Frisbie Pie Company made cookies, there is no evidence that they were called Mrs. Frisbie's Sugar Cookies. Recently, a cardboard box that once contained Frisbie's cookies was found. But there is no "Mrs. Frisbie" label.

• The company did make a small 4 inch (4-3/4 oz.) pie. The pie filling was placed into a paper or pressed cardboard container shaped like a pie pan and then placed into a box that had the Frisbie trademark name. The container (paper or cardboard) did not have the word Frisbie imprinted or stamped onto its surface. This fact will explain why no small Frisbie pie tins have been found. Evidently, these 4 inch pies were also sold in tins, but again these were not stamped with the company name. One can find many such small, unmarked tins in flea markets around New England, which may or may not be from Frisbie.

• The only pie pan that bears the Frisbie's Pies name is the standard 9-1/2" to 9-3/4" variety. But, recently I found a sample of the long rumored "original restaurant sized" pie pan. The at long last confirmed existence of this 10 3/4" perforated F tin is the happy conclusion of a long quest!

• The first Frisbie's Pies (10") of 1871 sold for 16 cents each wholesale. Through the turn of the century this small family bakery produced about

300 pies per day, but by 1940 its output had grown to a daily avalanche of 100 tons of pie a day! (about 65,000 large pies plus 135,000 smaller 5c pies).

• At the new three story bakery, a customer could purchase a broken pie for 5 cents. If there were none available, and you were known by the salesperson at the walk-up window, chances were good that a pie would suddenly experience a small accident and appear at the window. Many Bridgeport families, hard up during the Depression years depended on this source of inexpensive treats.

 • The Bridgeport community, rubbing its collective stomach in satisfaction, affectionately referred to the pie company as "Ma Frisbie."

• Large Frisbie trucks used to stock the company's distribution warehouses in places like New London, CT, Albany, NY, and Springfield and Worcester, MA had a carrying capacity of 10,350 pies each.

• The Frisbie Pie Company served 6,500 stores and restaurants. Most pies were delivered still warm from the oven!

• Frisbie's pie tin washing machine washed, sterilized, rinsed and dried 3,600 tins per hour.

• In 1956, The Frisbie Pie Company was sold to Table Talk Pies, Wagner Baking Corp.

• In 1958, the contents of the Frisbie Pie Company were auctioned off to the general public. One of the items on the list was 50,000 new pie pans of various sizes. These pie pans were probably unstamped.

• In 1979, the original Frisbie Pie Company building located on Kossuth St. in Bridgeport, CT was torn down. Many of the long time employees returned for a last time to take a brick or some other piece of the building home as a memento.

• Addresses for Frisbie plants and warehouse distribution points:

Bridgeport, CT plant: 363 Kossuth Street (originally 147 Kossuth Street before street renumbering took place in 1898).

Hartford, CT plant: (est. 1925) 754 Maple Avenue.

Providence, RI plant: (est. 1938 when Frisbie acquired the Plantation Pie Company) 124 Webster Avenue.

Poughkeepsie, NY plant: (est. 1938 when Frisbie apparently took over operations of the Hudson Valley Pie Company, and kept that name while producing Frisbie's Pies) 37 Corlies Ave.

New London, CT distribution warehouse: 72 Thames G

Springfield, MA (distribution warehouse) 67 Bliss Street

Worcester, MA (distribution warehouse)1145 Main Street.

• During one of the annual Frisbie-Frisbee family reunions, a used Frisbie pie pan was sold at auction for $200.00.

• Most Frisbie pie safes will have a "Frisbie's Pies" decal, serial number and "Property of the Frisbie Pie Co." stamped on the bottom of the case. But one or more of these features may be missing.

• In Back To The Future III, the character Marty (played by Michael J. Fox), is seen tossing a Frisbie pie tin at one of the bad guys. Two problems here: (1) The reproduced Frisbie pie tin used was wrongly designed with four compartments. (2) The movie's storyline takes place in 1885, but the word "Frisbie" did not appear on the real tins until the late 1930's!

A Collector's Guide to Different Pie Pan Styles

Lettering Types

There are four different lettering styles of Frisbie pie pans to collect. The major categories are as follows:

1. Perforated Letter F (PLF) (7/8 inch) consisting of 8 Holes.

2. Raised Letter F (RLF) (1-3/16 inch). (1 1/2 inch Segmented Letter F.)

3. Small Letter (SL) (7/8 inch) Frisbie's Pies Lettering.

4. Large Letter (LL) (1-1/4 inch) Frisbie's Pies Lettering.

Hole Patterns

Two sizes of vent holes are to be found on Frisbie pie pans; small (1/8")
and large (3/16" - 1/4"). There are 5 different vent hole patterns: (a) Star
made with 5 small holes in a circle and one in the middle. (b) Star made
with 4 large holes in a circle and one in the middle. (c) Cross made with
5 large size holes. (d) Circle made with six holes (large or small size). (e)
Double Circle made with 12 large size holes designed in two concentric
circles.

5c Dep. and Dep. Tins

During the Depression years and through the Second World War, the Frisbie Pie Company, concerned that many of its tins were not finding their
way back for reuse, required deposits. Some tins can therefore be found
with either "DEP." or "5c DEP." stamped in their centers. These stamps also
have variations— for instance, there are differences in the sizes of the lettering. In addition, some "DEP." and "5c DEP." lettering is backwards as you
look into the pan and can be either raised or sunken. Some rare pie pans
have a hand stamped (as opposed to machine imprinted) 5c DEP— these
are distinguished by the off center spacing or tilting of the letters and number. Hand stamped lettering is also thinner and sharper as well as smaller
than the standard machine formed style. In addition, a very few Frisbie tins
have been found with a hand stamped number 5, probably an antecedent
to the more formal machine formed stamps.

Shoulder

The Frisbie Pie Company made 27 kinds of pie baked in four basic styles
of pan. Different pies required different shaped tins. This helps explain the
various height and shape variations to be found in Frisbie tins. Square
shoulder pans (the area where the side of the pan meets the bottom)
were made for apple, cherry, peach and other fruit pies. ("Square" does
not mean 90 degrees, but rather refers to the sharp, distinct angle
formed where the shoulder intersects the base of the pan.) Semi-round
shoulder pans also exist which are something of a hybrid between round
and square shouldered types. On these, the angle where the shoulder
meets the base is softened, but not truly round.

Round shoulder pie pans were used for mince and custard type pies.
These are distinctly curved where the shoulder meets the base, and this
feature is obvious looking at the pan from both inside and out.

The oblique pan's shoulder flares out, is more obtuse than that of the sharply angled square shoulder tin. Still, there is a distinct angle where the oblique shoulder pan meets the base, so it cannot be called round. These are the smallest of the Frisbie pie pans, 9 1/2" in diameter, and also have the smallest bases. As is the case for round shoulder tins, all oblique shoulder ones are less than one inch in height.

The square shoulder pan is by far the most common. Being more rare, the round and oblique shoulder varieties should command a slightly higher price. They fly better too, though you will not likely want to put them to the test!

Wrinkles

Around the circumference of the shoulder, many pans have a feature known as "wrinkles," vertical lines or grooves mostly in the shape of a wavy letter V or U. These are the result of intense birth pangs during manufacture— the shoulder area subjected to such pressure against the mold that it caused the metal surface to be squeezed, forming these wrinkles. This feature does not add value to the pan.

Crimped Edge

Some pie pans can also be found with a "crimped edge," another result of the pan being handled by various kinds of equipment during the assembly line process used to form pie crust and filling. The crimped edge does not always contain the same amount of crimps and is not always in the same area of the rim. Although it may be nice to have a sample in your collection, this feature also does not add value to the pie pan.

Metal Gauge and Finish

Most pie pans were very consistent in thickness and weight. But there are specimens of significantly heavier and lighter gauges. These pans should be considered as being different and count as an additional item in a given collection. To be so classified, however, the differences in weight should be significant. Identical style pie pans with all the same features should have a weight differential of at least 33 percent to qualify as separate pieces. The lightest known pan is 97 grams, the heaviest 180 grams. You'll find that most pie tins weigh in at around 117-125 grams. A "hand rolled" perforated F pie pan may have been produced during the early days of the Frisbie bakery. These are rumored to have been manually rolled out over a wooden mold and trimmed to size. The metal gauge for these tins was probably thinner than standard; consequently these, if they do exist, will be lighter than the mass produced punch pressed pie pans.

There are two types of metal finish on Frisbie pans, a dull non-shiny "baked finish" found on many of the older ones, and a very shiny, reflective finish found mostly on the later pans, especially on the large lettering style variety. Most pie pans were manufactured from a large sheet of steel that was coated with a shiny finish of tin. The reheating of a pie pan in the oven will eventually cause the pan to lose its shiny finish, and many of the pans you collect, whether of early or of late manufacture, will show the dull sheen of worthwhile and productive oven labor. (As a matter of fact, pre-heating the pie tin at high temperatures was a part of the recommended process of preparing a pan for baking duty). But a number of shiny exceptions are to be found.

Prior to 1940, pie pans were made from a large sheet of steel that was "hot dipped" with tin for sanitary purposes. This shiny coating, though it would be nearly impossible to measure, is slightly thicker than the finish on the later pans. After 1945, most pie pans were coated with tin using the electrolytic process. These have a very thin coating that is more easily worn off than that of their hot dipped predecessors.

In general, Frisbie pie pans with a shiny finish are worth more than those with a dull, non-shiny baked finish. As a rule of thumb, the condition and amount of shiny finish is directly related to the overall value of the Frisbie pie pan. However, there are baked, finish tins with a "marbleized" appearance that is aesthetically pleasing and highly collectible. The application of oil will highlight and protect these features. Collectors may also come across baked finish pans that have a rich dark blue/black finish, and are free of knife cuts and rust. Despite their dull finish, such tins can be judged as being in excellent+ condition.

Different Plants/ Different Pie Pans

Why are there so many variations of Frisbie pie pans? In part the answer may be that the Frisbie Pie Company was in operation for nearly 90 years. Frisbie opened four different plants, in Bridgeport, and Hartford, CT., Poughkeepsie, NY., and Providence, RI. Likely, in some instances, these plants contracted with different sources to produce some of their pie pans. Differences in punch press operations and materials used also probably account for some of the variations. My research shows, though, that it was the Chicago Metallic Company of Lake Zurich, IL that produced most of the Frisbie pie pans.

Dating the Frisbie Pie Pan

Coming up with an accurate chronology of pie tin production has been one of the most difficult aspects of researching this book. There are no manufacturing records to refer to for accurate information. Former employees of the pie factories were not privy to such knowledge either. (A business licence for the Frisbie Pie Company was applied for in 1905). However, I secured a copy of the Frisbie Pie Company's U.S. trademark application, number 353,755, registration number 319,117 issued on November 13, 1934. This application stated that the trademark name had been in continuous use since 1910! However, the application did not actually state that the word "Frisbie's" had been utilized on the pie pans since 1910. This reference was intended to indicate that the word "Frisbie's" had been used in advertising and packaging since that date. The five examples supplied in the Frisbie trademark application included a small logo sticker which read, "Frisbie's Pies 20 cents," plus, a copy of the box (packaging) used for the small 4 3/4 oz. pie, labeled "Frisbie's Junior Pie 20 cents." There is also a copy of the banner name "Frisbie's" that appeared in advertising and on the now rare and highly sought after Frisbie pie safe. Though this trademark application provides much useful information, it unfortunately does not give much chronological insight regarding pie pan production. However, evidence has recently surfaced that indicates all Frisbie pie tins were of the "perforated letter F" style perhaps as late as the 1930's. Then, perhaps in response to competitive pressures, the spelled out "Frisbie's Pies" logo began to appear on tins.

It is known that the Perforated F style was the first of the Frisbie pie pans, having been produced as far back as the late nineteenth century. Surprisingly, considering their venerability these are some of the easiest pans to find (except for the restaurant size, of which only two are known to exist), and are often the least expensive. This is probably because many sellers in the New England area do not recognize that these "F" tins are indeed from Frisbie! Perforated Letter F (PLF) tins make up 22% of known Frisbie pans. (After the publication of this book, the percentage of surviving Perforated F tins should double to 45-50%!)

Following the "F" tin, the next variety produced was the small letter (7/8")

"Frisbie's Pies" pan, probably first made in the late 1930's. All small letter (SL) tins make up 28% percent of known Frisbie pans.

Those of most recent manufacture are the large letter (LL) (1 1/4") "Frisbie's Pies" pans, likely first produced just before the Second World War and remaining in production until the company folded in 1958. Not surprisingly, large lettered pans, being of more recent vintage, are more likely to be found by collectors than others, with the possible exception of the "F" pan. Especially common are those with a 1/8" diameter 6 hole star pattern, and square shoulder. Large letter (LL) tins make up 50 percent of all known Frisbie pie pans.

Dep. & 5c Dep.

Due a combination of the Depression years (when people were holding on to every thing they could), and the popularity of Frisbie pie pan tossing in the 1930's-40's, many Frisbie tins were lost or simply never returned. As a result of this low recidivism rate, the Frisbie Pie Company began to impose a two cent deposit on some of its pie pans during this period. However, no pie pans are to be found with a "2c DEP." inscription. Instead, such tins are inscribed with "DEP." Customers at the time of purchase were charged the extra two cents for these pies.

Keeping in mind the truism that prices rarely fall, it is clear that "DEP" marked tins were manufactured prior to those with the "5c DEP." stamp. These latter tins were produced during World War II when the economy, invigorated by the massive demands of war production, broke once and for all the stranglehold of the Depression. Interestingly, a very few "5c DEP." pans can be found with these labels off center or crooked. This is because the Frisbie Pie Company in certain instances took already used pie tins and hand stamped them with these new insignia. A good example of this is the rare "raised letter F" pan, which was probably made in the early 1900's, and then hand stamped with a 5c DEP thirty years later. Although rare, the hand stamp was probably applied to whichever tins happened to be on hand in the bakery at the time of need. Because it's unlikely that two tins of the same style could have a hand stamped 5c DEP located exactly in the same place, I feel that each of these hand stamped 5c DEP tins, and tins impressed with just the number 5, should be classified as being visually different. All DEP and 5c DEP tins make up only 13.4 percent of known Frisbie tins.

Care and Cleaning of Frisbie Pie Pans

The last Frisbie pie pan was manufactured prior to 1958. The first ones (the perforated F restaurant size) were probably made near the end of the nineteenth century. Frisbie tins, therefore, will be found in a wide range of conditions— from totally rusted, to shiny and virtually unused. It is very important not to apply any foreign substance or use a mechanical process in an attempt to upgrade, polish or enhance the condition of these antique pie pans. Serious collectors look for tins in as good an original condition as possible. Therefore, any attempt to remove prominent blemishes can be easily detected and will only lower the overall value of the pie pan.

Also, avoid the temptation to shine up an old Frisbie pie pan that may come into your possession. The discoloration of the metal surface found on many pie pans is a natural process that is desirable, especially on the older ones, and should not be altered in any way. All in all, the fewer scratches that mark a pie pan, the better. In many cases, a tin will have been used only once. There may be only a few noticeable scratches from a kitchen knife used to slice the fresh pie, and if you're very lucky, you may find an unblemished Frisbie tin. After the pie was consumed, pans were generally either thrown out, stored in basements or garages, or returned to the pie company for the deposit.

I have even found Frisbie pie pans that still had some dirt or fruit residue encrusted on them. Another collector, a college instructor, put one of his students to good use— on pie tin lookout. This alert student almost literally spirited away a valuable Frisbie tin out from under noses gathered around a Thanksgiving table, sniffing its delicious contents. Yes, Fris-bie pie pans can still be found doing what they were made for—baking pies! This particular tin also came with an encrusted little souvenir of pie filling, which begs the question, what can the collector do to clean up a tin without compromising its value?

One method is to soak it for one hour in hot soapy water. Then, wipe it with a very soft cloth or better, a sponge, then dry it very thoroughly. If you are cleaning a shiny pie tin, do not rub too hard against the surface, or you will leave fine scratch marks on the shiny tin finish.

Now, immediately apply a little *boiled* linseed oil over the entire surface, rubbing the oil into the pan with a soft cloth only. The light coating of boiled linseed oil will protect the pie pan from rust and will highlight the features of a baked finish "marbleized" pan. It is a very effective enhancer and rust preventative that will dry to the touch. (Three in One type oil is also effective in rust prevention).

It's very important to apply such surface protection, because wherever rust forms it will leave behind pitted marks on the surfaces of the pan. Remember, especially in humid climates, that without adequate protection, rust inevitably has its way with metal, be it ever so slow and gradual. Don't be in the position of a collector living in Hawaii who after some years of storing his 29 valuable and rare Frisbie pie pans in a moist environment, retrieved them one day to find them claimed by their dull red host! Hot water, soap, and the application of protective oil or like substance is the only procedure for pie pan enhancement and preservation that is generally accepted by Frisbie collectors. (Oven cleaner can be used for very dirty, rusted, or residue encrusted pie pans). Then, store your pie pans in a cool dry place. Shiny tins can be stored in an unsealed plastic bag. Stacking them one on top of the other will not damage or warp the pie pans unless you pile up 50 or more. But, no doubt, you will want to put at least some of your pie pans on display. Any collector should have at least one Frisbie pie pan prominently highlighted. They make a great conversation piece!

Standard Measurements for the Frisbie Pie Pan

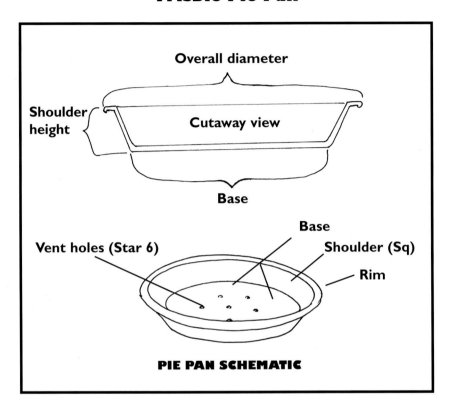

Overall diameter

Shoulder height

Cutaway view

Base

Vent holes (Star 6)

Base

Shoulder (Sq)

Rim

PIE PAN SCHEMATIC

Avid Frisbie collectors are interested in trying to find every different Frisbie pie pan ever produced. There are a number of subtle and not so subtle variations in Frisbie pie pan measurement. Most of these are so minor as to not be significant. Close attention should be paid to the DEP. and 5c DEP. scripts and lettering styles. It is in such variations where the collector could discover a new style Frisbie pie tin. However, differences in overall pie tin diameter, base or shoulder height must be significant, for the tin to be so classified. It is possible that you could have a Frisbie pie pan that is not listed in this book— we are always looking for information on new finds. Therefore, if you think you possess a Frisbie tin that is visually different from the 40 variations described herein, please inform me of your find! In the last year or so at least 14 previously unknown variations of pie tins have been unearthed, and there are likely more awaiting their day in the sun! Here is an overview of the range of size differences found on basic pie pan features:

Pie Pan Lettering

Again, there are only four major styles and measurements for the lettering found on Frisbie pie pans. The first of these is the distinctive, perforated letter "F" tin. Eight holes punched into the pan form this 7/8 inches moniker. Most pie tins will be found with the words "Frisbie's Pies" in letters either 7/8 inches or 1 1/4 inches in size. Raised letter F pie tins measure 1 3/16 inches in height and the Segmented Raised letter F is 1 1/2 inches high.

Because of variable pressure and very slight differences in die sizes from one punch press machine shop to another, some of the lettering type for "Frisbie's Pies" may seem to vary ever so slightly from the standard sizes listed above. But, as with the minuscule variations to be found in rim diameter measurements, etc., any such slight lettering deviations should be considered insignificant. Again, the goal here is to standardize criteria that *obviously* distinguish one Frisbie pie pan from another!

Overall Diameter

Most diameters for Frisbie pie tins will be from 9 1/2 to 9 3/4 inches in width. The most common diameter is 9 5/8." But the recent exciting discovery of a very old "F" pan, proves the long rumored "restaurant" sized tin did exist. This tin measures 10 3/4 inches in diameter.

Base

The base measurements for all known Frisbie pie pans (excluding the restaurant "F" tin) are from 6 3/4" to 7 3/4" The most common base measurement is 7 3/8 inches.

Shoulder

Shoulder height can measure from 11/16 to 1 1/4 inches. All tins with an oblique shoulder will be under one inch in height; all square and semi-round shoulder pie pans are one inch or more high. The one inch measurement is the most common.

Vent Holes

There are only two sizes for vent holes: Small (1/8 inches) and Large (3/16 inches - 1/4 inches). Small holed Frisbie pie pans are by far the most numerous.

DEP. and 5c DEP. Stamps

The "DEP" and "5c DEP" imprints to be found on some pans add interesting and distinctive varieties for the Frisbie pie pan collector to seek out. In part because they were intended to be returned, these are some of the rarer Frisbie tins to be found, and are highly sought after by collectors.

The DEP. script was produced with at least three distinctions of lettering. The main differences appear in the sharpness of the lettering. These differences are slight and were caused by variations of tools used to make the imprint. The most significant differences will be found between those that were hand stamped as opposed to those that were machine stamped.

Hand Stamped 5c DEP. Script

The hand stamped "5c DEP." insignia was produced with a chisel like tool that was placed onto the surface of the tin and then struck with a hammer to force the imprint into the pie pan. The number and letters on such hand stamped tins will have (comparatively) very thin and sharp edges, as if made with a knife edge. On these, the 5c script measures 1/2" the DEP 3/8." There is only one known design for the hand stamped 5c DEP. (See photo on page 197).

Two known varieties of hand stamped number 5 tins also exist. The number 5 was to signify 5c DEP. They measure to 1" x 3/4" on small letter (SL) pie tins, and there's a 3/4" x 1/2" version to be found on a few perforated letter F (PLF) tins. (See photos on pages 193 and 195.)

DEP. & 5c DEP. Machine Formed Stamps
DEP. Small Letter Tins

There are two different styles of machine stamped "DEP" lettering appearing on small letter pie pans. One is the square angled style. This "DEP" stamp can be identified by an imprint with a more severe square (as opposed to rounded) angle delineating the sides of the letters. The letters for this style are reversed, off-centered and slightly smaller, measuring out to 7/16 of an inch in height. (See item SL-05A.)

The oblique edged lettering "DEP" style is identified by lettering that is slightly wider and more rounded than the square angled variation, the letters demonstrating less sharp delineation on the surface of the pan. Consequently, this "DEP" will be centered on the tin and measure slightly larger than the former, to 9/16 of an inch. These differences are most noticeable on the letter "D." (see item SL-06A on page 194.)

5c Inscription
Small Letter Tin

Tins with 5c script may vary slightly in size, either 5/8" or 11/16." But consider the 5c found on all such small letter pie pans to be 5/8 of an inch in height (excepting, of course, hand stamped ones.) The cent mark (c) is basically the same size, 3/8" on small letter pans, and 7/16" on their large lettered brethren. In either style, this mark does not differ enough to warrant distinction.

5c DEP.
Large Letter Tins

With one exception, "5c DEP." script found on all large lettered pans, measures 7/8". For large letter tins with just the "DEP" stamp, the "DEP" will also measure 7/8". (The one exception is the hand stamped 5c DEP.) Therefore, a 5c script that measures to 7/8" in any large letter pans, except hand stamped ones, should correspond in size to the letter "D" in DEP.

Grading the Frisbie Pie Tin

Pie pans usually spend their tin bound lives doing what they are meant to do—baking pies, and the Frisbie ones certainly were a hard working bunch—it's not often that one is found in mint condition! This is not surprising, especially taking into account that the Frisbie company ceased operations 40 years ago, with its oldest tins dating back to around the turn of the century. Nonetheless, some Frisbie tins have been found in near mint condition, though these are rare. It is also very difficult to find a Frisbie pie pan not embossed with the eager scratches of pie slicers. The dreaded kitchen knife! But dull finish, unmarked pie pans do exist in collections, and still occasionally turn up! These, if otherwise unblemished, should be considered as being in excellent+ condition, though not quite as desirable, and therefore, valuable as a mint condition shiny tin, which is near the top of the list of "Holy Grail" wish items!

Tins will also usually show the marks of their busy, productive lives—

along with knife scratches may be found wrinkles, warpage, crimps, stains, spots of rust and an uneven tin coating especially on the inside of the pan. Because the Frisbie pie pan is a premier collectible item, one found in near mint condition will command a slightly higher price percentage wise than a collectible plastic flying disc in comparable condition. In other words, scuff marks, etc. on a frisbee will detract more from its value than similar wear and tear on a Frisbie pie pan. Here's a guide for appraising the condition of pie pans you may come across:

MINT CONDITION: There must be absolutely no sign of any defect, blemish, stain, warpage, scratch, scuff mark, rust, dent, wrinkle or crimp anywhere on the surface of the pie pan. The shiny tin coating should be flawless. Though you are unlikely to find a shiny metal Frisbie pie tin of such immaculacy, tins approaching such perfection are out there.

NEAR MINT CONDITION: The pie pan will have a mirror-like shiny coating on its entire surface. The shiny tin coating will be even through-out. There can only be one or two minor signs of a blemish, stain, scratch, or scuff mark. The tin must be free of wrinkles and crimps. The base and rim of the pan must be flat and straight. *Near mint condition will command 90 percent of the mint price.

EXCELLENT CONDITION: A pie pan can only have minor signs of one or two blemishes, and a few light surface scratches. The shiny tin finish will be intact. There can be only one set of kitchen knife cuts. No rust, wrinkles, crimps or dents anywhere on the pan. The base and rim will be straight and flat. (Note: There are pie pans which due to oven duty, have lost any sign of their shiny tin finish. If this is the only defect, then such a pan should be considered as being in excellent+ condition). *Excellent condition will command only 75 percent of the mint price.

VERY GOOD CONDITION: Many pie pans will be found in this condition. These will have noticeable signs of either scratches or stains, perhaps a small spot of rust, some blemishes, wrinkles and one or two minor dents. The kitchen knife cuts will look as if only a few pies were cut while still in the pan. Although not complete, the shiny tin surface will still be visible on both sides of the pan. The base and rim will be relatively flat and straight. *Very good condition will command only 50 percent of the mint price.

GOOD CONDITION: The pie pan will have many signs of scratches, stains, dents, rust, wrinkles, crimps, and kitchen knife cuts. The base and rim should be relatively flat or straight. Little or no shiny tin finish will remain on either side of the pan. *Good condition will command only 35 percent of the mint price.

FAIR CONDITION: The pie pan will have numerous signs of scratches, knife cuts, wrinkles, crimps and some rust spots. No tin finish on either side. Base and rim are not flat. Badly beaten up, but not trashed. *Fair condition will command only 15 percent of the mint price.

POOR CONDITION: The pie pan will have numerous signs of scratches, dents, holes caused by rust, wrinkles, crimps, stains, a badly bent base and rim, and many kitchen knife cuts. Such a tin will have none of its once shiny tin luster. Tin will be trashed. *Poor condition will command only 5 percent of the mint price.

THE
FIRST OFFICIAL
FRISBIE PIE COMPANY COLLECTIBLE
PRICE GUIDE

Frisbie Pie Pans

Pie tins are some of the most important and popular of frisbee memorabilia to collect and are the mainstay of any collection.

PERFORATED LETTER F
Restaurant Size.
Size: 10 3/4" x 8 1/4" x 1".
Rare.
Letter F is off-centered.
Semi Round Shoulder.
PLF-01 L1800's
Mint:$1250. Very Good:$625.

PERFORATED LETTER F
Standard Size. 9 5/8".
Letter F is centered. 7/8".
Square Shoulder.
PLF-06 E1900's
Mint:$250. Very Good:$125.

PERFORATED LETTER F
Number 5
Hand Stamped.
Square Shoulder.
PLF-09 M1900's
Mint:$400. Very Good:$200.

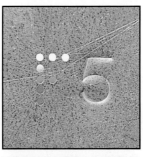

PERFORATED LETTER F
PLF-09A Close-up: Hand Stamp Number 5 (3/4" x 1/2").

RAISED LETTER F
5c DEP. Hand Stamped.
5 Large Holes Cross Pattern (CR).
Square Shoulder.
RLF-02 M1900's
Mint:$500. Very Good:$250.
(See close-up next page)

RAISED LETTER F
RLF-02A Close-up: Raised.
Letter F (1 3/16") & Hand
Stamped 5c DEP. (1/2 x
3/8).

RAISED LETTER F
Segmented (1 1/2").
F is off-centered.
Semi Round Shoulder.
No Holes.
RLF-04 M1900's
Mint:$400.Very Good:$200.

SMALL LETTERS
Raised. (7/8")
Reverse Letters.
DEP. Square Edge. (7/16")
DEP. is off-centered.
Square Shoulder.
Circle Holes (6).
SL-05 L1930's
Mint:$450.Very Good:$225.

SMALL LETTERS
SL-05A Close-up: DEP.
With square edge letters (7/16").

SMALL LETTERS
Raised.
DEP. Oblique Edge (9/16").
DEP. is centered.
Square Shoulder.
Star Holes (6).
SL-06 L1930's
Mint:$450.Very Good:$225

SMALL LETTERS
SL-06A Close-up: DEP.
With oblique edge letters
(9/16").

SMALL LETTERS
Sunken.
Hand Stamped Number 5.
Oblique Shoulder.
Circle Holes (6).
SL-07 L1930's
Mint:$425.Very Good:$213.

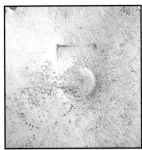

SMALL LETTERS
SL-07A Close-up: Hand
Stamped Number 5
(1" x 3/4").

SMALL LETTERS
Sunken.
5c DEP.
Oblique Shoulder.
Circle Holes (6).
SL-09 1940's
Mint: $575.Very Good:$288.

SMALL LETTERS
Raised.
5c DEP.
Reverse Letters.
Square Shoulder.
Circle Holes (6).
SL-10 1940's
Mint:$675.Very Good:$338

SMALL LETTERS
Sunken.
5c DEP.
Hand Stamped.
(1/2 x 3/8)
Oblique Shoulder.
Circle Holes (6).
SL-12 1940's
Mint:$475.Very Good:$238.

LARGE LETTERS
Sunken. (1 1/4")
Square Shoulder.
Star Holes (6).
LL-01 1940's
Mint:$350.Very Good:$175.

LARGE LETTERS
Sunken.
"Marbleized Pie Tin."
Square Shoulder.
Star Holes (6).
LL-01A 1940's
Value is higher than the
common variety.
Very Good: $200.+

LARGE LETTERS
Sunken.
Square Shoulder.
No Holes.
LL-03 1940's
Mint:$350.Very Good:$175.

LARGE LETTERS
Sunken.
Semi Round Shoulder.
Large Circle Holes (6).
This particular tin is
known as "Angel's Hair"
because of its artistic
design. Value is higher than
the common variety.
Very Good:$200.+
LL-05 1940's
Non-artistic tin of this type.
Mint:$350.Very Good:$175.

LARGE LETTERS
Sunken.
Square Shoulder.
Large Holes.
Double Circle (12).
LL-06 1940's
Mint:$350.Very Good:$175.

LARGE LETTERS
Raised.
Reverse Letters.
Square Shoulder.
Star Holes Large (5).
LL-07 1940's
Mint:$425.Very Good:$213.

LARGE LETTERS
Raised.
DEP. Reverse Letters.
Square Shoulder.
Star Holes (6).
LL-08 1940's
Mint:$550.Very Good:$275.

LARGE LETTERS
Raised.
5c DEP.
Reverse Letters.
Round Shoulder.
Star Holes (6).
LL-13 1940's
Mint:$550. Very Good:$275.

LARGE LETTERS
LL-13A Close-up: 5c DEP.
(7/8").
(Photographed from
bottom of pan.)

LARGE LETTERS
Sunken.
5c DEP. is Hand Stamped
and Reversed.
Round Shoulder.
Star Holes (6).
LL-15 1940's
Mint:$475. Very Good:$238.

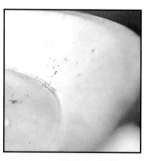

**HAND STAMP
5c DEP.**
LL-15A Close-up: 5c DEP.
Hand Stamped
(1/2" x 3/8").

**RUST DAMAGED
PIE PAN**
JK-01 (#SL-09)

SHOULDER TYPE
SH-01 Close-up: Oblique
Shoulder Angle (Ob/Sh)

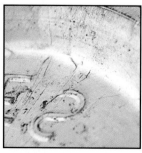

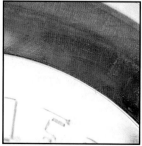

SHOULDER TYPE
SH-02 Close-up: Semi
Round Shoulder
(S/Rd/Sh)

SHOULDER TYPE
SH-03 Close-up: Round
Shoulder (Rd/Sh)

SHOULDER TYPE
SH-04 Close-up: Square
Shoulder (Sq/Sh)

Frisbie Pie Safes (Cases)

Where better to display your Frisbie treasures than in one of these? The Frisbie pie safe is at the top of every collector's most wanted list.

FRISBIE PIE SAFE
(Malafronte)
Standard size 5 pies.
Dimensions: 16 5/8" x 12 5/8" x 12 5/8".
Case Number: L-29417.
"Property of the Frisbie Pie Co." stamped on bottom of case.
FPC-01 E1900's
Mint:$1000.VeryGood: $500.

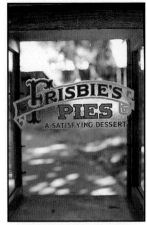

FRISBIE PIE SAFE
(Malafronte)
FPC-01A Close-up: Frisbie's Pies decal. "A Satisfying Dessert."

FRISBIE PIE SAFE
(Mangone)
Standard size 5 pies.
Dimensions: 18 1/2" x 13 1/8" x 11 5/8".
Case Number 625312
FPC-02 Close-up: Frisbie's Pies Decal. "Fresh Here Everyday." E1900's
Mint:$1295.Very Good:$648.

FRISBIE PIE SAFE
(Mangone)
FPC-02A Metal label made by: General Display Case Co. N.Y.C.

FRISBIE PIE SAFE
(Mangone)
FPC-02B Close-up: "Property J.P. Frisbie Co." stamped on bottom of case.

FRISBIE PIE SAFE

(Beckerer) Decal: "A Satisfying Dessert".
Large Size: Glass/Metal frame. Holds 9 pies.
Dimensions: 28" x 12" x 11 1/2".
FPC-03 1900's. Mint: $1650. Very Good:$825.
*Frisbie Pie Safe. (No Photo) Large Size: Glass/Wooden.
Holds 9 Pies. FPC-04 1900's. Mint: $1995.Very Good: $998.

FRISBIE PIE SAFE

(Johnson)
Standard size 5 pies.
FPC-05 Close up: Decal.
"Frisbie's Pies".
Mint:$900.Very Good:$450.

FRISBIE PIE SAFE

(Johnson)
FPC-05A Close up: "Property of Frisbie Pie Co."
stamped on bottom of case.
No case number. 1900's.

Frisbie Pie Company Misc.

There is quite a variety of Frisbie memorabilia that exists to be sought after by the avid collector.

CASCADING RACK

FPC-06A Close up:
Frisbie's Pies sign with
picture of boy sampling
pie. (Tin).

CASCADING FRISBIE PIE RACK

Holds 6 Pies.
FPC-06 1900's
Mint:$650.Very Good:$325.
(Without tins).

FRISBIE'S PIES SIGN
Pure Aluminum Sign.
(12" x 8").
FPC-07 1900's Wilson-
Hurd Co.
Mint:$175. Very Good:$88.

FRISBIE'S PIES X-MAS SIGN
6 Color Lithograph Card-
board. (14 3/8" x 12 3/4").
FPC-08 1930's
Mint:$250. Very Good:$125

FRISBIE'S PIE SERVER
FPC-09 1900's
Mint:$195. Very Good:$98.

FRISBIE'S PIE SERVER
FPC-09A Close up: "Fris-
bie's Pies" on handle.

FRISBIE'S LUNCH COOKIES 5¢ DISPLAY BOX
FPC-10 1930's
Mint:$350. Very Good:$175.

FRISBIE'S PIES KEY CHAIN
Poker Chip.
FPC-11 1950's
Mint:$50. Very Good:$25.

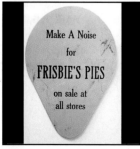

FRISBIE'S PIES SNAPPER
FPC-12 1940's
Metal.
Mint:$50. Very Good:$25.

FRISBIE'S PIES PENCIL
FPC-13 1950's
Mint:$50. Very Good:$25.

BRICK FROM THE FRISBIE PIE CO.
Building demolition in 1979.
FPC-14 1915.
"Priceless."

Price List of All Known Frisbie Pie Pans

Frisbie Pie Pans With Visual Differences

This is the only method to use to identify and collect different Frisbie pie tins. Differences are mainly determined by visual features. There are 40 known different pie pans to collect. (Of course, any samples of hand stamped letter F, number 5, or 5c DEP, and heavy weight tins are counted as being different, even if found on the same basic style.) Tins with "Marbleized" and "Angel's Hair" type features are worth more than conventional ones because of the aesthetic appeal of their natural art. But these are not classified as different tins.

Perforated Letter F (PLF)

ITEM NO.	VISUAL FEATURES	MINT PRICE	VERY GOOD
PLF-01	Restaurant Size. F is off-centered. (10 3/4" Diameter) S/Rd/Sh.	$1250.	$625.
PLF-02	Shallow Shoulder 3/4". Base 6 3/4". Rd/Sh (AKA-Little Boy).	$500.	$250.
PLF-03	Shallow Shoulder 3/4". Base 7 3/4". Rd/Sh (AKA-Low Boy).	$450.	$225.
PLF-04	Oblique Shoulder.	$325.	$163.
PLF-05	Semi-Round Shoulder.	$325.	$163.
PLF-06	Square Shoulder.	$250.	$125.
PLF-07	Square Shoulder 1 1/4" High. Heavy Weight.	$400.	$200.
PLF-08	Square Shoulder 1 1/4" High. Average Weight.	$325.	$163.
PLF-09	Hand Stamped Number 5 (3/4" x 1/2") Square Shoulder.	$400.	$200.

Raised Letter F (RLF)

RLF-01	Raised Letter F (1 3/16") No Hole Square Shoulder	$425.	$213.
RLF-02	Raised Letter F (1 3/16") 5c DEP. HS 5 Large Holes CR Sq/Sh	$500.	$250.
RLF-03	Raised Letter F (1 3/16") (5c DEP. HS RL) No Holes Sq/Sh	$550.	$275.
RLF-04	Raised Letter F (Segmented) (1 1/2") No Holes S/Rd/Sh	$400.	$200.

Small Letters (SL)

SL-01	SU Circle Holes Square Shoulder	$350.	$175.
SL-02	SU Circle Holes Oblique Shoulder	$350.	$175.
SL-03	SU No Holes Square Shoulder	$350.	$175.
SL-04	SU No Holes Oblique Shoulder	$450.	$225.
SL-05	RA DEP Square Edge RL Circle Holes Sq/Sh	$450.	$225.
SL-06	RA DEP Oblique Edge Star Holes Sq/Sh	$450.	$225.
SL-07	SU Number 5 HS Circle Holes Ob/Sh	$425.	$213.
SL-08	SU 5c DEP Circle Holes Sq/Sh	$550.	$275.
SL-09	SU 5c DEP Circle Holes Ob/Sh	$575.	$288.
SL-10	RA 5c DEP RL Circle Holes Sq/Sh	$675.	$338.
SL-11	RA 5c DEP RL Circle Holes Ob/Sh	$675.	$338.
SL-12	SU 5c DEP HS Circle Holes Ob/Sh	$475.	$238.

Large Letters (LL)

LL-01	SU Star Holes Sq/Sh	$350.	$175.
LL-02	SU Star Holes Rd/Sh	$350.	$175.
LL-03	SU No Holes Sq/Sh	$350.	$175.
LL-04	SU Large Holes Circle Sq/Sh	$350.	$175.
LL-05	SU Large Holes Circle S/Rd/Sh	$350.	$175.
LL-06	SU 12 Large Holes Double Circle Sq/Sh	$350.	$175.
LL-07	RA RL 5 Large Star Holes Sq/Sh	$425.	$213.
LL-08	RA DEP RL Star Holes Sq/Sh	$550.	$275.
LL-09	RA 5c DEP RL No Holes Sq/Sh	$750.	$375.
LL-10	RA 5c DEP RL Star Holes Sq/Sh	$750.	$375.
LL-11	SU 5c DEP Star Holes Rd/Sh	$550.	$275.
LL-12	RA 5c DEP Star Holes Rd/Sh	$775.	$388.
LL-13	RA 5c DEP RL Star Holes Rd/Sh	$550.	$275.
LL-14	SU 5c DEP HS Star Holes Rd/Sh	$450.	$225.
LL-15	SU (5c DEP. RL HS) Star Holes Rd/Sh	$475.	$238.

Explanation of Legend

Lettering Styles

LL   Large Letters: Refers to a certain style of pie tin. (1 1/4" size "Frisbie's Pies" lettering). This was the last style produced.

PLF   Perforated Letter F: Refers to the 7/8" letter F that is made with 8 holes. The first Frisbie pie tin.

RA   Raised: The lettering of "Frisbie's Pies," letter "F", "DEP" or "5c DEP." is raised off the surface of the pie pan when looking into the pie pan.

RL   Reverse Letters: The lettering of "Frisbie's Pies," letter "F," "DEP.," or "5c DEP." is reversed when looking into the pie pan.

RLF   Raised Letter F: The letter "F" is raised off the surface of the pie pan, (1 3/16" high) and, 1 1/2" high for the segmented letter F.

SL   Small Letters: Refers to a certain style of pie tin. (7/8" size "Frisbie's Pies" lettering). This was the second style produced.

SU   Sunken: The lettering for "Frisbie's Pies," "DEP.," or "5c DEP." is sunk into the metal surface when looking into the pie pan.

Shoulder Types

Ob/Sh   Oblique Shoulder: The shoulder of the pie pan has a shallow, more flared out angle to the base, and therefore is more oblique than that of the square variety. Oblique shoulders are found only on perforated letter F (PLF) and small letter (SL) tins, and measure under one inch in height.

Rd/Sh   Round Shoulder: This feature is only found on large letter (LL) tins. The shoulder/base area is truly round and not oblique. All round shoulder tins will measure under one inch high.

S/Rd/Sh   Semi-Round Shoulder: The shoulder is slightly rounded near the base. These are mostly found on letter F and large letter pans of 7 1/4" base measurement. Semi-round shoulder tins are something of a hybrid falling between true round & square shoulder styles. All semi-round shoulder tins will measure to at least one inch in height.

Sq/Sh   Square Shoulder: The shoulder of the pie pan intersects the base at a sharp, as opposed to shallow angle, producing a well defined edge. Square shoulder tins are always one inch or more in height, and are also the most common, appearing in all the basic styles.

Dep. & 5c Dep. Variations

DEP.   Deposit: "DEP." is stamped onto the pie pan.

5   The number 5 (1" or 3/4" high) is hand stamped onto the pie tin. This number 5 stands for 5c DEP.

5c   Five Cents: Deposit amount is stamped onto the pie pan.

HS   Hand Stamped: 5c DEP (or the number 5) was stamped onto the pie pan by hand. The lettering style is different from the standard machine made stamp, in that it is thinner and sharper and usually off centered.

OBE   Oblique Edge: The lettering for "DEP" is more oblique (rounded edge) than the square (SE) style lettering. Oblique DEP script is larger than square edge DEP and will measure to 9/16" in length. This feature is only found on small letter pie pans.

SE   Square Edge: The lettering for DEP has more of a square right angle edge than the oblique style. SE DEP script is smaller than the oblique edge (9/16") and will measure to 7/16" in length. This SE feature is found only on small letter (SL) pie pans.

Hole Patterns

C   Circle: The pattern of six holes in a circle.

CR   Cross: Four holes in a wide cross pattern and in the middle. (Only found on RLF tins).

DOU   Double: The pie pan has two sets of holes (total of 12) arranged in a double circle pattern.

S   Star: The pattern of holes has four or five holes in a circle and one in the middle.

Chapter VII

THE FRISBEE CONSPIRACY

A major investigation revealing that Wham-O may have wrongly applied for a registered trademark on the generic term "frisbee"!

Introduction

Frisbee. The name is so seemingly generic that anything plastic, disc-like, and flown for fun is universally called a frisbee. But to the surprise of many, frisbee is not a generic term, in fact is owned by Wham-O, Inc. (which in turn now is owned by Charterhouse Group International of New York). For nearly five decades, Wham-O has controlled this universally recognized trademark.

What's in a name? Everything! How would the development and growth of frisbee sports have been affected had not this universally recognized term been monopolized? Arguably, the sport would have achieved a far greater prominence in American life. But healthy competition which would have spurred growth of the sport has been limited because companies (and potential sponsors), barred from calling their products "frisbees," have been reluctant to venture into the flying disc business. The vital questions that beg to be answered, therefore, are: 1) What were the circumstances leading Wham-O to trademark "Frisbee" in the first place, and 2) Does Wham-O have a valid claim on the term?

It depends on who you ask. I first started asking questions about the origin of the "frisbee" name in the early 1970's when I first learned of the Frisbie Pie Company and naturally became curious about its association with Wham-O's trademarked name. So, I went to the public relations people at Wham-O and asked. The story I was told (which eventually appeared in many newspapers and other publications throughout the country) was that Wham-O's co-founder, Rich Knerr, hearing of the popularity of his company's new Pluto Platter Flying Saucer, traveled to the Northeast on a fact finding tour to visit Ivy League Schools where the disc flying fad was really taking off. But supposedly, as this standard story is told in Panati's *Extraordinary Origins of Everyday Things*, Knerr "to his astonishment...discovered students at...Yale and Harvard, playing a lawn game that involved tossing metal pie tins which they called "frisbieing" (Of course, we know now that this term, and most likely the tins played with were from the Frisbie Pie Company of Bridgeport, Connecticut!)

Having heard and liked the term, Mr. Knerr, the story goes, decided to "adopt" it for Wham-O's new Pluto Platter, and "unaware of the existence of the Frisbie Pie Company, he trademarked the word "Frisbee." This is the standard explanation Wham-O offered for almost 40 years.

At first this seemed to me on the face of it to be a plausible account. But as I learned more over time, its credibility eroded. As someone who began collecting frisbees in 1968 and had an intense interest in their history, I repeatedly requested Wham-O to provide me with information regarding production dates for the pre-1960 collectible frisbees I'd found. But Wham-O's response was to shut up tighter than a giant clam threatened by a spiny sea urchin. Though over the years many other collectors have made similar requests, Wham-O to this day has not given us one iota of enlightenment regarding its early disc production. Needless to say, I became increasingly suspicious regarding the company's seeming code of silence. What did Wham-O have to hide? A lot it seems, based on what I've found! Here's what I've found to be the real story pieced together from much new research and evidence, and revealed here for the first time:

The Generic Evidence

Through the Freedom of Information Act, I requested and received a complete copy of Wham-O's Frisbee trademark application file submitted to the Patent and Trademark office in 1958. A trademark application, among other things, requires the applicant to attest to sole ownership of the trademark being applied for, with the right to use said mark in commerce. In other words, the applicant must assert that the trademark being applied for is a term not already in common use. This was so sworn by Arthur "Spud" K. Melin, Vice President of Wham-O, on July 25, 1958. Also of great importance, the document records that the trademark (Frisbee) was first used on (Wham-O) goods on June 17, 1957.

But wait a minute! Undeniable evidence exists that the term was already free and floating in the public domain well prior to this! Photographs, advertisements, stories about frisbee competitions (the term variously spelled) can be found in college newspapers and other publications dating back at least to 1949! I have also received many personal written accounts describing frisbie/frisbee play as a result of my queries. For instance, at Amherst College as early as 1949, some students were playing a game called "frisbie" with potato chip and pretzel can covers, a game which they claimed was named after the popular English Professor George F. Whicher whose middle name just happened to be Frisbie!

This story about Professor Whicher lending his middle name to a new sport called Frisbie, received national exposure in the September 1, 1957 edition of the *New York Times* (letter to the editor). But it's quite likely that Professor Whicher wouldn't have been singled out were it not for the already widespread acclaim of Frisbie pie tin throwing at New England college campuses. Frisbie's Pies were no strangers to Amherst; the company had a distribution warehouse in nearby Springfield. Likely, the students seized on the fact that their well regarded Professor Whicher shared his name with that of the popular pastime, and gave their Frisbie-ing some local color!*

Other Ivy League schools were also very much caught up in frisbee play. In fact, in 1955, two years prior to Wham-O's first claimed use of the frisbee term, *The Shield*, a publication of the Theta Delta Chi fraternity of Dartmouth College in Hanover, New Hampshire, featured a long and detailed account of the November 7, 1954 "World Frizby Championships" waged between the Delta Chi men and a visiting All Star Rowing team from the Westmount Rugby Football Club of Montreal, Canada. Match play which consisted of each team tossing back and forth a cookie tin cover, was governed by a complete set of rules which even included etiquette; coats and ties were required! (See Chapter II)

But it is at Princeton University where the most compelling evidence of "frisbee" in that spelling, already in use in the public domain well prior to Wham-O's first claimed use, is to be found. A query letter to one of Princeton's assistant archivists, Nanci Young, rewarded me with a number of dated articles from the Spring of 1957 that featured the word, "frisbee,"

*Amherst College is notable for its long tradition of frisbee play. In fact, the college has the distinction of being the source of the oldest photo I have yet found of tin tossing. The photo, showing three students in a game of catch with a metal cookie can cover, appears in the Amherst College 1939 yearbook! (see page 62) in some instances, better than two and one half months before Wham-O 's claimed June 17, 1957 first use of the term in its trademark application! That spring, Wham-O's gracefully aerodynamic Pluto Platter had just hit the campus in a big way. But press coverage clearly shows that for Princetonians the Pluto Platter was but the latest innovation in an established tradition of disc play. For them, the Pluto Platter no doubt represented a welcome ascension of the familiar frisbie/frisbee pastime from out of a clunky tin age into a new soaring epoch of plastic. Clearly, Wham-O was not ahead of the curl on this one! The fact is, the company was a late comer to the frisbee band wagon.

Here's the Princeton evidence: "Frisbee" first appears in the March 27, 1957 issue of *The Daily Princetonian,* in the caption under the photos of two men catching a flying disc. The disc in this photograph is a Wham-O Pluto Platter. The Wham-O (wam-O) sticker is just barely distinguishable on the underside of the disc in the photo. Then in the April 29, 1957 issue, a front page article about "frosh weekend," with a photo of a young woman tossing a disc, notes that "games of frisbee" were among activities featured.

Next, on May 2, 1957 is a reference that proves that this frisbee fad had truly made its mark. It's an ad for an eating establishment, a sophomoric little ditty entitled "Fanfare For Frisbee." "Someone tossed me in the air/ It had to land and knew not where; /And during flight my hunger grew,/

So to the Food Mart straight I flew." The ad goes on to reassure that the Food Mart is "friendly to all Frisbee Fans." Obviously the burgeoning frisbee crowd was beginning to represent a formidable marketing opportunity! Then in a May 17 article from the *Daily Princetonian* describing the activities of the "Princeton Graduate Lawn Frisbee Association," the word "frisbee" appears six times! (Remember, all these references appeared well prior to Wham-O's claimed first use of the term!)

Other Spring 1957 press references give more proof that Princeton was not an isolated outpost of pre-trademark frisbee expression. On May 10, 1957 in the *Yale (University) Daily News* an ad for the Yale Co-op includes a picture of disc pioneer, Bill Robes' Space Saucer with the caption "Frisbies." Underneath, the ad copy reads "Space saucers (frisbies to many) designed for easy fun." These and numerous other references from various

"The Princeton Graduate Lawn Frisbee Association." Frisbee aficionados pose in dinner robes with Wham-O Pluto Platters and refreshments in hand. Credit: David Jackson. Courtesy by Robert S. Haller. 1957. Statue of Dean Benjamin West, first dean of the Graduate School. Back Row:(L-R) Frank Newman, Eugene Sirmans, Richard Chambers, John MacAllister, Hal H. Smith, Mr. X. Front Row: (L-R) Fred C. Crews, Robert S. Haller and Robert C Landen.

Northeast college campuses dating back as early as 1949 are compelling evidence that Wham-O was wrong claiming "Frisbee" as its own! Before Wham-O got a hold of it, the term was free and floating about in the public domain as "Frisbee," "Frisbie," "Frizby," "Frisbey," "Phrisbee," and "FRISBIEING," each in its various spellings denoting games or activities played using flying discs.

Even after Wham-O's June 17, 1957 claimed "first use" of "Frisbee," published references appeared with spelling variations of the term, reflecting how well it was established on a grassroots level. For instance, The *Pontefract*, the newspaper of the Pomfret School of Pomfret, Connecticut, in its November 9, 1957 issue gave an account of spirited debate that took place in the school governing body as to whether or not, "Frisbie be accepted as a major sport." (On December 30, 1957, *The New York Times* in a short reference to the Pomfret debate also used the "ie" spelling).

Likewise, the *Amherst Alumni News* of October, 1957 using alternative spellings of the term, notes that "Phrisbee or Frisbey" has for some years been established on the Amherst campus" and that, "A commercial manufacturer is now making plastic phrisbee trays under the name of "pluto platter." From Amherst's perspective, Wham-O's Pluto Platter was the new kid on the block! To them it was the new fangled version of the familiar "phrisbee tray" a "bar tray or similar appurtenance" that had been used in games for years. As these and many other references and anecdotes show, "frisbee" in a variety of spellings was not only a familiar term long before, but continued to be used well after Wham-O's first commercial introduction of it in June of 1957 with the "ee' spelling. Clearly, the term had long been in the public domain, and it seems obvious Wham-O had no business co-opting it for its own!

So formidable was the "frisbee" fad at Princeton in the Spring of 1957 that it was the springboard for the term's first national exposure, as featured in the May 13, 1957 issue of *Sports Illustrated* in an article entitled "Events and Discoveries." This article is of crucial historical significance for two reasons. First, it confirms without a shadow of doubt that the term "frisbee" not only was in wide generic use, but was also given national exposure well before Wham-O's claim of first use (6/17/57) in its trademark application. Secondly, it clearly points to why Wham-O seems to have proceeded with such extreme haste to trademark "Frisbee." Describing the frisbee fad at Princeton, the *S.I.* article notes, "*the air has been filled lately with flying objects, everyone of which can be identified as a Pluto Platter made* by Wham-O. The undergraduates ignore the official name, though, and call the curious gadgets Frisbees." (Author's italics) This article elicited responses from a variety of sources, three of which were published in the May 27, 1957 *Sports Illustrated*. Each used the word "frisbee," one from Miami University in Ohio (Frisbee: Ohio Version), one from Princeton (Frisbee: Historian's Report), and the third emanating from Amherst College (Frisbee: Phrisbee). These references further indicate how widespread use of this term was in its various spellings before Wham-O trademarked it.

What a dilemma this must have posed to the folks at Wham-O! Likely they read the *Sports Illustrated* account and follow up letters, all spawned by the success of *their* new product, and noted it had been universally dubbed that strange frisbee name. Instantly recognizing that this was the catchword for a new pastime, it seems obvious Wham-O knew it had to act fast to "reap the whirlwind," (5,300 Pluto Platters were sold by one Princeton stationary store alone in the spring of 1957!). With its Pluto Platter receiving national exposure but being called a "frisbee" instead of its given name, (in the *Sports Illustrated* piece as well as in follow-up letters), Wham-O likely concluded it had to trademark the term before the knock-off artists pounced. The company, in what the evidence overwhelmingly points to as having been a "rush to trademark," hastily added the word "Frisbee" onto the already existing artwork for its Pluto Platter packaging in the early summer of 1957. (See item AT-25 on page 116) In other words, Wham-O evidently seized the day and pounced first, unfairly cornering a name and a market.

All this raises questions about just when the Pluto Platter, the

"Yale Does Not Understand Frisbee '57 Uniform." The great frisbee rivalry between Princeton and Yale. (Note the Mickey Mouse hat.) Princeton Alumni Weekly July 5, 1957. Credit: Seeley G. Mudd Manuscript Library. Department of Rare Books and Special Collections. Princeton University Libraries.

disc that became the first Frisbee, was first produced. Through the Freedom of Information Act, I tried to secure a copy of the patent application file for inventor Morrison's Pluto Platter and found it missing! I've long suspected that Morrison had his Pluto Platter in production as early as 1955, and that when he (now teamed up with Wham-O) found out of the popularity of his flying disc in the northeast, and that everybody called them "frisbees," he hastily applied for a design patent on July 22, 1957.

Interestingly in a period of just 38 days, the *Yale Daily News* advertised Bill Robes' Space Saucer as "Frisbies," *Sports Illustrated* published its "Flying Frisbees" article, the word "Frisbee" appeared on Wham-O's existing Pluto Platter package, and Wham-0 declared June 17, 1957 as the date of its first use of the frisbee word, and July 8 as its first use in commerce. To top it off, Fred Morrison applied for a design patent on July 22, 1957. Evidently, that little article in *S.I.* describing Morrison's Pluto Platter as a "Frisbee" provoked a "warp drive" response from Wham-O!

In summary, as the evidence overwhelmingly shows, the term "frisbee" had for a number of years enjoyed wide recognition among Ivy League flying disc faddists and many others in the Northeast. It had been much used in one spelling or another dating back to the first Frisbie pie tin tossing at Yale perhaps as early as 1930. And most certainly the fad spread from campus to campus in the tight knit Ivy League, as well as to other colleges. (Some of that traditional Ivy League rivalry is in healthy evidence on a placard sign displayed on the back of a Princeton student which taunts, "Yale does not understand FRISBEE!" This picture appeared in the July 5, 1957 *Princeton Alumni Weekly*.)

With frisbee so obviously having been a term of common use in the Northeast, it's not at all surprising I along with many others were met with such a stonewall of resistance from Wham-O when we requested pre-1960 disc production information! It's hard not to conclude that Wham-O knew it had a shaky hold on its trademark, and felt the need to conceal this. It also seems to explain why Wham-O personnel took such pains to try to convince me and everyone else that it was a July 8, 1957 piece in *Newsweek* which gave the first national exposure of the "Frisbee" term. Wham-O's trademark application claims this same date as its first use of the Frisbee term in commerce. Is this a coincidence? The time line fits well with their chronology, but not with ours. Obviously, it was the May 13, 1957 *Sports Illustrated* article which first brought the term national attention, and in all likelihood, to Wham-O's attention!

Co-founder Rich Knerr's 1957 "fact finding" trip to the Ivy League Schools, the one mentioned in many of Wham-O's standard accounts of how it came to trademark the frisbee, can now be seen as a reflex reaction to *Sports Illustrated's* May 13, 1957, first national exposure of the frisbee fad and the stir it was causing at Princeton , not Harvard or Yale, as Wham-O's account contends. My searches through both the Harvard and Yale archives, and many published "letters to the editor" in the New England area have to date, contrary to legend, found comparatively little describing frisbee/frisbieing on these campuses. Rather, it's Princeton that first flung the frisbee word into national consciousness!

Why is this venerable institution not given credit in the Wham-O version of events? It's probable that Wham-O upon learning of the Princeton frisbee fad, hastily trademarked the term. Then, likely all too aware it had snared a term in common use, it appears Wham-O laid down a smoke-screen for potential trademark challengers by deflecting attention away from Princeton where common usage of the frisbee term was well chronicled, to Harvard and Yale where at best fuzzy corroborative evidence of Frisbie play was to be found. This is not to say that Harvard and especially Yale did not play important roles in the development of frisbee play. But here for the first time, Princeton assumes its rightful place as the institution that introduced the frisbee term to the world!

Wham-O and the Knock-offs: A Too Peaceable Kingdom

Companies, needless to say, zealously defend their trademarks, in effect warning any would be usurper, "Try a knock-off and we'll knock your block off!" In other words they'll be on you in a New York second! In this light, Wham-O's delayed reaction to very blatant challenges to its Frisbee trademark and design patent by rival manufacturers in the late 1950's and early 1960's is curious to say the least. But Wham-O, as we've shown with its very challengeable Frisbee trademark, probably had good reason to go easy on the competition!

Take the case of Premier Products Corporation of Brooklyn, New York. This company was in the process of manufacturing and selling a near identical copy of Wham-O's Pluto Platter Flying Saucer as early as 1958. The only real difference was that Premier called its disc the "Mars Platter." (Premier even included the words, "Play Frisbee" on the packaging; trademark infringements don't get any more explicit than that!) Perhaps Wham-O was unaware of this usurper? They were aware from the start, and I have the documentation to prove it! But Wham-O took no action against Premier, even when sometime around 1960 the company added "Frisbee" onto the disc itself. It wasn't until March of 1963, five years after the Mars Platter was first produced, that Wham-O very belatedly filed suit.

In 1958, Empire Plastics of New York also marketed a knock-off disc. The Zolar Flying Saucer was an "in your face" challenge to Wham-O, which also had the words, "Play Frisbee" on the packaging. One or two years later the company produced two additional models with "Frisbee" in large letters molded into the discs. These are the so called "Mystery Y Frisbees" dubbed that because the word Frisbie appears on the disc and is there is the letter Y on the T-shirts of one of the players depicted on the discs, a reference, we believe, to Yale University and its Frisbie pie pan throwing history. On the packaging for a giant model disc the company also sold, are the words, "The New Campus Craze."

All this clearly indicates that Empire Corporation, located in New York State, was well aware of the popularity of "FRISBIEING" on college campuses in the Northeast, and that it marketed its discs to exploit this fad. Empire also marketed a very attractive box set of its two discs which highlighted in large letters the word "Frisbees." So here was Empire Plastics, an ambitious New York company, marketing a variety of "Frisbee" labeled knock-offs in the largest toy market in the country, as well as nationally. Where was Wham-O's challenge to protect its design patent and trademark? Empire was not a small, obscure company. According to the Federal Trade Commission, its retail sales were $2,000,000.00 in 1958. Wham-O knew of Empire's trademark and patent infringement in 1958. Yet as in the case of Premier Plastics Corporation, Wham-O did nothing about it for five years, a very curious delay. This was especially curious because the design patent for their (Fred Morrison's) Pluto Platter, issued on September 30, 1958, was only in effect for 7 years (expiring on September 30, 1965).

Why Wham-O's attitude of "live and let live" in the corporate world of "eat or be eaten?" It seems Wham-O feared that if it did initiate court action against these trademark violators, it would in turn be challenged as to the legitimacy of its trademark, and rightfully so as the evidence produced here for the first time indicates! (Morrison/Wham-O's disc design patent, being derivative, was likely vulnerable to challenge too). It's hard not to conclude that, faced with these blatant trademark violations, Wham-O waited five years to react because after five years in use a trademark is said to be "incontestable." Wham-O was likely well aware it had a shaky hold on its Frisbee trademark and therefore delayed responding. When Wham-O did finally act against Premier Products in 1963, co-partners and brothers, Nathan, Morris D. and Louis Newman stated in their defense that "Frisbee" was a common, derivative, descriptive and arbitrary term that had been in use long before Wham-O applied for its trademark. The brothers also argued that the design patent for the Pluto Platter was devoid both of artistic merit and invention, being of a typical shape widely known and used in the past.

The Newman brothers put up a good fight against Wham-O's civil action, even filing a counter claim. But for reasons still unknown to me, both Wham-O and Premier dropped their actions against each other (settled by consent on September 15, 1964). The end result was Wham-O ended up acquiring the Mars Platter mold, and Premier quit the frisbee market. It's not unreasonable to speculate that Wham-O avoided a potentially embarrassing examination of how it had arrived at its Frisbee trademark, by quietly resolving this dispute before it came to trial.

Wham-O succeeded in similar fashion in its action against Empire Plastics which did not put up a strong defense against Wham-O's suit when it too was belatedly filed in 1963. Consequently Empire lost (settled by consent) and had to turn over all flying disc molds and related materials to Wham-O. That put an end to Empire's marketing of flying discs.

The Federal Trade Commission Gets Involved

If the reader is not convinced by now of Wham-O's dubious hold on its Frisbee trademark, the particulars of the Federal Trade Commission investigation of the company and its trade practices will be revealing. This investigation took place in 1980 as a result of persistent complaints from a wide spectrum of frisbee players who had had enough of what they perceived to be Wham-O's control tactics. Through the Freedom of Information Act, I have gained access to investigation 801-0148, conducted by the Denver Regional office of the F.T.C.

This is in two parts. First, is a detailed report of the findings and recommendations of the Denver office resulting from its investigation both into Wham-O's alleged monopolistic activities, and into the legitimacy of its Frisbee trademark. Second is a detailed response to the field investigation by F.T.C. economist Alan A. Fisher. His job was to evaluate the evidence presented, and to recommend what actions, if any, the Federal Trade Commission should initiate.

The upshot is, the Denver office strongly advocated an F.T.C. investigation of Wham-O for both monopolistic, exclusionary marketing tactics and "the apparently fraudulent registration of a already generic term." In no uncertain terms the report states that, *"Wham-O's trademark is generic and was improperly obtained and promoted. Wham-O's assertion of an exclusive right in such an invalid trademark has resulted in its monopoly position."* (Author's italics)

The Denver Office investigation also found strong evidence of monopolistic, questionable business practices by Wham-O to the extent that it recommended "a full investigation with compulsory process of Wham-O Mfg. Corporation's monopolization of the frisbee or disc, market." The F.T.C. report also examined how the International Frisbee Association (I.F.A.) formed by Wham-O to promote the sport of frisbee, either "terminated" or "charged higher prices for frisbees" to I.F.A. "Regional Directors" who also sold non Wham-O flying discs. The report labeled such practices "exclusionary," and that Wham-O had "used the I.F.A. to police the frisbee market."

In addition, the F.T.C. report cited Wham-O as having quashed competition in the disc field by "acquisition of its former competitor, C.P.I., behavior long held to be clear example of exclusionary conduct." The report describes C.P.I. as having been Wham-O's "most aggressive competitor, and indeed, C.P.I. was a formidable rival. Its disc, the Saucer Tosser, was the best product on the market from the early to the mid 1970's, outperforming Wham-O's Pro model. In fact from 1974-1976 the Saucer Tosser held the world record for distance! The report found no justification of Wham-O's acquisition of C.P.I. other than to eliminate this source of formidable competition, citing this as further evidence of the company's pattern of monopolistic/exclusionary practices.

The *Frisbee World* publication also gave the appearance of promoting flying disc play in general, when in fact, Wham-O seems to have created both the I.F.A. and *Frisbee World* solely to promote Wham-O's line of Frisbees, and to control the sport by using exclusionary practices on competitors and other manufacturers. For instance, the F.T.C. report noted the prohibition of "other manufacturers advertising in *Frisbee World*," and that "its efforts to foreclose rival tournaments" in favor of those exclusively using Frisbee products "directly (excluded) competitors from tournaments and the tournament market for frisbees."

Players and player organizations that broke away from Wham-O's I.F.A. also suffered discrimination. For instance the Freestyle Players Association (F.P.A.) was formed in 1980 as an organization apart from the control of the I.F.A, in part because players wanted to compete with flying discs being manufactured that they felt were superior to Wham-O's product. In response, Wham-O insisted in payment in full for any of its discs ordered by these disloyal players, whereas other players and organizations loyal to the I.F.A. were granted more flexible payment plans.

Also, (though this was not cited in the F.T.C. report), in one incident at the 1981 Senior World Flying Disc Championships, an HBO film crew was instructed not to film a certain player because he was "too commercial." Well, that "too commercial" player just happened to be me. I guess I was being discriminated against because I was working for Brand X Mfg. Co., a very small Wham-O competitor. By the way, I won that 1981 Master Overall World Flying Disc Championships, and set a Master World Distance Record with a new Brand X Golf Disc. I was only trying to make a living. All this occurred one year after the F.T.C. investigation of Wham-O. At this time, I marketed my disc with the imprint, "Used by World Frisbee Champions," and was never challenged. Was this because the F.T.C. investigation was fresh in the minds of the folks at Wham-O?

The F.T.C. Denver Office investigation also found that Wham-O's monopolistic practices had a dampening effect on upstart flying disc manufacturers who wished to market competitive discs. Three such companies which were, as the report states, "effectively excluded from the retail market" by Wham-O's control of the frisbee term, were Brand-X, Disc Sport, (probably referring to Discraft) and Whirley Industries. The report adds that "at least one major sporting goods manufacturer, AMF Voit, entered the retail frisbee market. Within two years, AMF decided not to continue selling retail discs because its market research studies indicated Wham-O's trade mark gave Wham-O an insurmountable competitive advantage."*

*Any other flying disc companies or individuals are welcome to present frisbee evidence or complaints directly to the F.T.C.'s Denver Office: (Wham-O) Investigation Number 801-0148. Federal Trade Commission, Denver Regional Office, 1485 Curtis Street, Denver, CO 80202. 303-844-2271. Please send the author a copy of your complaint or evidence.

Still sought are additional pre-July 1957 published uses of the word "frisbee" in its various spellings. Personal written accounts of the origin of the frisbee word as used in toss and catch games are also needed.

The Sport Suffers

What cannot be ignored is the effect Wham-O's demonstrably exclusionary marketing and trade practices had on a number of the up and coming ambitious frisbee players who were in many cases dedicating their whole lives to the development of disc play in the 1970's, and by their sheer enthusiasm and hard work were doing a great deal to advance and promote frisbee sports. For instance, in Santa Cruz, California, frisbee promoter Tom Schot almost singlehandedly organized annual World Flying Disc Championships.

Through his promotional efforts, Tom attracted nearly 250 competitors and regularly filled the 4000 seat Cabrillo Stadium at $4.00 a head. The competitions featured an array of crowd pleasing events such as frisbee dogs, sky diving, and long distance throwing off the Santa Cruz pier. Tom also installed a premier, 27 hole championship frisbee golf course (Delaveaga) at the base of the Santa Cruz mountains. A small army of talented and determined frisbee players have worked with similar zeal to promote frisbee sports across the country and overseas, efforts which continue to this day. (These are some of the players who continue to make major contributions to the sport, and have been for 20 years or more: Peter Bloome, Harvey Brandt III, Mike Conger, John David, Dave Dunapace. Harold Duvall, Kevin Givens, Ed Headrick, John Houck, Steve Howle, Dr. Stancil Johnson, Jeff Jorgenson, Mary Jorgenson, Jim Kenner, Hero Kobo, Nobuya Kubayashi, Irv Lander, Dan Mangone, Gail McCall, Charlie Mead, Tom Monroe, Leonard Muise, Rick Neil, Seppo Nieminnen, Snapper Pierson, Derek Robins, Dan Roddick, Tex Robertson, Rick Rothstein, Tim Selinske, Kozo Shimbo, Jan Sobel, Ralph Williamson, Bruce Willis, Lavone Wolfe, Bill Wright.)

Despite the heroic efforts of these players and others, the F.T.C. report amply demonstrates, Wham-O and its I.F.A. organization through their controlling practices had a real dampening effect on the growth of frisbee sports by discouraging healthy competition that would have allowed continued exponential growth of the pastime. In fact, my suspicions are Wham-O purposely slowed the growth of the sport when after 1981 it ended its support and sponsorship of the North American Championship Series and Rose Bowl World Championships. This ended an eight year tradition where

Wham-O had sponsored the high profile World Frisbee Championships and generously flown in competitors from all over the United States and from as many as 10 foreign countries to Pasadena, California for an all expense paid week of competition that culminated finals held in the Rose Bowl to which the general public was invited.

As many as 50,000 spectators attended these Rose Bowl extravaganzas! A documentary film of one of these, "Floating Free" by Jerry Buss, was nominated for an Academy Award, and ABC sports provided national coverage of several competitions. It was a sport rapidly gaining exposure and public acceptance, and this was reflected in phenomenal increases in sales of Frisbees. But Wham-O's withdrawal after 1981 from these kinds of aggressive sponsorship and promotion effectively ended an era which had seen dramatic development of frisbee sports at the grass roots level across both the U.S.A. and Canada.

The figures support this. Wham-O increased from five million in sales in 1974 to 25 million in 1980 (as cited in the F.T.C. report). Undoubtedly, a large factor in this exponential increase was Wham-O's strong marketing and support of frisbee competitions during those years. In fact when the company was sold to Kransco in 1982, Wham-O's over the counter stock had increased in value by 400 percent! During the go get 'em promotion years, the Frisbee had evolved from a toy found at Woolworth's to being a respected item of superior design, displayed and sold in sporting goods stores nationwide. This evolution would not have taken place without Wham-O putting its all into it!

But when Wham-O withdrew, organizers who tried to substitute with championships of their own had neither the reputation, resources, nor the free use of that all important "frisbee" term. The dizzying momentum of the previous eight years was lost. It's obvious to me that had a healthy competitive market been in place in 1981 to take up the slack, instead of one which Wham-O effectively monopolized, this would have never occurred. Either Wham-O responding to the competition, would have kept up its aggressive promotions, or other manufacturers would have seized the day and jumped in. With an even playing field allowing healthy competition, the soaring 1970's of frisbee sports would have continued to arc through the 1980's and to this day, instead of having so grievously stalled out as I feel has been the case.

Outcome of the F.T.C. Investigation

Allen Fischer, the F.T.C. economist, responsible for evaluating the Wham-O investigation and recommending action, counseled caution, though he conceded the Denver office had detailed "an interesting and complex market situation worth investigating." He also concurred on the likelihood of the illegitimacy of the Wham-O Frisbee Trademark: "If indeed, "Frisbee" (or some other spelling pronounced the same way) was already a generic name when Wham-O applied for the registration, then the registration was fraudulent and presumably is cancellable."

But Fischer nonetheless concluded that the Denver Office study was "far too preliminary to justify compulsory process." That's where things were left to stand. This was likely a politically inspired recommendation on Fischer's part with Wham-O being but a very small potato in the field of billion dollar sales corporations where the F.T.C. normally finds itself expending its investigative energies. For Fischer and his compatriots, Wham-O likely did not merit the kind of attention and commitment of resources that a compulsory process action would have required.

How would frisbee sports have evolved without Wham-O's control of the Frisbee name? Would the term if it had remained in the public domain have inspired a number of other companies to aggressively design and market flying discs they could freely call "frisbees?" As a result of healthy competition would the entire sport have grown exponentially to the point where television coverage of disc competitions would now be commonplace with opportunities for a significant number of top players to make a living from endorsements and prize monies? The Denver Office F.T.C. investigation concluded there was strong evidence that Wham-O had hindered the growth of the sport by using "unfair methods of competition" resulting in "Wham-O's monopolization of these markets." The report went so far as to state that "Dedication of the FRISBEE trademark to the public" would be "an appropriate remedy" for "the exclusionary conduct Wham-O employed to achieve and maintain its monopoly." We concur.

Frisbee vs Flying Disc

So what's the big deal? Why this crusade to return the frisbee to its generic roots? Here's your answer. The evidence is pretty clear that it's been a deliberate policy on Wham-O's part since the early 1980's, to redefine the frisbee as just another fun toy. Undeniably, Wham-O originally marketed the Frisbee that way, but with the introduction of the "Pro" in 1964, the frisbee became increasingly the centerpiece of a number of sports and competitions that evolved with its use.

The increasing popularity of these competitive pastimes in the 1970's both dramatically increased Wham-O's sales, and attracted the attention of competitors contemplating getting into the flying disc business themselves. Indeed, other flying disc companies, AMF Voit, Destiny Discs, Discraft and Brand X Mfg. Co. sprang up at this time. In 1981, Wham-O, likely concerned that this increased competition would result in unwelcome scrutiny of its shaky trademark, and culminate in a decisive punitive response from the Federal Trade Commission, stopped its aggressive promotions.

Then Wham-O's support for the sport chilled further in 1982, when the company was sold to the Kransco Corporation. Kransco responded with even deeper cuts of funding for tournaments and the players were again the casualties. (Wham-O doesn't want the public to think of Frisbee as a sport; that would only dilute the validity and value of its registered trademark. Players have been forced to use the term "flying disc." What do we have to show for it? Not much. Just a protected trademark that sold for millions of dollars).

In 1994, the Wham-O trademark became the property of Mattel and was put on a shelf with Barbie. Players were given the ever shorter shrift as tournament support eroded further. Now the Frisbee trademark, as if being bandied about by a pack of dogs fighting over a scrap, has changed hands yet again. In other words, the frisbee that has inspired and captivated so many over the years for all the right reasons, continues in all the wrong hands. For too long it's been controlled by people whose only obvious attachment to it is as investment flavor of the day. Needless to say, this does nothing for the good of our beloved pastime!

As a result of what I perceive to have been Wham-O's restrictive actions and policies protecting its trademark, the many who participate in frisbee sports today are without the benefit of a level playing field. They and the general public have been deceived as to the true origins of the frisbee, and the long and venerable history of competitive play associated with this pastime. But as a former Marine sworn to protect truth, justice and the American way, I will not let this stand!

What players need to realize is that Wham-O personnel are now, and for too long have been interested only in protecting their stock value! Do you think those New York City investors, the Charterhouse Group would have just paid many millions of dollars to purchase Wham-O without the all important ownership of that universally recognized trademark FRISBEE?! You've read the evidence here for the first time— what do you think? Has Wham-O done us all injustice by lifting the generic term frisbee from the public domain and adopting it for its own all these years?

Players who may never have given all this much thought need to realize that the general public and potential corporate sponsors recognize our international sport as FRISBEE, period, not flying disc! But as long as FRISBEE continues in the control of those whose self-interest prevents expansion and growth of this pastime, all of us involved in frisbee sports will continue to be short changed. Sporting goods companies and corporate sponsors will continue to stay out of the disc market because of this strangle hold.

Disc golf, for example, has been an organized sport since 1968, ideal for inexpensive recreational play, yet the masses have yet to catch on. How many more of these wonderful recreational outlets would exist today if we'd been allowed to use the term, "Frisbee Golf" which brings instant recognition to the man on the street? Even now, there is no real sponsorship money outside of a few player owned golf disc companies. There are no companies competing for players' endorsements. There is no Coke or Pepsi Frisbee Golf Tour. And there won't be until players realize what's going on and take decisive action. What's to be done? Based on the evidence in this book, the time is ripe for a flood of letters to the Federal Trade Commission demanding a full compulsory investigation of the legitimacy of the Frisbee trademark. Then sit back and let the F.T.C. take care of the rest. It will have plenty to work with.

Postscript: Mr. Knerr Meets Mr. Frisbie?!

Memories play tricks, but as bizarre as this? In 1987 Wham-O cofounder Rich Knerr suddenly changed his story of how Wham-0 came up with the term "Frisbee." In the May 11, 1987 issue of *Sports Illustrated* in an article by Mark Danna, entitled, "After 30 High Flying Years, Frisbee Still Soars" (which I found during my research in 1994), Knerr claimed the Wham-O Frisbee was named after a mid twentieth century comics character called Mr. Frisbie! There are at least 3 other newspaper articles that each include this from out of nowhere Mr. Frisbie allegation.

Why all of a sudden change the story the Company had put forth for 40 years about the term's Frisbie Pie Company associations? Was it a clumsy handed attempt to throw researchers like me off the trail? Was Wham-O going through ownership changes at the time this article appeared? If someone could prove that the company had taken an already existing generic term and falsely trademarked it, would such a revelation have brought its stock, and therefore its market value tumbling down? Quite possibly.

What's undeniable is what this bizarre "Mr. Frisbie" revelation did to me—it insulted my intelligence and resulted in my redoubling my efforts to find out the truth! In a letter to Knerr's partner, Wham-O cofounder Spud Melin, I asked Mr. Melin to give his response to this story. I even mailed copies of Mr. Knerr's statements to Mr. Melin. In his reply, Mr. Melin contradicted his partner's "Mr. Frisbie" tale, informing me that the frisbee term had indeed originated with the Frisbie Pie Company.

With this final contradiction added to all the rest of the incongruities I have found, I feel like Dorothy in the Wizard of Oz who finally pries the curtain aside and finds the Wizard is not what he says he is! As the evidence amply shows, Wham-O as spinmeister and Wizard of Discdom has obscured much of the truth of the origins of the frisbee, and run its disc kingdom from behind a smokescreen of convenient myth. For instance, the story repeated in popular accounts that Rich Knerr misspelled the term "frisbee," confusing the bakery's "ie" spelling is a myth. In fact, most early references to the pie company, especially in national publications, used the "ee" spelling. Very likely it was the "ee" spelling that Wham-O first saw in print referring to the name being given to its Pluto Platter Flying Saucer by Princeton college students. Frisbee is the generic name Wham-O took for its own!

And it's almost certainly Princeton, not Yale or Harvard where Mr. Knerr, visiting in the late spring of 1957 (if he actually made the trip), witnessed the evolution of his company's Pluto Platter Flying Saucer into a FRISBEE phenomenon! Princeton is where 5,300 Pluto Platters were sold within a few months of their being introduced. At Princeton frisbee playing was already a full fledged, good old fashioned college fad by the time of Rich Knerr's alleged visit. And Princeton students already called their game frisbee, an alternative spelling of the term that had been variously, Frizby/Phrisbie/ Frisbey/Frisbie. The fact that the plastic Space Saucer by

New Hampshire inventor Bill Robes was on May 10, 1957 being market-ed by the Yale Co-op as "Frisbies," (before the May 13, 1957 national expo-sure of "Flying Frisbees" in *Sports Illustrated*) shows how commonplace recognition of the term had become in the northeast. It had been spread far and wide, beginning with those tin tossing ambassadors, the delivery drivers of the Frisbie Pie Company!

"The truth will out," it is said, and it is time Wham-O and all the people who in one way or another have allowed this "Frisbee Conspiracy" to linger all these years, unburden themselves and acknowledge the truth! After all, Wham-O is not some Darth Vador of an evil corporation, nor has it ever been in its various forms. Without a doubt, from founders on down the line, this has been essentially a group of people who have found joy in a job whose whole premise is the promotion of fun! And without a doubt the frisbee and all the games it has inspired have brought untold joy to millions. But the many smokescreens and obscurations of this "Frisbee Conspiracy" have acted as a burden not only to the advance-ment of frisbee sports, but to all those who for so long have known the truth and kept it hidden in their hearts. It's time they liberate their pas-sion and ours, once and for all unburden themselves by letting the frisbee fly free as it was meant to from the start. Then we can all soar together! Peace.

Appendix I

MAJOR EVENTS IN FRISBEE HISTORY
AN HISTORICAL PERSPECTIVE

776B.C. Discus throwing becomes one of the Pentathlon events at the Greek Olympics. The method that these athletes used to toss a disc (called a "diskoi") was an underhanded throw and not the body-whirling overhand wrist flip used by today's Olympians. The longest recorded toss of that era was 105 feet by Phayllos. The winner of the event received the discus as his prize.

1300   The popular disc game of quoits is played in England and Scotland.

1644   Edward Frisbie of England settles in Branford, CT.

1773   The first account of trapshooting appears in a British publication called *The Sporting Magazine*. Many of the early "disc shaped" clay pigeons were designed to be thrown in particular trajectories with a hand held launcher.

1848   William Russell Frisbie is born in Wallingford, CT.

1869   Mr. H.H. Olds hires William R. Frisbie to help sell his pies in Bridgeport, CT.

1871   The W. R. Frisbie Pie Bakery is founded in Bridgeport, CT as Mr. Frisbie takes over Olds' business and established routes.

1891   Mr. Charles Schwartz of Brooklyn, NY, applies for a U. S. patent for his "Spinning Toy," (#476,825). This invention is one of the first disks that could be thrown from one person to another. A hand held stick was used to engage a cone shaped center to keep the wood/metal disk spinning on the stick. However, no samples of this device have been found.

1903   Upon the death of his father, Joseph P. Frisbie becomes president of the W. R. Frisbie Bakery, and expands it from production of a few hundred pies a day into an enterprise with routes across much of New England and adjacent New York State. This sets the stage for Frisbie to become a widely known term that will lend its name to a developing pastime.

1905   The W. R Frisbie Pie Bakery is now called the Frisbie Pie Company and becomes a Connecticut corporation.

1910   The Frisbie Pie Company starts to use the "Frisbie's Pies" logo on its products and in advertising.

1915   Joseph P. Frisbie builds a three story Frisbie bakery in Bridgeport, CT. Employees are playing throw and catch with pie pans in the parking lot. Company truck drivers become the first frisbee ambassadors, having honed their skills in the spacious enclosed loading dock, the birthplace of Frisbieing.

1920   Yale is credited as starting the Frisbieing craze. However, there is relatively little evidence to support this story. This could have been a public relations ploy by Wham-O to associate its Pluto Platter Flying Saucer with higher learning or, possibly to steer people away from Princeton University where the word "frisbee" appeared in print well prior to Wham-O's claim of first use in its trademark application.

1922   Ten year old, Tex Robertson and neighborhood friends in Sweetwater, TX are playing everyday flying disc games with metal can covers.

1926   Ronald F. Gibson and classmates at the Bladworth Elementary School located in Bladworth, Saskatchewan are playing an informal game on a prescribed course that they call Tin Lid Golf. They are modifying the metal can cover so that it can be more easily thrown for distance with a backhanded motion.

1930   Earliest written report (letter) of Frisbie pie pan tossing at Yale University.

1933   Walter V. Heekin receives a U. S. patent for his "Exhibition Device" Patent No. 2,011,813. This metal pie pan was equipped with a handmade color wheel, whistles and a light source. (Only a few samples were made.)

1933   Michigan professor, Dr. Harold Copp establishes The Wolverine Day Camp in Ann Arbor, MI. This is where Tex Robertson first introduced the flying disc game called Sa-Lo, making the Wolverine Day Camp the birthplace of organized frisbee playing.

1936   At Princeton University, Albert Einstein stops to admire a disc throw and catch game conducted with a round metal can cover. He is quoted as saying, "Very beautiful!"

1937   Walter A. Darby applies for a U.S. patent for his Disk Scaling Game, patent #2,126,245. This early example of the frisbee golf game used adjustable laundry type baskets that could be laid out on a pre-scribed course. The disk was made of light-weight metal, fiber or rubber.

1937   Tex Robertson and Jack Nendell perform the first of its kind Sa-Lo frisbee demonstration before a capacity crowd at a University of Texas (Austin) basketball game.

1937   Buck Roger's Flying Saucer arrives. This is one of the first "throw and catch" flying discs to be marketed in the United States. It was made of two paper plates joined together and fastened with a strip of metal around the edge.

1938   At Kimball Union Academy located in Meriden, NH (near Dartmouth), the cookie can cover game becomes popular. (Bill Robes, inspired by the can cover tossing at KUA, designs his plastic Space Saucer in 1953.)

1938   Campers and staff of Camp Choconut, PA are playing throw and catch games with large metal pretzel can covers.

1939   That spring, students are playing an informal game of frisbee golf on the campus of Harvard University. They use metal cookie can covers for their discs. Both natural and man made objects are used as targets. No standard course is set up— each hole is selected by mutual agree-ment, or by each player in turn.

1939   Tex Robertson and his wife start Camp Longhorn on the shores of Inks Lake in Burnet, TX. The Sa-Lo flying disc game was used to sign up its first campers. Sa-Lo is still offered to the nearly 3,200 campers who attend every year.

1939   Five students from Middlebury College, VT travel to Lincoln, Nebraska to attend a Delta Upsilon National Fraternity Convention. Traveling in a 1931 Model A Ford, they stop at a gas station in the New England area to refuel and purchase a fresh pie made by the Frisbie Pie Company. (The pie tin was not found in a corn field in Nebraska as some accounts have reported!) After consuming the pie, the tin is tossed around for amusement at every rest stop along the way. Paul Eriksson, Cole Elbert, Dick Barclay, Porter Evans and Bob Gale bring their newly discovered frisbie tossing skills back to Middlebury College. Result—pie pan tossing spreads throughout the campus.

1942   Students at Kenyon College, Gambier, Ohio are playing a game they call "Ace Ball." (frisbee football). They are using a metal Oven-Ex cake pan. This activity was photographed at Kenyon (but not published) in 1950 by *Life Magazine* photographer Eliot Elisofon.

1946   Walter (Fred) Morrison makes a drawing of the first plastic disc design that he called the "Whirlo Way." Morrison's disc design went on to become the 1948 Flyin Saucer.

1948   The first plastic flying disc is created by Walter (Fred) Morrison and Warren Franscioni, machine formed from a block of Tennessee Eastman's Tennite and called the "Flyin Saucer." The original prototype breaks during its initial test flight. Fred and Warren start the Pipco Company in San Luis Obispo, CA.

1948   Arthur "Spud" Melin and Rich Knerr start Wham-O (Wam-O) Mfg. Co. by self-producing and marketing wooden sling shots.

1949   The Hall Manufacturing Company of Los Angeles, CA., markets the Sky Pie, (patent #2,690,339), a plastic flying disc with a wire catcher. A disc with a 3 inch hole in its center is thrown into the air and caught onto the wire catcher.

1949   Mr. Ezra Bowen (who later became a writer for *Sports Illustrated*) returns from spring break to Amherst College with several Pipco Flyin Saucers that he purchased from lifeguards in Daytona Beach, FL.

1950   The Li'L Abner Flyin Saucer appears. Several hundred of these 2nd period Flyin Saucers are produced by the Pipco Company as part of a failed promotion with Capp Enterprises.

1950   Students and members of the Phi Delta Theta Fraternity at Amherst College are playing a disc version of tennis with a metal cover from a State Line potato chip can. They refer to the game as Frisbie. It is reported that they named the game after English Professor, George

"Frisbie" Whicher.

1953   Ernest "Bill" Robes is marketing his homemade (first generation prototype) Space Saucers at the Dartmouth College bookstore. Sheets of plastic are heated in an oven and formed over a mold made from a washing machine agitator, then trimmed to size and hand stamped with the "Space Saucer" name.

1953   Students at Amherst College are playing frisbee football games called Phrisbee/Frisbey with a serving tray. The basic rules are similar to the modern and internationally popular game called Ultimate.

1954   Ernest (Bill) Robes of Hanover, NH creates the (second generation) plastic Space Saucer by injection molding, along with a standardized Space Saucer court game. He receives a U.S. patent for his Space Saucer in 1958, (#2,822,176).

1954   The International Frizby Championship is played at Dartmouth College; (November 7, 1954). The Blossom Brothers of Theta Delta Chi defeat the Tweedy Free-Throwers from Montreal, Canada. The disc they use is referred to as a "unit," which is a 5 inch metal cookie can cover. More than 150 people witness the event. Participant, David Oberlander, won the National Fraternity Award (Theta Delta Chi) for his cover story about this historic event which appeared in the March 1955 issue of *The Shield*, entitled, "World Frizby Championships."

1955   The first reported contest of a game called "guts frisbee" is played using a metal cookie can cover, in front of Lockhart Hall on the Princeton University campus.

1955   Dartmouth's Chi Phi Fraternity brothers and friends are using 6" metal can covers to play regular Frizby matches with 4 person teams. The game is popular enough to force other teams to "Call for Winners."

1955-6 (Approx.) Fred Morrison designs the Pluto Platter Flying Saucer. His design becomes the standard for almost every flying disc manufactured since then. He receives a Design Patent 183,626 on Sept. 30, 1958. (Application date is 7/22/57).

1956   Fred Morrison teams up with the Wham-O Mfg. Co. to market his Pluto Platter Flying Saucer.

1956   The Frisbie Pie Company is sold to the Wagner Baking Corp.

1957   Wham-O Mfg. Co. of San Gabriel, CA, markets Fred Morrison's Pluto Platter Flying Saucer. On January 23, 1957, the first of nearly 300 million Wham-O Frisbees start to fly and the craze begins.

1957   In the spring, Princeton University students start a campus fad with Wham-O's Pluto Platter Flying Saucer. They are calling their game-frisbee. (5,300 Wham-O discs are sold). The word "frisbee" makes its earliest known published appearance in the March 27, 1957 issue of *The Daily Princetonian.*

1957   On May 10, 1957, the *Yale Daily News* is advertising Bill Robes' Space Saucers as "Frisbies."

1957   *Sports Illustrated* publishes its first article on frisbee playing (May 13, 1957), entitled "Flying Frisbees." This is the first national exposure of the term "frisbee" being used to describe a game of throw and catch with a flying disc.

1957   The Graduate College Lawn Frisbee Association is formed at Princeton University. This frisbee club is founded in rebuttal to the May 13, 1957 *Sports Illustrated* article suggesting that the game of frisbee can be learned or mastered by undergraduates in only ten minutes.

1957   Frisbee playing becomes very popular on the campus of Phillips Exeter Academy in Exeter, NH. A major article on frisbee playing as a sport appears in the school newspaper.

1957   Students at Miami University, (Oxford, OH) are playing disc games called Night Frisbee, Wandering Frisbee, and Guts Frisbee with a blunt-toothed circular saw blade (Gloves are permitted!)

1957   In September, a solid brass plaque bearing the inscription "Fris-bee Field Sept. 1957" is presented to Thomas Worthen at his Magoon Point summer house located on the eastern shore of Lake Memphremagog (Canada), which is just across the border from Newport, VT. The plaque was in appreciation for the many great frisbee times enjoyed by Mr. Worthen's friends, George "Bud" Snow, John Lyman and Lee Foster, at this location.

1957   In a Dec. 30, 1957 *New York Times* survey, titled "Prep School Sports," by Michael Strauss, students from the Pomfret Prep School (Pomfret, CT), express their desire to have Frisbie playing declared a national sport. (The "Frisbie" spelling is used by the *Times*!) This sentiment was first publicized in the November 9, 1957 *Pontefract*, the newspaper of Pomfret Prep, in an article entitled, "Frisbie Becomes Overwhelming Pastime; Try it This Weekend." (Photo accompanying article is of a student catching a flying frisbee).

1958   The first International Frisbee Tournament (IFT) is reportedly held at Eagle Harbor, MI during a picnic for the Healy family and their friends. This, it is believed, begins the longest running frisbee tournament in the world.

1958   Wham-O applies for a trademark on the word "frisbee." The application is filed on July 28, 1958. (First use, June 17, 1957; in commerce, July 8, 1957).

1959   Wham-O receives a Registered Trademark #679186 on May 26, 1959, for the word FRISBEE. Category: Toy Flying Saucers For Toss Games, in class 22.

1959   The COPAR Company of Chicago, IL introduces its versions of flying disc games, with complete equipment and a rule book for playing Sky Golf and Sky Croquet.

1964   "Steady Ed" Headrick becomes the Vice-President of Sales and General Manager for Wham-O Mfg. Co. This visionary is probably more responsible than anyone else for starting the modern day era of frisbee sports. He invented and patented the Professional model Frisbee for the serious player in 1964. He also started the International Frisbee Association in 1967, which claimed 112,000 members. In 1965, he was the first frisbee player to appear on the Johnny Carson Show, and in 1967, he established the Junior Frisbee Championships. Nearly 10 million youngsters have participated in this annual event. In 1974, he established and organized the World Frisbee Championships held annually at the Rose Bowl until 1981. This was the biggest and most prestigious frisbee event of its kind. In 1975, "Steady Ed" invented and patented standardized equipment for the game of disc golf, and established the Disc Golf Association, and in 1979, organized the $50,000 Frisbee Disc Golf Tournament. Today, there are over 700 disc golf courses located in 13 countries and 12,000

PDGA members. He has also won numerous World Championship titles.

1964   Wham-O introduces the Professional model Frisbee, the first "high tech" model for the serious player.

1966   Luci Baines Johnson marries Pat Nugent on August 6, 1966. The two travel to the Bahamas for their honeymoon under the alias of Mr. and Mrs. Frisbee.

1967   Wham-O's International Frisbee Association is formed in the interest of promoting frisbee play. During its existence over 112,000 frisbee enthusiasts become IFA members.

1967   Students (and local residents) at U.C. Berkeley develop a type of frisbee freestyle play they call "jamming." Trick throws and catches, hand and foot tipping, boomerangs, and a variety of skip shots with a stylized flow of throwing and catching with the same continuous motion are all incorporated into this activity.

1968   The California Masters win the 11th Annual IFT Guts Frisbee Championships held in Eagle Harbor, Michigan. This powerful and talented team included, "Steady Ed" Headrick, Jay Shelton, Steve Sewall, Tom Boda and Ken Headrick. This was also Wham-O's first introduction to organized/competitive frisbee playing.

1968   Students from Columbia High School in Maplewood, NJ develop rules for a game they call Ultimate frisbee. This team game, today known as "Ultimate," is now played at hundreds of educational institutions and clubs around the world.

1969   "Steady Ed" Headrick's All-Comers Meet is held at Brookside Park in Pasadena, CA. Distance, golf, accuracy and team Guts are contested. Jay Shelton, the overall winner, wins the first organized frisbee golf contest. Bob May takes distance and Gary Headrick wins accuracy.

1969   The first Ultimate frisbee game is played at Columbia High School in Maplewood, NJ. In a blow against parliamentary procedure, the student council is defeated by the staff of the school's newspaper, The Columbian, 11 to 7.

1969   The first National Junior Frisbee Tournament is held at Madison

Square Garden, in New York. Darrell Lewis wins the event and a $1000.00 U.S. Savings Bond.

1970   Buzzy Hellring writes the first version for the rules of Ultimate Frisbee.

1970   On May 23, 1970, at the El Cerrito, CA Parks and Recreation Dept. Frisbee Tournament, Victor Malafronte sets a new World Distance Record by throwing a Wham-O Pro 92 yards using the behind the back delivery.

1970   The Berkeley Frisbee Group (BFG) establishes a standardized 18 hole frisbee golf course on the campus of U.C. Berkeley. Players use man-made and natural objects as targets. Berkeley is gaining a reputation as the "Mecca of Frisbee."

1971   Bill Schneider is teaching the first accredited frisbee course at Sacramento State University in California.

1972   The CPI Saucer Tosser is introduced. Berkeley Frisbee Group players discover it to be a superior to the best Wham-O's product line has to offer. Wham-O would eventually buy out the CPI company in 1978.

1972   Bill and Mike Schneider are hired by a German company to perform frisbee demonstrations throughout Europe. They are the first professional players to go on tour.

1972   While competing in the 15th annual IFT, Ines Sam of the Berkeley Frisbee Group sets the new women's world distance record of 67 yards. It is her first tournament.

1972   The Canadian National Exhibition stages the first Canadian Open Frisbee Tournament. C & R Losers win the Guts frisbee match over the World Champion Highland Avenue Aces.

1972   The first intercollegiate Ultimate match is played between Rutgers and Princeton on November 6, on the same field where the first Intercollegiate football was played 103 years earlier. 1000 spectators and ABC Sports see Rutgers win, 29 to 27.

1972   Goldy Norton publishes the first frisbee book entitled, *The Official Frisbee Handbook.* (Bantam Books)

1973   Victor Malafronte wins the first freestyle "individual" event at the second annual Canadian Open Frisbee Championships.

1974   The American Flying Disc Open is held at John Hopkins University, Rochester, NY. The first standardized frisbee golf targets are used. (Shallow wooden boxes placed on the ground are used as targets or pins) Dan Roddick wins the overall and a new Datsun 210. The game of Double Disc Court makes its debut. (John Kirkland wins the first DDC event.)

1974   On August 25th, the first official Invitational World Frisbee Championships is held at the Rose Bowl in Pasadena, CA. Nearly 100 competitors and 25,000 spectators attend. Victor Malafronte and Jo Cahow win the world championships. Monika Lou and John Kirkland prevail in the world champion distance event.

1974   The Swedish Frisbee Federation is formed. Nine years later in 1983, frisbee is accepted as a "traditional sport" by the Swedish Federation of Sports. There are now numerous Ultimate teams and 50 frisbee golf courses located throughout the country.

1974   The first frisbee dog championships is held at California State University at Fullerton, CA

1974   Jim Kenner and Ken Westerfield win the first "pairs freestyle" event at the 3rd Annual Canadian Open Frisbee Champions.

1974   The first Octad (8 Disc-defying Events!) Is held in New Jersey at Rutger's University. Here, the superior qualities of the CPI Saucer Tosser disc are seized on by players as it becomes the first non-Wham-O disc to hold the world's distance record. On this chilly spring day with strong northwesterlies, the author gets first crack at immortality, setting the record with his "Two Finger Macho Sidewinder" shot of 375', but east coast powerhouse Dave Johnson answers with a backhand shot of 378' (using one of the author's own CPI's!)

Dave's CPI world distance record will stand for the next two years. (Some 23 years later, we are still very good friends, and have had a rewarding collaboration on this book with Dave as editor—just one of many long lasting, close relationships that have flourished in the Frisbee Family!)

In 1978, Wham-O purchases all shares of CPI stock, and the All Star Saucer Tosser is never seen in competition again.

1974   Jim Palmeri and his brother John open the first frisbee retail store called, "The Flying Disc and Chess Shop" in Rochester, NY.

1974-5 John Kirkland and Victor Malafronte are hired by the Harlem Globetrotters to perform choreographed frisbee shows set to music. While on this 6 month national tour that covers nearly 200 cities, we perform for over 2 million people.

1975-6 Women's World-Multi Frisbee Champion Monika Lou and Victor Malafronte conduct three major frisbee tours throughout Japan.

1975   The Japanese Frisbee Association is created by the Iwamoto Trading Company.

1975   Freddie Haft and Kerry Kolmar develop the nail delay which revolutionizes freestyle play. This is a specialized technique of "catching" by balancing a spinning disc on the end of one's finger nail. This breakthrough allows frisbee freestyle to become more of an art form, with choreographed routines done to music and Olympic style judging.

1975   The first Indoor Frisbee Distance Championships is held at the Los Angeles Convention Center. Dave Johnson wins with a world record 277 feet. Monika Lou sets the women's indoor world record with a toss of 209 feet.

1975   The first Intercollegiate Ultimate Frisbee Championships is held at Yale University. Eight teams participate. The team from Rutgers is the winner.

1975   Doctor Stancil E.D. Johnson's book, *FRISBEE: A Practitioner's Manual & Definitive Treatise,* is published.

1976   The U.S. All Star Frisbee Team made up of players from the Berkeley Frisbee Group, wins the overall championship against the All

Japanese National Team in Tokyo.

1976   "Steady Ed" Headrick and his son Ken invent and patent a standardized frisbee catcher called a "Disc Pole Hole." In 1975, they install the first permanent disc golf course at Oak Grove Park located in La Canada, CA. During its first year of operation, nearly 5,000 people play disc golf during a given week. "Steady Ed" markets the first line of golf discs, the "Night Flyer."

1976   The first issue of *Frisbee World Magazine* is published by the IFA/Wham-O Mfg. Co.

1978   The Smithsonian Institution adds a frisbee display case to its "Flying For Fun" exhibit.

1978   The International Guts Frisbee Hall of Fame is established at the Copper County Chamber of Commerce building on Michigan's Upper Peninsula.

1978   The IFA/Wham-O Frisbee Hall of Fame is established in San Gabriel, CA

1978   The first Santa Cruz Flying Disc Classic is organized by Tom Schot. Don "The Rocket" Hoskins wins the overall. This event evolves later into the Flying Disc World Championships.

1979   Wham-O and the Disc Golf Association sponsor the $50,000 Frisbee Disc Golf Tournament held at Huntington Beach, CA. In sudden death, Tom Kennedy wins the event over John Connolly.

1979   The Ultimate Players Association is formed. Tom Kennedy is elected Director.

1979   The first 35 plus age division overall world champion titles are contested as part of the 1979 WFC. Winners are: Jim Palmeri Master 35+; Johnny Roberts, Grand Master 45+.

1979   Scott Zimmerman wins the first of four consecutive overall world championships!

1981   Brand X Mfg. Co. markets the first two-to-one ratio golf disc. The

40X Mold sets a new Master World Distance Record of 118 meters at the 1981 Senior World Flying Disc Championships.

1981   The European Flying Disc Federation is created.

1981   The last Wham-O sponsored World Frisbee Disc Championships (WFC) is held at the hallowed Rose Bowl in Pasadena, CA. According to Federal Trade Commission figures, Wham-O's Frisbee sales reached 25 million dollars in 1980, an unbelievable 500% increase from the FTC cited figure of 5 million dollars sales in 1974. Evidently, the sport is growing too fast for Wham-O, and it cancels future WFC Rose Bowl competitions. This event continues as the U.S. Open Flying Disc Championships, with at best, lackluster Wham-O support.

1981   The first Senior World Flying Disc Championship limited to players 35 and over is held in Springfield, MO. HBO is there to cover the event. Victor Malafronte 35+, Ron Widel 55+, and Jack Roddick 65+ are the overall winners.

1982   AMF VOIT enters the flying disc market with its two-piece disc called the Vector Hyperfoil.

1982   Wham-O and its Frisbee trademark are sold to Kransco, a large toy company.

1982   The first Professional Disc Golf Association (PDGA) World Championships is held in Charlotte, NC. Harold Duvall is the winner.

1983   Innova Champion Discs markets the first beveled edge golf disc, the Eagle. The beveled edge allows for far greater throwing distances than had before been possible, radically changing the game of disc golf.

1983   The First World Ultimate Championships is held in Gothenburg, Sweden. The Santa Barbara Condors are the winners.

1981-90 Numerous frisbee-related organizations, clubs, Ultimate teams, and disc golf courses are appearing throughout Europe and Asia.

1986   The Cub Scouts offer a new activity badge for participation in the frisbee team game of Ultimate.

1987   The General Association of International Sports Federations welcomes the World Flying Disc Federation (WFDF) as a member.

1987   The first World Flying Disc Federation (WFDF) Overall Championships is held at Ft. Collins, CO. Peter Bowie of New Zealand wins the event.

1988   Snapper Pierson is the first player to win the Masters overall, and the WFDF (open overall) world championships in the same year.

1989   Ultimate is a demonstration sport for the World Games held in Karlsruhe, Germany.

1989   Amy Bekken wins the first of four consecutive overall world championships.

1990's   So far, Elaine King has won five Professional World Disc Golf Championships!

1991   Wham-O sends 20,000 Frisbees to our Desert Shield troops in Saudi Arabia.

1992   World multi frisbee champion Ralph Williamson, grand collector and historian, opens the first frisbee museum in Seattle, WA.

1993   The Disc Golf Hall of Fame is established in Huntsville, AL

1994   Mattel buys the Frisbee trademark From Kransco.

1995   Scott Stokely becomes the first person to break the 200 meter distance barrier in competition. (World Record toss of 200.1 meters.)

1997   Ralph Williamson wins the first World (PDGA) Legends Disc Golf Championship.

1997   Ken Climo of Clearwater, FL wins his eighth consecutive Professional Disc Golf Championship!

1997   Nearly 350 qualifying competitors from 7 countries participate in the 16th Annual Professional Disc Golf Championship held in Charlotte, NC. Total cash purse is $50,000.

1997   Mattel sells the Frisbee trademark to New York City investors, Charterhouse Group International.

1998   A year of important Frisbie/Frisbee anniversaries! It's the 50th anniversary of the invention of the first plastic flying disc, the 40th anniversary of the closing of the Frisbie Pie Company, the 40th IFT, and the 30th anniversary of the creation of the game of Ultimate.

1998   On May 30th a large celebration is held in Bridgeport CT, birthplace of the frisbie/frisbee, to commemorate and honor the Frisbie Pie Company as the institution that spawned the frisbee game. This celebration features frisbee demos, a display of Frisbie memorabilia, a float parade and a period accurate re-creation of one of the Frisbie "pie wagons," whose drivers both delivered the pies and pioneered a pastime!

2001   Look for frisbee to be a full metal sport at the International World Games in Akita, Japan.

Appendix II

GLOSSARY OF FRISBEE TERMS

ABSOLUTE MINT CONDITION: This is an extremely rare grading of a disc and package (and pie tin) so perfect you will probably never find one!

AESTHETIC VALUE: The beauty, artistic appeal, and creativity of a disc, its design or decoration.

ANTIQUE: Any flying disc which is at least 25 years old.

APPRAISAL/PRICING: Any professional evaluation of a collectible flying disc or an entire collection.

ARCUATE VANES: A series of curved diagonal ribs or channels designed to trap air flow over the top surface of flying disc. This action will cause a disc to rise or fall as it travels through the air. Examples: The Flyin Saucer or the Magic Saucer.

ATLANTIS: Refers to the "Holy Toledo!" disc originally discovered by Dr. Stancil Johnson while walking along the beach. It was speculated to have washed up from the drowned civilization of Atlantis, as good an explanation as any!

BACK TO BACK DISC: A flying disc which has the same or nearly the same disc design on the top and bottom sides. Usually designed rimless and hollow inside. Example: The Magic Saucer.

BERKELEY FRISBEE GROUP (BFG): One of the early modern day frisbee clubs (circa 1969), a fulcrum of frisbee sports development; created "Jamming Freestyle," the individual field events of MTA/TRC, and the concept of frisbee collecting. Also, performed professional demonstrations and educational clinics, and was the starting point for many world frisbee champions and world record holders.

BERNOULLI PRINCIPLE: The decrease in pressure as the velocity of a fluid or air increases over the top surface of a disc while in flight. Named after Jakob Bernoulli, a Swiss mathematician and physicist (1654-1705).

BEVELED EDGE: A term used to describe the tapered outside leading edge of a golf disc.

BLOCK STAMP: A decoration or logo shaped like a block and used by the manufacturer to market a particular line of Innova-Champion golf discs.

BOLTERON: An early plastic material used by Bill Robes to hand make his first period Space Saucer in 1953.

BOOTLEGGED: A term used to describe a disc that was illegally copied by

another company without permission from the owner. (AKA: Knock-off.)
BRAND X MFG. COMPANY: A former flying disc (ASI/Premium) company which produced one of the first two-piece discs (Connection/AMF Vector Hyperfoil) and an early line of golf discs.
BRICKBAT: A disc which has an extra firm or stiff flight plate, usually, the first run of a new mold. (e.g. Pro mold #15.)
BUTYRATE: An early plastic mixture used by the Pipco Company to mass produce the first plastic flying discs in 1948, called, The Flyin Saucer.
CAMP WOLVERINE: (Ann Arbor, MI) From here comes the earliest account of organized frisbee playing (SA-LO). Sa-Lo was introduced by Tex Robertson in 1933.
CAPITAL THRUST: An term used at Dartmouth College in the early 1950's to describe a good throw of the unit, (cookie can cover) that scored a point in the game of "Frizby."
CLASSIC SUPER PRO SERIES: A specialty item created with Wham-O's Super Pro model. Classics have an astrology theme label.
CLASSIFICATION: A means of grouping together respective or similar flying discs into a particular kind of group or category.
CLASSIFICATIONS: One of 20 different groups of flying discs, a particular kind or type of collectible.
CLEAR: A disc that doesn't have any pigment (color) in the plastic. AKA-Unpigmented.
CLUB DISC: A collection of flying discs which represent any of the various frisbee clubs; usually commemorative of its founding, or the flying disc tournaments and events sponsored by that club.
CM: Refers to the metric system of measurement (centimeter). Used to measure the width of golf discs.
COLLAPSED RIM: Found on Fastback #3 mold discs (FB3). Due to wear and tear, the mold partially collapsed causing the plastic by the rim to be pushed slightly inward. This will allow the FB3 to turn more readily during the field event of MTA (hang time).
COLLECTIBLE FLYING DISCS: Refers to any type of flying disc which has been classified as a collectible item.
COLLECTOR: An individual interested in obtaining certain collectible flying discs for his or her personal collection and for historical value.
COLLECTOR'S ITEM: Any flying disc which is deemed collectible due to its popularity, age, classification or rarity, etc.
COURSE PRO: A person responsible for maintaining a disc golf course. General contact person for information on disc golf course design, tournaments, site-locations, demonstrations, clinics and golf disc sales.
CPI: Canadian flying disc company first called Continental Promotions

Inc., later changed to Concept Products Inc.

CRIMPED EDGE: A feature found on some Frisbie pie pans. The top edge of the rim of such a pan was crimped during the pie manufacturing process.

CUPOLA: The central raised section of Wham-O's Pro model; the area where the label is attached.

DEALER: A disc collector interested in purchasing or trading for collectible flying discs for the purposes of reselling or trading to another collector.

DELAY: The act of catching a spinning disc on a fingernail or device to prolong its rotation during the event or activity of freestyle play.

DELAY MARKS: Usually concentric circles or loop marks caused by a fingernail or device on the surface of a disc during the activity of "delay" while playing freestyle.

DES. PAT.: A design patent issued by the U.S. Patent Office to protect a certain design or shape.

DGA: The Disc Golf Association. Founded by "Steady Ed" Headrick PDGA #001. The creator and inventor of disc golf equipment, course designs and the original line of golf discs.

DISC AUCTION: An event staged to auction off highly collectible and popular flying discs. Some of these events are held to raise money for non-profit organizations; i.e. Save The Children Foundation; Friends of the Park, etc.

DISC COLLECTING: The gathering of collectible flying discs as a hobby, business or just for the fun and uniqueness of the activity.

DISC GOLF: "Disc Golf" was a registered trademark of the Disc Golf Association for standardized equipment used for the game of disc (frisbee) golf. Founded by "Steady Ed" Headrick. The term "Disc Golf" has been given to the public domain by "Steady Ed."

DISC GOLF COURSE: Usually an 9-27 hole course, with mostly par 3 holes; designed to challenge a player's skill in traversing a prescribed course around trees, rolling hills and manmade objects etc. Similar to a ball golf course, but with more obstacles and variety of approach possibilities.

DISC IN THE PACKAGE: Any collectible flying disc which is still in its original package. Add 35% to the near mint price for collectible discs still in the package.

DISC OF THE YEAR AWARD: An annual award given to the most artistic, aesthetic and creative flying disc design or decoration.

DISCRAFT PRODUCTS: A leading manufacturer of golf, freestyle and Ultimate flying discs and accessories.

DISC POLE HOLE: A flying disc entrapment device designed to capture a disc during the game of disc golf. It's counterpart in "ball" golf is the "hole" or "cup."

DISCUS: A disc shaped projectile usually made of forged metal and used for the distance hurling event that originated at the Greek Olympic Games around 776 B.C.

EAGLE HOT STAMP: A foil decoration of an eagle which appeared on one of Wham-O's Super Pro models, but was covered over by an over-sized paper label of an eagle. A collector's item.

EARLY: Term used to identify the 2nd period of the Wham-O Pluto Platter that has ribs on the center dome.

ENGRAVING: Any lettering or design which is tooled into the mold of a flying disc.

ESKER: A small narrow band, or bands, strip, or bar of plastic which is engraved into the mold to cover unwanted script or to add a new inscription over the original inscription on a disc.

EXCELLENT CONDITION: An appraised grading which determines that a frisbee, Frisbie pie tin, or related memorabilia, has only a few slight imperfections. Not good enough to be graded as in near mint condition. Excellent condition value for plastic is only 70%; for Frisbie pie pans, 75% of the near mint price.

FASTBACK: (FB) A light-weight toy disc design with sloping shoulders and a flat center area for the application of art design or imprinting. Usually given away with admission to an event or with retail goods purchase, etc. Also known as a premium disc. A very poor flyer that turned a lot of people away from the sport of frisbee.

FISH EYE: A term used to describe a small, circular shaped imperfection in the decoration of a disc caused by a particle of dust, dirt or air bubble.

FLAMED BLACK RING: Found on the first (prototype) Wham-O Pro model made only in 1964. The ring band was spray painted on the disc and then flame cured or dried. Flamed ring Pros have a dull finish and rough looking edges. All other Pros were hot stamped and have a shiny finish with sharp edges.

FLASH: An excess amount of plastic found around the parting line of a disc after manufacture.

FLAPJACK GUTS: Game played like Guts with a rubbery soft disc (Flapjack) that will twist and turn unpredictably in flight.

FLIGHT PLATE: The top surface of a disc from the center to the shoulder.

FLIGHT RINGS: Same as ridges. Concentric lines or grooves cut into the shoulder area of Wham-O Frisbee flying discs. Invented by "Steady Ed" Headrick.

FLYING DISC COLLECTOR: A person involved in the collecting of flying discs and related memorabilia. Many collectors will specialize in a particular classification or classifications of flying discs.

FLYING RING: Any flying ring where the diameter of the hole in its center is larger than the shoulder area of the ring plate itself.

FLY MART: A scheduled meeting of frisbee collectors for the trading and selling of collectible items. Always open to the general public. Fly Marts are held at most major frisbee tournaments.

FOOTBALL STAMP: A standard decoration or logo shaped like a football and used by the Innova Company in manufacturing and marketing a particular line of its golf discs.

FOREIGN DISC: Any flying disc produced outside the U.S.A.

FRANKENSTEIN: The practice of creating non-issued discs in an attempt to pass them off as a collectors item. There's a fair chance that if you hear, "there were only a few made," or you notice a disc just doesn't "fit in," or can't be readily categorized, it could be a Frankenstein. These discs (also known as "bastardized discs,") are unacceptable to most collectors. They should not be confused with art work and test run samples which are collectible. However, it is sometimes impossible to determined the exact history of a given disc, so, buyer beware!

FREESTYLE PLAYERS ASSOCIATION (FPA): Governing association which develops, regulates, organizes and sanctions major freestyle events.

FRISBEE: The now universally recognized term, the first published use of which appeared in the *Daily Princetonian* (Princeton University) on March 27, 1957, to describe the game of throw and catch with a round flying disc. The word Frisbee was first used by Wham-O on 6/17/57.

FRISBEE BRAND FLYING DISCS: The word "Frisbee" is a registered trademark of the Wham-O Inc., for flying discs used in sports games.

FRISBEE COLLECTOR: A person involved in the collecting of frisbees and related memorabilia. Many collectors will specialize in a particular classification or classifications of flying discs.

FRISBEE SPORTS EQUIPMENT: Flying discs and assorted equipment used during certain competitions or events.

FRISBEY: A term used by Amherst College students in the mid-1950's (also phrisbee) to describe a team passing game of frisbee football that was played on campus with a serving tray used as the "Frisbey."

FRISBIE: (1): The family and business name for the bakery located in Bridgeport CT- (circa 1871-1958). (2): A 1949 term used by Amherst College flying disc enthusiasts to describe the game of throw and catch with a metal pie pan or cookie can cover, the term reportedly derived from the middle name of English Professor George Frisbie Whicher. (3): The word "Frisbies" was also used on May 10, 1957 to advertise Bill Robes's Space Saucer in the *Yale University Daily News*.

FRISBIEING: A pre 1957 term used to describe the game of throw and catch with a metal pie pan made by the Frisbie Pie Company of Bridgeport, CT. More than likely started by the Frisbie truck drivers and other bakery employees early in the 20th century. (C.1915).

FRISBIE PIE PAN: A metal pie tin from the Frisbie Pie Company frequently used in games of toss. A highly collectible specialty item, the Frisbie pie pan is responsible for the name of today's popular and well known activity commonly referred to as frisbee playing.

FRISBIES: A term used by Yale University on May 10, 1957 to market Bill Robes's Space Saucer in the *Yale Daily News*.

FRISBY: A term used by students at Kimball Union Academy, Meriden, NH (KUA) in the late 1940's to describe the game of throw and catch with a metal pie pan or can cover. Frisbie was also used at KUA.

FRIZBY: A pre 1957 term used by Dartmouth students in the early 1950's to describe their game of throw and catch with a Frisbie pie pan or cookie can cover. The Frizby word was first recorded in a March, 1955 fraternity publication, *Shield* cover story entitled, "World Frizby Championships" by David Oberlander-Dartmouth College '55.

GALAXIE SWIRL: A disc decoration or logo that resembles a galaxy, first used for The 1983 World Disc Golf Championships-Santa Cruz.

GENERIC STAMP: A decoration or logo used by a manufacturer as a standard means of identifying a particular disc or product line.

GLO: A term used to describe a color of a disc that has phosphorescent material (glow-in-the-dark).

GLOW IN THE DARK: Any of a group of flying discs designed to glow in the dark, due to the phosphorescent material within the plastic mixture. (AKA Glo).

GOLF DISC: A specialized collection of mostly beveled edge, weighted and high performance throwing discs designed to perform various types of flights patterns, for use on an 18 or 27 hole frisbee golf course. One of the newest and most popular classifications of collectible flying discs.

GOOD CONDITION: An appraised grading which determines that a flying disc or Frisbie pie tin has many signs of wear and tear, not of the quality to be graded as being in very good condition. Good condition value for plastic is only 30%, for Frisbie pie pans, 35% of the near mint price.

GRADING: The means of determining the condition and market value of collectible flying discs etc.

GRASP: A term used by Dartmouth students in the early 1950's to describe a good catch of the cookie can cover employed in the game of "Frizby."

HDX SERIES: A high density (nearly unbreakable) performance disc. Part of Wham-O's World Class classification or weighted series.

HISTORICAL SIGNIFICANCE: Usually referring to an antique disc, or first of its kind, that is recognized for having had an important impact on frisbee history.

HORSESHOE CRAB: An early term coined to describe the 1948 Flyin Saucer because of its resemblance to the Coney Island, NY crustacean.

HORSESHOE GAME: Game apparatus consisting of four flying discs to be thrown at a stake or through a hoop imbedded in the ground.

HOT STAMPING (HS): A metal foil decoration or design applied to the center of a disc by a heat transfer process.

I.F.D.C.A.: The International Flying Disc Collectors Association: An organization where members receive a certificate, and a newsletter all about collectible flying discs. A good contact point for both new and experienced frisbee collectors.

I.F.T: The International Frisbee Tournament: This frisbee guts tournament is still held annually every Fourth of July weekend in the state of Michigan. It is the longest running annual frisbee tournament in the world.

INJECTION POINT OR PIN: The area where molten plastic is injected into the metal mold. Usually found in the center of a disc, top or bottom.

INNOVA/CHAMPION DISCS: Disc manufacturer considered the leader in golf disc design, sales, and related equipment.

INSERT: Usually refers to a cardboard or paper decoration, or product information sold with, or as part of the flying disc.

IN THE PACKAGE: Refers to a disc which is in its original packaging. Add at least 35% to the listed near mint price for each collectible disc within its original package. The condition of the package should also be rated.

JAMMING: A form of freestyle frisbee play developed by the Berkeley Frisbee Group in the late 1960's. A quick time throw and trick catch game where speed, power and accuracy is used to perform many different skip shots, straight flights and boomerang throws on a concrete surface protected from the wind. Basic "flow of the game" is to catch and return throw in the same motion. (Birthplace: Lower Sproul Plaza, U.C. Berkeley Campus).

KUA: Kimball Union Academy, Meriden, NH; an early center of frisbee play and inspiration for Bill Robes 1953 Space Saucer.

KNOCK OFF: A replication or illegal copy of an existing disc by an unlicenced company or person.

LABEL: Usually a self-adhesive paper or foil decoration which is applied to a disc.

LATE: Term used to identify the 2nd period Wham-O Pluto Platter that does not have ribs on the center dome.

LID: Common term used to describe or refer to a large disc. Originally coined for Wham-O's Master Frisbee (later, the World Class Series 165 gram disc).

LIGHTNING DISCS: A leading company in golf disc design, sales and related equipment.

IVY LEAGUE: Refers to a group of prestigious colleges located in the northeastern United States.

MAIL ORDER: An individual or company in the business of representing many flying disc companies and related equipment. Products are usually listed in a catalog.

MANUFACTURER ONLY: A category of collectibles where all discs come from the same manufacturer, i.e. Wham-O Inc.

MARBLEIZED: A swirl of different colors within a plastic flying disc caused by multiple color pigments or plastic colors added during the manufacturing process. Example: the Space Saucer. Also, the artistic combination of a baked and tin finish design found on certain Frisbie pie tins.

METAL GAUGE: Refers to the Frisbie pie pan and the type or thickness of the metal used in its manufacture.

MIMETIC: Any flying disc which is designed to mimic another object or thing, e.g. a cookie, tire or pizza etc. AKA- Flying Disc Impersonators.

MINI DISCS: Any of a group of flying discs which are under 5" in diameter. Many mini discs have been utilized as premiums, personal, business, or greeting cards.

MINT CONDITION: The best possible condition attainable for any collectible flying discs and related items.

MODERN DAY FRISBEE SPORTS: Refers to the period, circa 1964 to the present, when frisbee playing has been considered as an evolving sporting pastime rather than as just a simple throw and catch game.

MOLD: A metal casting of the actual disc in which molten plastic is injected to produce a particular part.

MOLD FAILURE: Condition caused by mold collapse, cracking, deformation, due to excessive or improper use.

MOLD NUMBER: A single or double digit number or letter engraved into the mold for identification purpose i.e. 1, 10, 1-4, 40X, 80, A or B, or FB 1, etc.

MOONLIGHTER: A Flying disc which has phosphorescent material within its plastic mixture, designed to make it "glow in the dark." i.e. Wham-O Moonlighter Frisbee/DGA Night Flyer.

MTA: Maximum Time Aloft. A competitive field event where a player throws the disc into the wind in an attempt to keep it high and aloft for as long as possible before making the required one handed catch before it hits the ground. Stop watches are used to measure time. The world record MTA is almost 17 seconds!

MYSTERY Y: A term coined to describe Empire Plastic's discs which used the word "Frisbee" and a Y (probably for Yale University) in its disc design and packaging.

NEAR MINT CONDITION: An appraised grading which determines that a flying disc or Frisbie pie tin has only very slight imperfections (but not good enough to be graded as in mint condition). Near mint condition value for plastic is 85%; for pie tins, 90% of the mint price.

NON-PLASTIC FLYING DISC: Any disc made of metal, wood, clay, rubber, fabric or stone etc.

NORTH AMERICAN SERIES: Sub-series disc of Wham-O's World Class "weighted" Series Frisbees.

NOVELTY DISC: Any of a group of discs designed to produce an unusual effect such as those with unusual shapes, ones that light up, make noise, etc. General retail, mimetic and two-piece discs are included in this catch all category.

OCTAD: Refers to a frisbee tournament in which 8 different events were contested. First held at Rutgers University starting in 1974.

OLYMPIC DISC: Any of a group of discs with the official Olympic logo or script in its design or decoration.

OLY PRO: Wham-O Professional Model Frisbee with an Olympic logo label. Can also refer to Wham-O's Mini Oly disc.

PARTING LINE: The area where both parts of the mold come together during production. They usually produce a very thin line of plastic located along the outside leading edge of a disc's rim.

PAT. APPLD. FOR: A patent application has been filed with the patent office.

PATENT NUMBER: A number (or letters) issued by the Patent Office to protect the claims of an invention or device, etc.

PATENT PENDING: An inscription to advertise that there is a patent pending on an invention, such as a new disc design or device.

P.D.G.A.: The Professional Disc Golf Association. The governing body concerned with the development, sanctioning, regulation and future of the game of disc golf.

PERFORATED LETTER F: Refers to the first style of Frisbie pie pan that can be identified by the letter "F" which is formed with eight holes cut into the center of the pan.

PERIOD: A means of identifying which particular disc was first produced, and then retooled with additional information or design features that earmark a later period. (i.e. Pluto Platters).

PHOSPHORESCENT: A chemical powder added to the plastic mixture to increase the disc's weight, and causing it to "glow in the dark."

PHRISBEE: An early 1950's term used by Amherst students to describe the Ultimate like game of frisbee football played with a round serving tray.

PIE TIN: A metal pie pan used for the baking of pies. Herein, referring to the pie tins of the Frisbie Pie Company of Bridgeport, CT.

PIE SAFE (also known as PIE CASE): A metal and glass, or wood and glass case with a screen door used by restaurants to store and display fresh Frisbie's Pies.

PING PONG BALL: Refers to the type of plastic used to make most of the antique back to back discs and the Eureka U1 Saucer. The material feels and sounds just like a ping pong ball.

PITTING: A mold condition usually caused by small metal fragments, (wear and tear), or other foreign substances which find their way into the mold during operation. Pie tins will also show signs of pitting due to rust.

POLE HOLE: A patented flying disc entrapment device used as a pin for playing disc golf.

POLY: A term used to describe a disc that is made of straight, flexible polyethylene plastic and is not stiff or "weighted."

POOR CONDITION: An appraised grading which determines that a flying disc or pie tin has numerous imperfections, too many for it to be graded as being in fair condition. Poor condition plastic discs and Frisbie pie tins are valued at only 5% of the near mint price.

POPULARITY: The degree of appeal of a certain disc or classification of collectible discs which are most popular with collectors. Age, condition, rarity, aesthetics and historical significance are some of the factors that make a given disc popular and collectible.

PRATTLE: A term used at Princeton University in the late 1950's to describe a flying disc.

PREMIUM DISC: A light weight toy disc design for advertising a product, company or event etc. Usually given away with price of admission to an event, purchase of, or promotion of products. (Not designed for normal play).

PRICE GUIDE: A publication designed to list the standard value for collectible flying discs. Only meant to be a guide and not the only price for all flying discs and related items.

PRICING: Determined by age, condition, rarity, historical significance, aesthetics, and popularity.

PROFESSIONAL FRISBEE DISC: A group of discs in Wham-O's Pro model line.

PRO SHOP: A small retail operation offering a variety of golf discs and accessories for sale. Usually located at a disc golf course site or a local sporting goods store.

PROTOTYPES: Any of a group of discs which originate from the first run of a new mold which is later retooled, made with a different material mixture or discontinued. Production runs are usually low in numbers (50-200).

PUDDLE: A small bead or bubble of plastic usually located on the top, or underside center of a disc near its injection point.

PYRAMID STAMP: A decoration or logo shaped like a pyramid to market a particular line of golf discs (e.g. Destiny Puppy discs).

QUOIT: A disc shaped projectile weighing up to 3 pounds with a 1"-3" hole in the center for ringing around or near a stake imbedded into the ground. Similar to the game of horseshoes.

RAISED LETTERS: Inscription or lettering engraved into the mold as a part of a disc's design, rendered high enough for the inscription to be above the plate of the disc, i.e. the 1st period Flyin Saucer, or the Frisbie Pie Company's raised letter F pie tin.

RARE: A category in which very few discs of that type have been found, or very few were produced.

REGISTERED COLLECTOR: A flying disc collector who is registered with the International Flying Disc Collector's Association (IFDCA). Benefits include networking, advertising, a newsletter, and additional information on collectible flying discs.

REGULAR MODEL: Refers to Wham-O's Regular Frisbee model, or designates usually the smaller of two otherwise identical disc models.

REISSUE: An older or previously produced mold or disc discontinued for many years, then brought back into production. i.e. (Empire Plastics) Wham-O's Mystery Y Giant model in yellow, or Wham-O's Sailing Satellite in white; both were reproduced in 1979.

REJECT: A disc with a serious enough imperfection to render it not marketable.

RETAIL OUTLET: An individual or company selling current stock items and accessories, and/or collectible flying discs from a store front or disc golf pro shop.

RETOOLED: The engraving or retooling of an existing mold cavity to correct a problem or to change its design.

REVERSE LETTERS: Usually refers to Frisbie Pie Company tin lettering.

Some Frisbie pie pans were produced with the inscription "Frisbie's Pies" stamped into the metal pie tin from the underside, resulting in lettering which appears backwards when viewed by looking into the pan.

REVERSE OLY LABEL: Upside down Olympic logo with two interlocking rings on top and three on the bottom. Example: Wham-O Oly Mini Frisbee Disc.

RIBS: Found on the underside of the 2nd period Space Saucer after retooling, and on the shoulders of some Frisbie pie pans.

RIDGES: Concentric lines, "spoilers," or flight rings which are engraved into the shoulder area of a Frisbee. Usually found only on Wham-O products.

RIM: The outside vertical lip of a disc.

ROUND OF SNAPS: A term used by Dartmouth students in the early 1950's to describe the gathering of players in a circle to celebrate an excellent throw or catch, by all teammates snapping their fingers together.

ROUND SHOULDER: Refers to the Frisbie pie pan where the bottom edge meets the outside wall or shoulder. This is rounded, as opposed to the sharp intersection found on the square shoulder pie pan.

SAFE: Refers to the pie case or "safe" used to store the fresh pies from the Frisbie Pie Company. (Highly collectible).

SA-LO: The name given to the first organized public frisbee game offered by Tex Robertson at Camp Wolverine, Ann Arbor, MI in 1933. ("Sail It Low And Level.") Sa-Lo has been offered at Camp Longhorn, Burnet, TX since 1939.

SECOND: A flying disc which is determined to be unmarketable due to an imperfection in the molding process or in the application of art work.

SERIES DISC: Refers to a group of 5 different series of Frisbees created with Wham-O's World Class "weighted" Series: 97G, 100G, 119G, 141G and the 165G discs. The different series include World Class, North American, Signature, World Frisbee Championships and the HDX series.

SHOULDER: The area of a disc from the rim to approximately 2" onto the flight plate depending on the diameter of the disc. Usually where your thumb is when throwing a disc.

SIGNATURE SERIES: A group of Frisbees from Wham-O's World Class Series. The signatures belong to the World Frisbee Disc Champions for any particular year (1975-1979).

SILK SCREEN (SS): An ink based decoration or design applied to a flying disc and related items.

SIZE: The diameter of a flying disc measured across the center of the disc to the opposite outside rim.

SKY GOLF: A version of disc golf where a player had to throw through a series of six wire hoops. Introduced by the COPAR Company in 1959.

SNAFFLE: A term used at Princeton University in the late 1950's for a one handed catch of a flying disc.

SOFT-POLY: Refers to the 1953 version of the 1948 Flyin Saucer made with the softer polyethylene plastic. Also denotes the late 1950's, Bill Robes Space Saucer.

SPECIALTY AREA: A sub-class of a major flying disc classification, i.e. WFC Signature Series Frisbees mentioning a certain state, those with a certain mold number, etc.

SPLIT DIGIT: A mold number found on early Wham-O Pro model Frisbees. The number is located on the opposite sides of the puddle at the underneath center of the disc. i.e. (#1-4 and 1-6).

SQUARE SHOULDER: Refers to the Frisbie pie pan where the bottom edge of the pan meets the wall or shoulder. This intersection is sharp rather than rounded as in the round shoulder pie pan.

STARTER KITS: Any number of flying discs usually of the same classification, or a grouping designed to represent a cross section of available items. Frisbee dealers/collectors can provide starter kits for beginning collectors.

SUNKEN LETTERING: Refers to the type of lettering found on the Frisbie pie pan that is pressed into the inside of the pan.

SUPER PRO: Any of the flying discs from Wham-O's Super Pro model series. Includes the Classic Super Pro.

TENNITE: The plastic material used to machine form the first prototype of the 1948 Flyin Saucer.

THROWING STOCK: An assortment of flying discs used for playing frisbee games.

THRUST: An early term used at Dartmouth College (in the 1950's) to describe the act of throwing a cookie can cover.

TIN: A pie pan, or cookie can cover made of metal.

TOOL: Term referring to the creating or making of a new (flying disc) mold.

TOURNAMENT: An organized competition played by either professionals and or amateurs, with professional rules, prize money and or titles.

TOURNAMENT DIRECTOR: The person responsible for the organization and management of competitive (professional/amateur) frisbee events.

TOURNAMENT DISCS: Any disc which commemorates or advertises a local, state, national or world championship event.

TOURNAMENT MODEL: Usually refers to Wham-O's Master Frisbee model.

TRAPSHOOTING: The sport of shooting at metal, clay or limestone disc shaped objects that are launched into the air by mechanical means or by a hand held launcher. Live birds were originally used as targets.

TRC: Throw Run and Catch: A competitive field event where the player throws from within a circle, runs after, and attempts a one handed catch of the disc as far away from the throwing circle as possible. The world record is nearly 100 meters!

TUBE TONE: A pole sounding device designed with chains and used as a pin or target in the game of frisbee golf.

TWO-PIECE: Any disc designed and manufactured in a two step process. Usually a rim, or rim and shoulder of one construction is attached (molded or fixed to) the flight plate of another construction, forming one complete flying disc. Example: the AMF Vector Hyperfoil or Wham-O's Spectra disc.

ULTIMATE PLAYERS ASSOCIATION: Governing body for the development, regulation and sanctioning of major Ultimate tournaments or events.

UNI-COLOR: A classification of flying discs which are of the same color: red, or blue or green etc.

UNIT: A term used by Dartmouth students in the early 1950's to describe a 5" cookie can cover they were using for their Frizby games.

UNPIGMENTED DISCS: Any disc which has no color pigment in the plastic. They are usually transparent or translucent.

VARIEGATED: A disc which has swirls of different colors in its plastic mixture. Or it can appear to be a combined shade of gray, brown and black, looking; i.e. the 1955 Space Saucer.

VERY GOOD CONDITION: An appraised grading which determines that a flying disc or pie tin has some obvious signs of wear and tear, and is not in good enough condition to be graded as excellent. Very good value is only 50% of near mint price for both plastic discs and Frisbie Pie pans.

WAM-O: This is the alternative spelling of the Wham-O Company name that can be found on early small foil labels that were attached to the underside of its 1st period Pluto Platter, and to the wooden stakes packaged in the Pluto Platter Horseshoe game. (It was not a misspelling of the company name).

WEIGHTED DISC: Refers mainly to high tech golf discs produced with weighted materials for playing the game of frisbee golf on a prescribed course. (Golf discs are very heavy for their relative size. Some weigh in at 7 ounces!).

WELLISHES DISEASE: The peeling or blistering of plastic away from a flying disc. Usually found in thin narrow sheets, sections or blisters. (Noncontagious!)

WFC SERIES: Any disc which commemorates the World Frisbee Disc Championships held between 1974-1981 at the Rose Bowl in Pasadena, CA.

WHAM-O MFG. COMPANY: Founded in 1948. Since 1957, Wham-0 has been the leader in flying disc sales, sports promotion/education and popularity with collectors from around the world. Now known as Wham-O, Inc.

WOLF: Pet name for the senior frisbee players. "Wonderful Old Loveable Friends."

WORLD-CLASS SERIES FRISBEES: A high performance, weighted and sized collection of Frisbees produced by Wham-O in 5 different standard weights: 97G, 100G, 119G, 141G and 165G. There are 5 different specialty series created within this class: World Class Series, World Frisbee Championships Series, Signature Series, North American Series and HDX Series.

WRINKLES: Found along the shoulder of the Frisbie pie pan and caused by extreme pressure applied to a sheet of steel as it is being formed by a punch press.

Appendix III

FRISBEE RESOURCES

These companies provide a wide variety of frisbee sport products, accessories and services. Products include flying discs for every competitive event or recreational activity, including premium discs (for advertising) of all price ranges and sizes, disc golf bags, hand carts, custom t-shirts and other apparel. These establishments may also provide disc golf course design, equipment, rule books and a comprehensive listing of existing frisbee golf courses worldwide. Professional frisbee demonstrations, frisbee videos, lessons and education clinics for all levels may be provided as well by the frisbee consultants and historians associated with these venues, plus, you'll find a complete schedule of all major and local tournaments. Contact one of these providers in your area, and get a full fledged orientation into the world of frisbee!

RETAIL OUTLETS & MAIL ORDER ESTABLISHMENTS

Ace Mountain Wear, 825 Early Street, Suite B, Santa Fe, NM 87501 505-982-8079

AirBorn Sports, P.O. Box 767, Bowling Green, KY 42101-0767 Phone: 502-793-9597

Basket Heads, 4616 W. Sahara Suite 1-108, Las Vegas, NV 89102. Phone: 702873-1338

Circular Productions, P.O. Box 792, Austin, TX 78767-0792. Phone: 512-385-6789. Fax: 512- 385-7329. Email: jrhouck@aol.com. John Houck

Designwest/Graphics, 1170 Ninth St. #26, Alameda, CA 94501. Phone: 510-865-3800. Barbara J. Alexander. (My art director.)

Discarama, 2518 Nolensville Pike, Nashville, TN 37211 Phone 615-256-7738 John Knoch

Discards, 926 N. Ventura St., Anaheim, CA 92801. wwjj@aol.com Phone: 714-774-7077 Wil West

Disc Flights Inc., P.O. Box 470794, Tulsa, OK 74147-0794 Phone: 918-622-6648. Fax: 918-622-9251 Rick Neil

Disc Golf Association Inc., 16 Maher Road, Watsonville, CA 95076 Phone 408-722-6037. Fax: 408-722-8176. Email: steady01@ix.netcom.com. "Steady Ed" Headrick

Disc Golf Disc LTD., 3888 Hill Road, Lakeport, CA 95453 Phone 707-263-6304

Discimages, 1008 S. 32nd Street, Lincoln, NE 68510-3230

Disc Golf Specialties, 248 Litchfield Lane, Houston, TX 77024

Disc Golf World, P.O. 2252 Kansas MO 64142 Phone 913-648-1905 Rick Rothstein

Disc Golf Jewelry, Blums Jewelry, Big Spring Mall, Big Spring, TX 79720. 915-267-6335 Greg Brooks

Disc-N-Dat, 6009 Vine St. #2, Cincinnati, OH 45216 Phone 513-242-9030 Dan Bayless

Disc Sport Promotions, P.O. Box 19526, Centrepoint P.O., Vancouver, B.C. V5T 4E7 Canada. Phone: 604-535-1003. Fax: 604-535-6884. Email: discsports@bc.sympatico.ca. James Brown

Disc Sports Resource Center, Web Page: www.bioteca.com/discsports/ Phone: 800-281-2057

Discovering The World, Box 911, La Mirada, CA 90637 Phone 714-522-2202 Fax: 714-670-6340 Dan Mangone

Discovering The World (Retail Store) 6272 Beach Blvd., Buena Park, CA 90621 714-522-2202. Fax: 714-670-6340. Email: dtworld@aol.com. Web Site: http://www.dtworld.com

DiscWorld, 1829 W. Galbraith Rd., Cincinnati, OH 45239 Phone 513-931-1037. For Orders only: 1-800-626-2584 Doug Cepluch

Dymanic Discs, 5639 Meadow Vista Way, Agoura, CA 91301. 800-464-0434

Fantasy Flights Disc Golf Sales, 23301 66th Ave. W, Mountlake Terrace, WA 98049. Phone: 206-670-2548. Lowell Shields

Final 9 Sports, 6321 Main Ave. Suite R, Orangevale, CA 95662. 916-987-DISC, Fax: 916-987-3444. Jim Oates

Flying Aces Pro Frisbee Team, 13975 Dennison Road, Milan. MI 48160. Phone: 313-439-8182. Fax: 313-439-0162. Email: 102343.32@compuserve.com or, aces@flyingaces.com

Flying Eye Disc, 4021 Biscayne Drive, Winter Springs, FL 32708 Phone: 800-438-0701. Fax: 407-699-8881.

FSN 801-281-3312 (Steve)

GateWay Disc Sports, 15 Midland Ave., Maryland Heights, MO 63043. 314-770-9180

Heart of Texas Disc Golf, P.O. Box 684382, Austin, TX 78768-4382. FAX: 800-ASK-DISC Phone: 512-472-DISC.

Identified Flying Objects, 2426 NW 119th Ave., Gainesville, FL 32609. Phone: 352-378-6688. Email: afn12826@afn.org. Tom Monroe

IFO Graphics 404-296-8400

In Flight Sports, 911 Howard St., Kalamazoo, MI 49006 Phone 616-345-7040

In Flight Sports, 215 S. State St., Ann Arbor, MI 48104 Phone 313-995-3323

In Flight Sports, 507 E. Grandriver, East Lansing, MI 48823 Phone 517-351-8100. Fax: 517-351-2732. Http://www.inflightsports.com

Jams Sports Shop, 7601 Clifton Road, Fairfax Station, VA 22039 Phone 703-250-JAMS Tully Liddell

Jay Bird Discs, 735 Bon Air Rd., Lansing, MI 48917 517-323-4726 Jay Matthes. Email: jbird-disc@worldnet.att.net

Las Vegas DGC, 127 McLaren St., Henderson, NV 89014

Leading Edge, 3720 Springfield Drive, Orlando, FL 32818. Phone: 407-295-8713. Bob Lewis

Little Flyers, 11740 Madden Lane. Fishers, IN 46038. Phone: 317-598-0480. Email:discfly-er@iquest.net

Mini Discs, Blums Jewelers, #14 Highland Mall, Big Springs, TX 79729 Phone 915-267-6335 (TX & NM only 1-800-643-6336) Greg Brooks

Nam-Q Enterprises, 6040 Adams, Warren, MI 48092 810-979-6780 Michael Forton

On Course Disc Golf Productions 913 Gailliard Drive, Mobile, AL 36608. Phone/fax 334-343- 0490 Joe Sherrod & Family

Sandy Point Resort Disc Golf Ranch 1230 Sandy Point Lane, Lac du Flambeau, WI 54538. Phone: 715-588-3233. Email: sprdgr@aol.com. Mike and Michelle Cousins

Sky South, P.O. Box 9662, Mobile, AL 36691-0662 Phone 205-478-0379 (evenings) Jim Okum Fax: 334-470-8041

S & P Kite Co., (Disc Pro Shop) 5534 Albemarle Road Suite 111, Charlotte, NC 28212. Phone: 704-567-9006. Fax: 704-567-1760

Tom Schot Sports, P.O. Box 73, Capitola, CA 95010 Phone 408-462-5293 Tom Schot

Trophy Shop, Phone: 352-372-8551 (Rita or Charisma)

Tube Tone Concepts, 902 Terrell Hill Drive, Austin, TX 78704 Phone 512-444-9402 Fax: 512-476-2602 www.bhw.com/tubetone

Two Purple Disc 'N Dat. Web Page: http://members.aol.com/datdisc 1-800-815-7178

Ultimate Stuff, C Associates P.O. Box 14520. Washington, DC 20003

Wall City (Disc Bags) 512-385-6789. Web Page: www.wallcity.com

The Wright Life, 200 Linden St., Fort Collins, CO 80524 Phone 303-484-6932 (For Orders-Free Catalog) 1-800-321-8833 Fax: 303-490-2714 http://www.wrightlife.com

MAGAZINES & NEWSLETTERS
United States of America

Airwaves (Mid-Atlantic), 16085 Olmstead Lane, Woodbridge, VA 22191 Chain Mail (Raleigh NC), 3836 Sue Ellen Drive, Raleigh, NC 27604

Disc Golf Journal, P.O. Box 3577, Champaign, IL 61826-3577 Phone: 217-398-7880. Fax: 217-398-7881. Order line: 800-651-DISC. Email: kathyig@aol.com. Tom Schlueter Publisher.

Disc Golf World News, P.O. Box 2252, Kansas City, MO 64142 Phone: 816-471-3472 Fax:816-471-4653 Rick Rothstein Publisher/Editor Email: rickdgwn@aol.com

Disc Golfer (PDGA) P.O. Box 11693, Shorewood, WI 53211

Freestyle Players Association. P.O. Box 2612, San Diego, CA 92014

Guts Players Association, 5841 Haverhill Drive, Lansing, MI 48910

NEFA News, New England Flying Disc Association, 137 Chestnut St. North Reading, MA 01864

The Floater (MFA), P.O. Box 1481, Minneapolis, MN 55414

Tri-State Newsletter (NE), 176 N. Main Street, Pat. 6, Emmaus, PA 19049

Ultimate Players Association, 3595 E. Fountain Blvd. Suite J2, Colorado Springs, CO 80910

MAGAZINES & NEWSLETTERS
Foreign Countries

AFDA Newsletter. P.O. Box 149, Osborne Park, 6017, Western Australia

Disc Times c/0 JFDA. 1-19-2 Aoto, Katsushika-ku, Tokyo 125, Japan

Frisbeelagan, c/o Peter Lundmark, SFF, Andes Personsgatan 18, 41664 G teborg, Sweden

SPIN-B.C. News, Box 14281, Minneapolis, MN 55414

Sportime (GAISF), Jean-Louis Meuret, 26 Route de Grandvaux, 1096 Cully, Switzerland

Swiss Disc Golf News, Urs Hante, Landvogt-Waserstr 17, 8400 Winterthur, Switzerland

Ultimatum, AF Design, Grenaby Works, Grenaby Road, Croydon CR0 2EJ, UK

UP!, Albercht Tiefenbacher, Hans-Thoma-Str. 3, 76133 Karsruhe, Germany

Upside Down, Jean-Charles Dupin, 5, rue Robie b8, 1060 Brussels, Belgium

World Flying Disc Federation, Kathryn Middis, 47 William Smith Close, Cambridge, CB1 3QE, England.

MANUFACTURERS
Producers of various frisbee sport products for players of all levels

Discraft, 1042 Benstein Road #106, Walled Lake, MI 48390. 248-624-2250 Fax 248-624-2310. Email: discraft@aol.com. Jim Kenner & Gail McColl

Dynamic Discs, 5639 Meadow Vista Way, Agoura Hills, CA 91301 800-464-0434 Jan Sobel

Innova Champion Discs, 11090 Tacoma Drive., Rancho Cucamonga, CA 91730 Phone: 909-481-6266. Fax 909-481-6263. Email: innovagolf@aol.com. Web Site: http://www.innovadiscs.com/ Tim Selinske

Innova-Champion Discs (South) PO Drawer 4979, Rock Hill, SC 29732. Phone: 803-366-5028. Fax: 803-329-3472 Harold Duvall

Lightning Discs, P.O. Box 181025, Dallas, TX 75218. Phone: 214-328-9017. Fax: 214-328-9088 (Shop: 1402 Corto, Dallas, TX) Steve Howle

Wham-O Inc. 3830 Del Amo Blvd., Suite 101, Torrance, CA 90503-2219. Phone: 310-370-9100. Arthur Coddington. (Parent Company: Charterhouse Group International, NYC)

ORGANIZATIONS

Disc Golf Association Inc., 16 Maher Road, Watsonville, CA 95076. Phone: 408-722-6037. Fax: 408-722-8176. Email: steady01@ix.netcom.com. Web Site: http://www.discgolfassoc.com. "Steady Ed" Headrick

Disc International Sports Club, 1203 West 103rd Street, #333-C, Kansas City, MO 64114. Web Page: www.disc-sports.com

Double Disc Court Players Association. P.O. Box 3132, San Diego, CA 92163. 619-265-2632 Web Page:robbie.ddcpa@fatcity.com. Or, http://www.leland.stanford.edu/dam-on/ddc.html

European Flying Disc Association, c/o Alex Kloetzel, Reumont Str. 42, Aachen 52064, Germany

European Flying Disc Federation, Thomas Griesbaum, Briegerstrasse 8, D-76139 Karlsruhe, Germany. 49-721-608-4001

Federal Trade Comission Denver Office Wham-O Investigation #801-0148, 1485 Curtis Street, Denver, CO 80202. Phone: 303-844-2271

Freestyle Players Association. P.O. Box 2616, Del Mar, CA 92014 619-758-3771 Email: larri@rmii.com, or: Toml@mediacity.com

General Association of International Sports Federations (GAISF) Villa Henri, 7 Boulevard de Suisse, MC 98000, Monte-Carlo, Monaco 33-93-507413 or 33-93-252873 Fax

International Flying Disc Collectors Association, P.O. Box 470794, Tulsa. OK 74147-0794 918- 622-6648. Rick Neil

International World Games Association (IWGA) De Lepelaar 8, 2751 CW Moerkapelle, Netherlands. 31-79-593-3242 or 31-79-593-3357 Fax

Japan Flying Disc Association, Tsukuda Bldg 4F, 3-1-3 Moto-Asakusa, Taito-Ku, Tokyo, Japan

National Ultimate Association, 202 Green Meadows Drive, Wilmington, NC 28405. 910-791-8623. Toad Leber

Professional Disc Golf Association (PDGA), 65 Front Street West Suite 0116-24,

Toronto, Ontario, Canada W5J IE6. Phone: 416-203-9628 Fax: 416-203-9629. Email: pdga@front.net (Membership)Web Page: http:/www.discgolf.com/pdga/pdga.html Complete Disc Golf Course Directory (Worldwide) Http://www. home.netscape. com/ people/bfitler/pdgadir/. (For a copy of the directory send $10. 00 to the PDGA.)

Ultimate Players Association, 3595 E. Fountain Blvd. Suite J2, Colorado Springs, CO 80910 Web Page:http://www.upa.org/upa/ (UPA Rules Of Ultimate, 9th Edition 32 pages $3.00).

WFDF World Flying Disc Federation. Bill Wright, President: 200 Linden, FT. Collins, CO 80524. Phone: 970-484-6932, Fax: 970-490-2714, Email: bwright@wrightlife.com

COMPETITIVE EVENTS "WFDF"

The following descriptions of frisbee sporting events are provided by the World Flying Disc Federation's, *The Official Rules of Flying Disc Sports 1997 Edition*. This comprehensive and complete guide covers all the professional rules for competitive frisbee games, lists the associations responsible for designating these, discs approved for competition, plus all the 150+ World Records. (Cost $5.00) For a copy please contact: WFDF, 200 Linden, Ft. Collins, CO 08524.

AIMS OF W.F.D.F.

1. To encourage and protect the spirit of flying disc play where as partners rather than opponents we compete against the limits of our own abilities rather than each other. To foster a climate of peace in which disc play may be appreciated for its ability to bring people together in a communal rejoicing of skills and play. To ultimately learn to live together through playing togther.

2. To encourage disc play throughout the world and promote the establishment of new national flying disc associations, advising them on all flying disc activities and general management.

3. To achieve general acceptance of disc play as a sport.

4. To provide a forum for discussion on all aspects of disc play worldwide and to arbitrate between flying disc interests when and where conflict might arise.

5. To establish and uphold a tournament standard for all flying disc competition worldwide. To fairly distribute the right to organize World Flying Disc Championships to interested associations and to sanction other international tournaments.

SPIRIT OF THE RULES

Flying disc sports have traditionally relied upon a spirit of sportsmanship which places the responsibility of fair play on the players themselves. Highly competitive and committed play is encouraged, but never at the expense of the bond of mutual respect between players, adherence to the agreed upon rules of any event, nor the basic enjoyment of play. Protection of these vital elements serves to eliminate adverse conduct from the playing field. The responsibility for the maintenance of this spirit rests on each player's shoulders.

WFDF DESCRIPTIONS OF COMPETITIVE DISC GAMES

DOUBLE DISC COURT

Double disc court is a game played by two teams of two players each. Each team is charged with defending a court from the attack of the opponents. The attacks are made in two ways: by the throwing of one of the two discs in play into the opponent's court in an attempt to have the disc come to rest within that court without ever having touched out-of-bounds, or by causing both discs to be touched by a player or players on the opposing team at the same time. A team scores a point whenever they makes a successful attack or whenever an opponent throws a disc out-of- bounds. The first team to score the requisite number of points as determined by the competitive format shall win the game.

GUTS

Guts is a sport played between two teams of two to five players each. The objective is to be the first team to score 21 points. To start play, each team lines up facing each other 14 m apart. Play is accomplished by a player throwing the disc at the opposing team and within the reach of at least 1 player of that team, in such as manner that the opposing team cannot make a clean catch. Scoring is contingent on the success or failure of the throwing team. A good throw, without a catch, results in a point for the throwing team and a bad throw results in a point for the receiving team.

ULTIMATE

Ultimate is a passing game team sport in which the team with the higher point total at the end of the game wins. It is played with two teams of seven players on a rectangular field with endzone at each end. A goal, worth 1 point, is scored when a player/thrower passes the disc to a teammate and it is successfully caught within the confines of the end zone his or her team is attacking. The disc may be advanced solely by being passed by one teammate to another, with the receiver catching the disc without its touching the ground. A player may not run while in possession of the disc. While the team in possession of the disc seeks to advance the disc toward the end zone it is attacking, the opposing team seeks to thwart advancement and obtain possession by forcing a turnover. A turnover results whenever a pass is incomplete, caught or knocked down by an opposing player, touches the ground at any point, or is caught by a player out-of-bounds. No overt contact or tackling is allowed. The sport is played on a self-officiated basis, with no referees. All line violations, possession and foul calls are made by the players on the playing field.

DISCATHON

Discathon is a race in which players throw their discs, one at a time (each contestant may carry three discs, two which are in play, one which is a spare) through a circuitous 1 km course defined by a series of "test" and "mandatories." Mandatories are throw challenges which typically involve prescribed routes around poles, trees, or through hoops or other goal-like objects. Each mandatory describes a required flight path. The discs thrown by the players shall traverse the entire course, although the players themselves need not follow any specific path. The object is to complete the course in the shortest time possible.

FIELD EVENTS

Field events is a general term that refers to individual disc sport events, namely: accuracy, distance, maximum time aloft (MTA), throw, run and catch (TRC), and self-caught flight (SCF). The common link among the field events is the competitive measurement of a particular basic skill. Accuracy measures a player's ability to consistently throw a disc through a specified target from various distances from, and angles to, the target. Distance measures how far a player can throw a disc in flat arena of play. MTA measures the length of time a player's throw is in the air. TRC measures the distance a player can throw a disc and catch the throw, prior to the throw hitting the ground, SCF combines the events of MTA and TRC.

FREESTYLE

Freestyle is creative movement with a disc. Competitive freestyle is a game whereby a player, or a team of two or three players, perform a routine, which consists of a series of throws, catches and various acrobatic moves, done to music using one or more discs. The routine is compared to the routines of the other competitors through scoring done by judges, who evaluate the routine on the basis of difficulty, execution and presentation. The player or team with the best score is declared the winner.

DISC GOLF

The growing popularity of the game of disc golf begins with the essential fact that throwing a flying disc with power and accuracy is a marvelous sensation both for the thrower and the observer of the throw. The constant challenge, the social nature of the game, the good physical and mental conditioning, and the fact that it is inexpensive to play are also attractions. Disc golf is a recreational sport for everybody, regardless of age, gender, or ability. The object of the game is to traverse a course from beginning to end in the fewest number of throws of the disc. Each consecutive throw is made from where the disc came to rest after the last throw. Score is determined by counting the number of throws made on each hole plus any penalty throws, and then summing all holes. The winner is the player who completes the course with the lowest score

The course consists of a series of holes laid out so that when the player completes one hole he or she proceeds to the beginning of the next hole until all the holes have been played. The player is provided with a teeing area from which to begin each hole and a target to complete the hole. Ideally, disc golf courses are situated in mixed habitat of woods and field, testing both distance capabilities and finesse in the player. Natural obstacles encountered in the way of the flight of the disc are very much a part of the game and must not be altered by the players in any way to decrease the difficulty of a hole. Disc golf courses are normally 18 holes in length, but there are also 9-hole, 24-hole and 27-hole courses in existence. Courses can be found in each of the 50 United States as well as in Canada, Japan, Australia, New Zealand, Denmark, Sweden, Finland, Norway, the Netherlands, Switzerland, Germany, Hungary, the United Kingdom, Peru and even in parts of Africa.

WORLD RECORDS

There are nearly 150 different World Record categories for frisbee playing. Categories are determined by age, gender. Here is a small sample. For a complete listing of World Records, please contact WFDF. Ask for The Official Rules of Flying Disc Sports, 1997 (cost: $5.00.)

Open Distance Men: Scott Stokely 200.01 Meters
Open Distance Women: Anni Kremel 136.31 Meters

Open MTA Men: Don Cain 16.72 Seconds
Open MTA: Women: Amy Bekken 11.81 Seconds

Open TRC Men: Hiroshi Oshima 92.64 Meters
Open TRC Women: Judy Horowitz 60.02

Canine Distance-Owner Throwing with Dog by His/Her Side: Mark Molnar throwing to Cheyenne-Ashley Whippet 118.90 Meters

Two Person Marathon: John Fischer and Rich Hannah (4/5/90 to 4/10/90) 126 Hours and 21 minutes.

Wheel Chair Distance Men: Antwone Archie 91.84 Meters

COLLECTORS AND DEALERS

ALABAMA

Bill Wagnon
3019 Shadow Lawn Drive
Huntsville, AL 35810
205-859-2313
Email: bwagnon@hiway.net
Class: Antiques

Bruce Willis
2707 Trail Ridge Road
Huntsville, AL 35810
205-852-8224
Email: bruce.d.willis@boeing.com
Class: Wham-O Pro Model

Lavone Wolfe
P.O. Box 6332
Huntsville, AL 35824
205-772-8433
Email: slwolfe@ingr.com
Class: Antiques, Frisbie Pie Tins, Minis, Golf Discs for the Hall of Fame.

Terry Rester
P.O. Box 160841
Mobile, AL 36616-0841
334-645-0636 Fax: 334-694-3214
Class: Golf Discs, Minis.

ARIZONA

Harvey Y. Brandt
1332 E. Lawrence Lane
Phoenix, AZ 85020-3034
602-870-1913
Class: Tournament, Ultimate (All)

CALIFORNIA

Victor Malafronte
909 Marina Village Parkway
Alameda, CA 94501
Class: Antiques, Frisbie Pie Co., Novelty-Engineered Discs
Email: frisbee@pacbell.net

Mark Horn
239 TaosRoad
Altadena, CA 91001
818-798-8729
Email: mhornddc@aol.com
Class: 119 Gram, Wham-O 40 Molds

Don & Jeanine Bayless
1801 W. Cris Ave.
Anaheim, CA 92804
714-535-4112
Fax: 714-535-2293
Email: daynes@cyberpcs.com
Class: FB3 Green, Wham-O, Super Pro

Wil West
926 N. Ventura St.
Anaheim, CA 92801
714-774-7077
Email: wwjj@aol.com
Class: Minis, Golf, Discs, Novelty, Glo,
Olympic, All. (Green discs/Glo)

Mike Schneider
98 Maple
Atherton, CA 94027
650-328-6508
Class: All

Neal Hoellwarth
500 Laura Ann Ct.
Bay Point, CA 94565
510-458-4533
Class: Antiques, Ultimate, Golf Discs

Gregory "Reverend Che" McKean
P.O. Box 4981
Berkeley, CA 94704-4981
510-237-4269
Email: rvrndche@aol.com
Class: All.

Hal Erickson
1531A Berkeley Way
Berkeley, CA 94703
510-540-5784
Class: Antiques

Dave Moscoe
375 Huckleberry Lane
Boulder Creek, CA 95006
408-338-1441
Email: casamo0no@aol.com

Class: Ultimate, Antiques

Pete D'Agostino
P.O. Box 53
Canyon, CA 94516
510-376-6695
Class: Golf Discs, Ultimate, Antiques

Peter Sontag
3626 Pine St.
Castro Valley, CA 94546
510-581-1394
Class: Ultimate, Minis, Golf Discs,
Freestyle, HDX

Ron Widel
13971 Monte Del Oro
Castroville, CA 95012
408-633-4114
Class: Pros, Super Pros, World Class,
Antiques

Tim Selinske
752 N. Fifth Ave.
Covina, CA 91723
909-481-6266
Fax: 909-481-6263
Email: skeball@aol.com
Class: Antiques, Wham-O 50 Molds, Minis,
Golf Discs

John Kimball
8783 San Pedro Way
Elk Grove, CA 95624
916-685-6446
Class: Ultimate, Golf Discs

D. Fritz
Fernwood
Grove, CA 92643
Class: Aviar Golf Discs, Minis, Antiques, Glo

Geoff Lissaman
434 S. Auburn St.
Grass Valley, CA 95945
916-274-8326
Class: Golf Discs

Johnny Lissaman
434 S. Auburn St.
Grass Valley, CA 95945
916-274-8326
Class: Golf Discs

Kevin Randall
5799 13th Ave.
Hanford, CA 93230
209-584-1210
Class: Golf Discs (tournament).

Leonard Muise
26381 Whitman St. #46
Hayward, CA 94544510-885-1302
Class: Golf Discs, Foreign, Tournament.

Charley Barringer
P.O. Box 3167
462 Belvedere Street
La Jolla, CA 92038-3167
619-454-4732
Fax: 619-454-4732
Email: cbplaysdsk@aol.com
Class: Ultimate, Golf Discs, Minis

Shayne Dillahunty
4055 Highland Springs Road
Lakeport, CA 95453
707-263-3210
Class: Antiques, Minis, Wham-O, Club,
Golf Discs

Dan Mangone (DCW)
P.O. Box 911
La Mirada, CA 90637
714-522-2202
Fax: 714-670-6340
Email: dtworld@aol.com
Class: Antiques, Unpigmented (Clear),
Golf Discs, All.

Jon Freeman
512 South Ogden Drive
Los Angeles, CA 90036
213-937-6898
Class: Antiques, novelties, Foreign

Mike Tamada
Institutional Research Office
Occident College
1600 Campus Road
Los Angeles, CA 90041
213-259-2966
Email: tamada@oxy.edu
Class: Ultimate Discs.

Cliff Towne
P.O. Box 35525
Los Angeles, CA 90035

213-463-2253
Email: clifftowne@loop.com
Class: 80 Molds (Ultimate) 40 Molds,
Foreign, Fastbacks

Michael Kramer
1921 Sierra Ave.
Napa, CA 94558
707-253-0903
Email: mkramer@hamsoft.com
Class: Golf Discs, Wham-O (World
Class), Pro, Foreign

Harold Hampton
18001 Salmon Mine
Nevada City, CA 95959
Class: Golf Discs.

Michael Travers
18200 Rainbow's End
Nevada City, CA 95959
916-265-5358
Fax: 916-292-4205
Email: travers@oro.net
Class: Golf Discs, Glo, Foreign.

Kyle Burk
2100 Haven Place
Newport Beach, CA 92663
714-548-7290
Email: coolstuff@liberty.com
Class: Antiques-Pre 1965

Scott Riley
7065 Shirley Drive
Oakland, CA 94611
510-482-3357
Class: Glo Golf Discs Aeros and Puppies.

Dan (Stork) Roddick
655 Rim Road
Pasadena, CA 91107
310-252-4715
Fax: 310-252-3866
Email: cybe-stork@aol.com
Class: Antiques, Minis, Wham-O, Novelty
(Mimetic), Glo.

Jeff Soto
2581 Marty Way
Sacramento, CA 95818
916-442-0338
Class: Minis, All.

Tom Callan
2880 Calle Guadalajara
San Clemente, CA 92673
714-498-5696
Class: Antiques, Wham-O (promotional)

Don R. Olow
5589 Brunswick Ave.
San Diego, CA 92120
619-582-1697/619-635-6871
Fax: 619-635-6917
Class: Golf Discs, Ultimate, Freestyle,
Minis, Glo.

Michael Slonin
P.O. Box 900243
San Diego, CA 92190
619-283-2579
Fax: 619-487-0534
Email: tusor@inet1.inetworld.net
Class: Antiques, Foreign

Snapper Pierson
2657 Covington Road
San Diego, CA 92104
619-280-DISC
Fax: 619-692-3607
Email: snapfriz
Class: Golf Discs (Midnight Flyers), All

K. Daniel Clark
3218 Steiner St.
San Francisco, CA 94123
415-922-7761
Fax: 415-922-7761
Email: kclark@aol.com
Class: Antiques, Novelty

Keith Armstrong
526 Fifth Ave.
San Francisco, CA 94118
Email: kjam@aol.com
Class: Variety

Bill Schneider
155 Stratford Drive
San Francisco, CA 94132
415-333-1693
Class: All

Doug Korns
1386 Hillcrest Court
San Jose, CA 95120

408-268-5595
Email: doug@aol.com
Class: Wham-O 80 Molds-HDX, Ultimate,
Freestyle

John "Friz Whiz" Kirkland
4436 Wavertree St.
San Luis Obispo, CA 93401
805-545-0662
Fax: 805-545-8718
Email: frizwhiz@fix.net
Class: All

Kevin "Skippy Jammer" Givens
851 Happy Valley Road
Santa Cruz, CA 95065
408-425-4960
408-4254960 (work)
kdgivens@cats.ucsc.edu
Class: Minis, Club, Tournament, Golf Discs,
Ultimate, 80 Molds.

Tom Schot
P.O. Box 73
Capitola, CA 95010
408-462-0374
Class: Golf Discs

Anthony Allen
924 Mendocino Ave.
Santa Rosa, CA 95401
707-578-3903
Class: Fastbacks, Freestyle

Tom Ford
2613 Sage St
Santa Rosa, CA 95405
707-578-8158
Email: fordboys
Class: Minis, All.

Jimmy Zuur
P.O. Box 9392
Santa Rosa, CA 95405
707-544-2201
Class: Super Pros

Stephen Hey
1078 Oxford Way
Stockton, CA 95204
Email: krazyhey@aol.com
Class: Golf Discs, Minis

Amye Rosenthal
10000 Marnice Ave.
Tuhunga, CA 91042
818-353-4390
Class: Golf Discs, All.

Andrew Lemann
P.O. Box 156
Yorkville, CA 95494
707-895-Disc (3472)
Class: Golf Discs, Super Pro, Player's
Association, Wisconsin Tourn. Discs.

COLORADO

Sabrina Donaldson
7805 A Barbara Ann Road
Arvada, CO 80004
303-940-7078
Class: Antiques, Golf Discs, Minis

Scott Holter
10950 W. Florida Ave. #303
Lakewood, CO 80232
303-987-1986
Class: Pre-1980 Virginia State Discs

John Bird
1301 Lefthand Drive
Longmont, CO 80501
303-678-7448
Email: birdj@ci.boulder.co.us
Class: Antiques

Drew "Dno" Hall
1441 Laurette Drive
Colorado Springs, CO 80909
719-596-3036
Class: Golf Discs, Minis, Club, Tournament.

Scott Holter
10667 W. 8th Ave. Apt. #6
Lakeport, CO 80215
303-202-1706
Email: scottphizzb@cris.com
Class: Frisbie Pie Pans, Wham-0 40-70-
80C Molds, Pluto Platters, Minis, Virginia
State Tournament Discs pre-1982.

CONNECTICUT

Bob Beckerer
P.O. Box 3336
165 Holland Ave.

Bridgeport, CT 06605
203-333-1412
Class: Frisbie Pie Co. Memorabilia

Chris Montross
1532 Country Club Road
Middletown, CT 06457-2343
860-343-1645
Class: Antiques, Wham-O.

Richard Pancoast
255 Bunnyview Drive
Stratford, CT 06497
203-377-4286
Fax: 203-377-8708
Class: All with emphasis on Novelty.

Phil Kennedy
181 Ridge Road
Wethersfield, CT 06109
860-529-0398
Class: Antiques, Wham-O, Golf Discs,
Novelty, Foreign, World Class, Super Pro,
Pro

Shawn Kennedy
181 Ridge Road
Wethersfield, CT 06109
860-529-0398
Class: Minis, Wham-O, Golf Discs,
Ultimate, Novelty

DELAWARE

Troy Saville
418 Shai Circle
Bear, DE 19701
302-832-1916
Email: tsaville@taratec.com
Class: Golf Discs, Minis

FLORIDA

Bill Hileman
3611 NW 16th Blvd.
Gainesville, FL 32605
352-371-4208
Fax: 904-462-2581
Email: phryzbi@aol.com
Class: PDGA Golf Discs & Memorabilia.

Tom Monroe
2426 NW-119th Ave.
Gainsville, FL 32609

904-378-6688
Email: afn12826@afn.org
Class: Golf Discs (Midnight Flyers).

Lawrence Frederick
3904 Demery Drive West
Jacksonville Beach, FL 32250
904-223-4676
Fax: 904-249-0201
Email: frisbee@jax-inter.net
Class: 165G-Freestyle, Ultimate,
Tournament, Fastbacks, K-9

Bob Lewis
3720 Springland Drive
Orlando, FL 32818
407-295-8713
Email: blewis2.190@aol.com
Class: Golf Discs, Antiques, Minis, Novelty,
Glo, Uni-color-Black

Paul Kenny
1 Bluefish Place
Ponte Vedra, FL 32082
904-285-6969
Fax: 904-772-4523
Email: kenny%jx%psd@navair.navy.mil
Class: All

Tim Willis
2133 -5th St.
Sarsota, FL 34237
941-753-6636
Class: HDX/Golf Discs/Blanks/Florida
State Stamps

Nick Sartori
4706 Grainary Ave.
Tampa, FL 33624
813-968-8175
Class: Minis, Golf Discs, Novelty, Glo

GEORGIA

Geoffery Myers
1426 Towne Harbor Passage
Woodstock, GA 30189
770-924-8943
Email: geof@abraxis.com
Class: Tournament Discs

HAWAII

Lori Daniels
1902 Bertram Street
Honolulu, HI 96816
808-734-7727
Email: lorizdisc
Class: Tournament Discs

ILLINOIS

Bryan Wagler
18231 Illinois Route 9
Pekin, IL 61554
Class: Golf Discs

KANSAS

Ron Rice
RR#2 Box 75
Hays, KS 67601
913-628-8334
Class: All

Bill Paulson
7212 N. Meridian
Valley Center, KS 67147-8525
316-755-2681
Email: bempdgsct@feist.com
Class: Minis, Antiques

ILLINOIS

Rich Rand
1628 West 21st Place
Chicago, IL 60608
312-421-3038
Fax: 312-581-1030
Class: All pre-1980.

INDIANA

Allen Pier
RR #1 box 70-ap
Peru, IN 46970
317-473-5728
Class: All.

IOWA

Jeff Homburg
3920 Quebec St.
Ames, IA 50014

515-268-8042
Email: jhomburg@iastate.edu
Class: Golf Discs, World Class, NAS

Mike Waskowiak
2953 Middle Road
Davenport, IA 52803
319-359-3271
Fax: 319-324-1520
Email: mwaskowiak@aol.com
Class: Antiques.

Gary Johnson
P.O. Box 221
Stuart, IA 50250
Class: Minis, Glo

KENTUCKY

Neal "Doug" Aulick
3065 Brookwood Drive
Edgewood, KY 41017
606-341-7272
Class: PDGA Worlds Commemorative
Golf Discs

Steve Trauger
P.O. Box 623
Hebron, KY 41048
Email: platterman@aol.com
Class: Guts Frisbee Pros and all Guts
Memorabilia. Frisbie Pie Tins and Signs.

LOUISIANA

Roger Clark
6021 Rosemead Circle
Bossier City, LA 71111
318-742-5818 (phone & Fax)
Class: Golf Discs.

MAINE

Gordy Adell
5 Page Street
Kittery, ME 03904
207-439-2390
Class: Antiques, All

MASSACHUSETTS

Tiina Booth
c/o Amherst Regional High School
21 Mattoon St.

Amherst, MA 01002
413-549-3710 Ext. 253
Email: tbooth@k12.oit.umass.edu
Class: Frisbie Pie Pans, Ultimate

Tom Whiffen
237 Daniels Street
Franklin, MA 02038
508-553-9687
Email: twhiffen@aol.com
Class: Antiques, Minis, Wham-O, Golf
Discs

Dave Johnson
7 Lake Shore Ave
Monson, MA 01057
413-596-6966
Email: joandave@javanet.com
Class: Frisbie Pie Tins and other Company
Memorabilia.

John Dwork
P.O. Box 936
Northhampton, MA 01061
413-584-6317
Fax: 413-585-6317
Email: Dwork@well.com
Class: Antiques, Pros, Foreign, Novelties,
NAS Series, Super Pro

Steve Hartwell
137 Chestnut St.
North Reading, MA 01864
978-664-2888
Email: Shartwell@lotus.com
Class: Golf Discs, Wham-O.

Rick Williams
81 College Ave.
Somerville, MA 02144
617-666-5936
Email: rwilliams@genetics.com
Class: All

MICHIGAN

Dave Bourgeois
5784 University
Detroit, MI 48224
Class: Golf Discs (Black & Green)

Larry LaBond
3180 Chestnut Hills #301
Kalamazoo, MI 49009
616-372-2489
Class: Golf Discs, Minis, Ultimate

Mark Banghart
5004 Palisade Dr.
Lansing, MI 40917
Email: mb11524@aol.com
Class: All

Brian Hayes
13975 Dennison Road
Milan, MI 48160
313-439-8182
Email: 102343.32@compuserve.com
Class: All

MINNESOTA

Paul Thompson
4370 Brookside Court #317
Edina, MN 55436
612-920-1547
Fax: 627-2367
Class: Super Pros

Steve Born
5929 Upton Ave. South
Minneapolis, MN 55410
612-920-1593
Email: born0022@maroon.tc.umn.edu
Class: NAS Series, Freestyle-FPA, Minis,
MFA Discs

Randy Starck
2524 Hennepin #5
Minneapolis, MN 55405
612-374-1823
Class: Minis

Tim Mackey
2224 Clarke Court
St. Cloud, MN 56301
Email: csieben@magellan.cloudnet.com
Class: All

MISSISSIPPI

Dale McVeay
297-G McMahon Road.
Purvis, MS 39475
601-261-3820

Class: Golf Discs, Frisbie Pie Pans, Pluto
Platters.

MISSOURI

Ray Vuichard
821 Keeneland
Floirsant, MO 63034
314-839-7443
Class: Golf Discs

Ace Mason
5837 NE Spokane
Kansas City, MO 64119
816-453-8201
Email: ace@kcnet.com
Class: Antiques, Golf Discs, Novelty,
Foreign, All.

Bob Waidmann
680 Lindsay Lane
St. Louis, MO 63031
314-838-7907
Class: Minis, Golf Discs

NEBRASKA

Michael Jon Fleege
3224 N.48th Street
Lincoln, NE 68504
402-464-4620
Class: Golf Discs

NEVADA

Donn Blake
5104 Mandrake Lane
Las Vegas, NV 89130
702-645-7763
Class: All Wham-O

NEW JERSEY

Gary Seubert
22 Weyburne Road
Hamilton Square, NJ 08690-1947
609-890-1440
Email: garys@aosi.com
Class: Minis, Antiques, Frisbie Bakery
Items.

NEW MEXICO

Tom Lander
Star Route 2, Box 119
Kingston, NM 88042
505-895-5652
Fax: 505-895-3326
Email: blkrnge@riolink.com
Class: Golf Discs, Minis

NEW YORK

Krae Van Sickle
51 Dalmage Farm Lane
East Hampton, NY 11937
212-242-2317
Fax: 516-329-9205
Class: Antiques, Minis, Wham-O, Club,
Tournament, Ultimate, Foreign, All

David L. Einsidler
42 Bayberry Lane
Levittown, NY 11756
Email: eincycle@aol.com
Class: Antiques, Wham-O

Paul Stephens
453 Mountainview Drive
Lewiston, NY 14092
Email: writer20@aol.com
Class: Antiques

Keith A. Power
27 Cedar Dr.
Miller Place, NY 11764-1404
516-474-3863
Email: power@hawking.cad.bnl.gov
Class: Minis, Golf Discs and Ultimate.

Paul Brenner
71 Hollister Road
Freeville, NY 13068
607-539-6066
Email: pa5@cornell.edu
Class: Ultimate, Tournament, HDX

Doug Corea
414 W. Elm St.
E. Rochester, NY 14445
716-381-3047
Class: Golf Discs, Antiques.

Jim Palmeri
180 Norman Road
Rochester, NY 14623
716-292-0686
Email: jp@moscom.com
Class: Antiques.

NORTH CAROLINA

Phil Heitman
1013 Gunston Lane
Durham, NC 27703-3910
919-596-1906
Class: Olympic, Antiques.

Henry Griffin
909 Palmer Lane
Winston-Salem, NC 27107
910-784-4418
Class: Golf Discs, Minis, Novelty

OHIO

Peter G. Thielen
P.O. Box 292547
Columbus, OH 43229
Class: Novelty, Wham-O

OKLAHOMA

Tommy Parker
1218 Logan Ave.
Lawton, OK 73507
405-353-2279
Class: Golf Discs

Rick Neil
P.O. Box 470794
Tulsa, OK 74147
918-622-6648
Fax: 918-622-6398
Email: Via Steve Ward
Class: Antiques, Black/Gray, Club,
Tournament, and Foreign Golf Discs.

Steve Ward
7212 S. 90th E. Ave. #2049
Tulsa, OK 74133-5205
918-250-1120
Email: steve.ward@bgbbs.com
Class: HDX, Minis, Wham-O, World Class
(Tom Boda), Glo

OREGON

Bruce Sisson
922-E25th Ave.
Eugene, OR 97405
541-485-3275
Fax: 541-683-7212
Email: hyzerbomb@aol.com
Class: Golf Discs (Wintertime Open)

Jerry Miller
2658 S.E. 118th
Portland, OR 97266
503-760-2361
Class: Golf Discs, Minis

Jerry Schneider
4435 SE Crystal Springs Blvd.
Portland, OR 97206
503-775-3321
Class: Antiques, Minis, Wham-O, Glo,
World Class, Super Pro, Pro, Regular,
Olympic Discs.

Steve Tufty
6730SW-89th Place
Portland, OR 97223
503-244-5840
Email: pop@protocol.com
Class: Golf Discs-Eagles

Doug Drawbond
6930 Zena Road
Rickreall, OR 97371
503-835-8701
Class: Antiques, Minis, Golf Discs.

PENNSYLVANIA

Jon Merrill
517 North Fenwick Street
Allentown, PA 18103
610-740-0823
Email: Jamerrill@wow.com
Class: Frisbie Pie Pans, Tournament Discs.

Brian Case
1193 Shoreham Road
Camp Hill, PA 17011-6136
717-975-9476
Email: bcase@frisbee.microserve.com
Class: Antiques, Pie Pans, Prototypes,
Tournament, Club Discs.

Joe Lynn
RR 2 Box 77
Drums, PA 18222
717-788-6334
Class: Antiques, Signature Series, Glo
Golf Discs.

Dave "leb mets" Stembel
30 Tenmore Road
Haverford, PA 19041-1224
610-527-6419
Email: DMS@WRTdesign.com
Class: Prototype Golf Discs, Antiques,
NAS, World Class Series, Minis

Richhi Ross
246 School House Road
Lancaster, PA 17603
717-394-5650
Class: Minis, Microminis.

John Hanson
201 St. Marks Square
Philadelphia, PA 19104
215-386-5443
Fax: 215-386-5411
Email: has201@msn.com
Class: Ultimate

John "Jack" Roddick
601 Baltimore Road
Shippensburg, PA 17257
717-532-2248
jmrodd@ark.ship.edu
Class: Tournament Discs-Players Packages.

TENNESSEE

Darrell E. Lynn
97N. Holmes Street
Memphis, TN 38111
901-323-4849
Class: Minis, Glo-square top Fastbacks,
Publications

TEXAS

Paul Venable
6404 Woods Edge Drive
Arlington, TX 76016
817-572-0567
Fax: 817-572-2075
Email: keyaccts@oncomp.net
Class: Golf Discs-custom hot stamps.

Dave Moody
2606 Harris Blvd.
Austin, TX 78703
512-477-2360
Email: discgolf@bga.com
Class: Golf Discs

Jack McCulley
802 Glen Oak Drive
Austin, TX 78748
Class: Golf Discs

Dan R. Olsen
10700 Fugua #287
Houston, TX 77089
713-481-9770
Fax: 713-956-6163
Class: Tournament Minis, Prototypes

K. Kevin Morrow
511 S. Delaware
Irving, TX 75060
214-259-1046
Fax: 214-259-1060
Email: kevmo62@airmail.net
Class: Antiques, Minis, Wham-O, Club,
Tournament, Golf Discs, Novelty, Glo,
Uni-color

Jeremy Ohlheiser
2157 N. Pearson Lane
West Lakw, TX 76262
817-379-0795
Class: Antiques, Tournament, Golf Discs

VIRGINIA

Michael "Captain Snap" Conger
P.O. Box 43
Wallops Island, VA 23337-0043
757-824-1642
Fax: 757-824-2427
Email: snap.conger@gsfc.nasa.gov
Class: Pre & Post Wham-O S-ring and
Posters.

Dave Griffin
6153 Singletons Way
Centreville, VA 20121-2646
703-631-0833
Class: Antiques, Minis, Super Pros, Pros,
Golf Discs, Glo, HDX, 80 Molds

Tom Garber
6951 Birch Street
Falls Church, VA 22046
703-534-4821
Class: Antiques, Golf Discs

Duke & Bryan Stableford
608 Wood-ford St. #B
Fredericksburg, VA 22401-4435
703-371-9609
Class: Golf Discs-Midnight Flyers

Gary Foster
6821 Laban Road
Roanoke, VA 24019
540-362-3641
540-344-6265
Class: Club, Tournament

Tad Cronwell
6807 Linbrook Drive
Richmond, VA 23228
804-553-1101
Fax: 703-978-5353
Class: Antiques. Golf Discs, Wham-O, All

Mike McLaughlin
P.O. Box 607
Spotsylvania, VA 22553
Class: Glo

Dave Steger
16085 Olmstead Lane
Woodbridge, VA 22191
703-878-6870
Email: dbs1@nrc.gov
Class: Golf Discs, World Junior Frisbee
Championships

WASHINGTON

Jeff "Getty" Freeman
1606-149th Place SE #1
Bellevue, WA 98007
206-747-1440
Email: gettyf@aol.com
Class: Ultimate, Freestyle, Minis.

Sheryl Newland
2429-159th Ave. SE
Bellevue, WA 98008
206-641-8828
Email: newland@aol.com

Class: Glo, Antiques, Minis, Ultimate, Foreign, Wham-O.

Lowell Shields
23301 66 th Ave W
Mountlake, WA 98043
206-670-2548
Class: Golf Discs, Antiques

Ralph Williamson
11729 Exeter Ave N.E.,
Seattle, WA 98125
206-364-9808
Fax: 206-362-7802
Email: hdgezr@nwlink.com
Class: All, Golf Disc

WISCONSIN

Mike & Michele Cozzens
Sandy Point Resort
1230 Sandy Point Lane
Lac du Flambeau, WI 54538
715-588-3810
Fax: 715-588-3810
Email: sprdgr@aol.com
Class: Minis, Golf Discs, Glo

Randy Schukar
252 Georgia Street
North Stevens Point, WI 54481
715-341-6668
Email: platpus@coredcs.com
Class: Golf Discs

AUSTRALIA

Chris Himing
Unit #7
99 Clarke Street
Bunbury 6230
West Australia, Australia
Email: ozdisc@wantree.com.au
Class: Frisbie Pie Pans

CANADA

Glen Whitlock
RR#4 S10 C40
Gibsons, B.C. VON 1DO Canada
Class: Minis, HDX, Golf Discs

John Anthony
1653 Sheriff Way
Nanaimo, B.C. V9T 4A4 Canada
250-758-7987
Fax: 604-535-6884
Email: discsports@bc.sympatico.ca
Class: Antiques, Minis, Pros,
Tournament/Series Discs

Kevin Sparkman
1209 King St. West Suite 209
Toronto Ontario M6K 1G2 Canada
Class: Antiques

Adam Berson
507 E. 6th Ave. #202
Vancouver, B.C. V5T 1K9 Canada
604-874-1737
Class: World Ultimate Discs, Antiques,
Tournament Discs

Bill King
4494 W. 7th Ave.
Vancouver, B.C. V6R 1W9 Canada
604-224-2404
Fax: 604-535-6884
Email: discsports@bc.sympatico.ca
Class: Antiques, Pros, Minis, (T-Birds)

James Brown
P.O. Box 19526
Centrepoint PO
Vancouver, B.C. V4A-1R3 Canada
604-535-1003
Fax: 604-535-6884
Email: discsports@bc.sympatico.ca

Class: Antiques, Pros, Foreign, (Early Discraft)

Scott Lewis
476 W. 17th Ave.
Vancouver, B.C. V5Y 2A2 Canada
604-874-5636
Email: slewis@SFU.ca
Class: Antiques, Canadian Tournament Discs, HDX

James Anderson
Vancouver, B.C. Canada
Email: discsports@bc.sympatico.ca
Fax: 604-535-6884
Class: 165G (WOLF), Masters, Minis

ENGLAND

Derek Robins
50 Spring Lane
Kenilworth Warwickshire
England
Phone: 44 1203 523523 Ext. 2710
Email: d.j.robins@Warwick.ac.uk
Class: Minis, British Discs

Appendix IV

BIBLIOGRAPHY

"Battle of the Frisbee is Decided on the Playing Fields of Rutgers." *New York Times*. 11/7/72 Page 39.

Botermans, Jack and Burrett, Tony and van Delft, Pieter and van Splunteren. "Disc and Cross." *The World of Games-Facts On File*. 1995. Page 201.

Brillen, J.B. "Frisbee; They Are Pros, Gentleman." *Sports Illustrated*: (Letters). Page 79.

Buglione, Frances. "East side firm once made delicious 30 cent pies." *Bridgeport Post*: (Edmund C. Bond interview) Sept. 7, 1978.

Byrne, Tom. "Events in the Life of the Dartmouth Class of 1955." On the Hanover Plain. Page 18. 1995.

Caney, Steven. *Steven Caney's Invention Book*: "The Invention of the Frisbee". Pages 97-102.

Clark, W. Rockwell, Jr. "Production-Line Saves Ma The Job Of Making Pie." *Bridgeport Sunday Post*: 11/5/39.

Cohen, Tom E. "Who Started It." *New York Times Magazine*: (Letters) 8/25/57.

"Congratulations! To Bridgeport Life on its 1000th Issue." Frisbie Pie Company. *Bridgeport Life*: 5/26/34.

Croft, Georgia. "Profile: Bill Robes." *Echoes*: Kimball Union Academy. April 1986. Pages 11-14.

Danna, Mark. "After 30 High-Flying Years, The Frisbee Still Soars." *Sports Illustrated*: 5/11/87.

Eshman, Robert. "Ernest Robes: almost the father of the frisbee." *The Dartmouth*: 10/24/79.

"Fanfare For Frisbee." (Food Mart Advertisement) *Daily Princetonian*: 5/2/57. Page 5.

Faude, Wilson H. and Friedland, Joan W. "1920 Frisbies." *Connecticut Firsts: 1985*. Page 50.

Feld, Dorothy Baker. "Available Source Material On The History Of Branford, CT 1644-1800." An Excerpt From A Thesis Entitled, Branford In The Beginning: 1975.

Flint, Frank P. "Frisbee: Manners And Morals." *Sports Illustrated*: (Letters) 6/3/57. Page 79.

"Flying Frisbees." *Sports Illustrated: Events & Discoveries*. 5/13/57. Page 22.

"Friday Night Lake Party, Dance Highlights Frosh Weekend." *Daily Princetonian*: 4/29/57 Pages 1,3.

"Frisbee, Anyone?" *Amherst Alumni News*: January 1958. (Letters). Walt Meyer, '35, John Brown, Peter Schrag '53, Philip S. Thayer '45 and Ezra Bowen '48. January 1958 Pages 17-18.

"Frisbee Becomes Overwhelming Pastime; Try It This Weekend." *The Pontefract*: Pomfret Prep School. 11/9/57. Page 1.

"Frisbee Champions?" *Daily Princetonian*: 5/17/57.

Frisbee, Edward Selah. "Frisbie-Frisbee Genealogy."

"Frisbee: Ohio Version." *Sports Illustrated: 19th Hole. Readers Take Over.* (Letters) " 5/27/57. Pages 78-79. "Frisbee: Historians Report." Page 79. "Frisbee: Phrisbee." Page 79.

Frisbee, Oliver Libby A.M. *Year Book of The (John) Paul Jones Club of the Sons of the American Revolution.* 1897 Pages 15, 31-32.

"Frisbee: Pre-1957." Panati, Charles. *Extraordinary Origins of Everyday Things*: Connecticut. 1987. Pages 372-373.

Frisbie, Edward. "The last will and testament of Edward Frisbie, The Hearthstone." Branford CT. May 10, 1690.

Frisbie, Joseph P. *Frisbie Pie Company Salesman's Manual.* 1936.

Frisbie, Nora G. *Edward Frisbie of Branford and his Descendants. Vol. II.* Gateway Press. 1987.

Frisbie, Nora G. and Rousseau, Berniece Frisbie. "*Bulletin of the Frisbie-Frisbee Family Association of America.*" October 1990.

Gott, Peter H. "The First Frisbee." *Princeton Alumni Weekly*: (Letters) 7/1/75. Page 7.

Halpern, Eric. "Ultimate: Columbia High School and Beyond." U.S. History College Paper. Eric Halpern. 6/18/90

Henriksson, Peter. "Swedish Frisbee History." Stockholm, Sweden 1997

Horton, Stuart. "Maplewood Becomes Center of Frisbee." *The Evening News*: Newark, NJ: 11/7/70 Page 22.

"In Place of Kthunk." *Daily Princetonian.* 3/27/57.

Johnson, Stancil. E.D. *FRISBEE: a practitioner's manual and definitive treatise.* Workman's Press, NY. 1975

Joseph Cornwall '39, Water D. Bannard '56. "More Frisbee History." *Princeton Alumni Weekly* (Letters) 9/29/75. Page 5.

"Joseph Peter Frisbie." *Bridgeport Life*: 10/5/40.

"Joseph "Pious" Frisbie Speaks At Kiwanis." *Bridgeport Post*: 2/7/25.

Katz, Abram. "Whatever its origin, sales are high." *New Haven Register*: 9/2/89

Loomis, William. "A Gentleman's Sport." *The Exonian*: Phillips Exeter Academy. 9/21/57.

McKenzine, John. "Cultural Lag." *New York Times Magazine*: 9/1/57. (Letters) 9/1/57 Page 4.

McMahon, Jeff. "Where The First Frisbee Flew." *New Times Weekly:* San Luis Obispo, CA. 7/24-31/1997. Pages 10-13.

Morris, Robert. "Storytellers Put Own Spin on Frisbee's Beginnings." *Omaha World-Herald:* 8/17/89.

"Negotiations Reported For Sale of Frisbie Co." *Bridgeport Sunday Post:* 7/22/56.

Neil, Rick. *International Flying Disc Collector's Association:* Vol. 1 Number 1, Vol. 2 Number 1.

Nieminen, Seppo. "Let's Talk Frisbee: The language and Culture of Flying Disc with a Lexicon of Flying Disc Vocabulary." University of Jyvaskyla. Dept. Of English. 1995.

Oberlander, David. "World Frizby Championships." *The Shield:* Theta Delta Chi: Vol. 71. Number 3. (Dartmouth College). March 1955. Pages 103-4, 115.

Page, Anita. "Pie in the Sky." (Fred Morrison). *La Verne Magazine:* April 1977. Page 14.

Palmeri, Jim. "The Space Saucer: an important missing link disc." April/May 1980. Pages 46-47. "Collecting The Zolar." July/August. *Flying Disc Magazine.* Pages 40-41.

Panati, Charles, "Frisbee Pre-1957." *Extraordinary Origins of Everyday Things:* 1987. Pages 372-373.

"Phrisbee." *Amherst Alumni News:* October 1957 Page 21.

Price, Boby. Frisbie Pie Company Route Book. 1872

Rec. Sports. Disc: Internet News Group.

Roddick, Dan. Http://www.solving.com/discgolf/discuss/messages/197.html (9/10/97): "A Frisbee Disc-ourse from Stork." 9/10/97.

Seiler, Mike. "Wham-O Has Unique Legacy of Producing Some of the Hottest Toy Fans of All Time." *San Gabriel Valley Business Journal:* May 1994 Pages 1, 5.

Stow, Edith. *Boys' Games Among The North American Indians:* 1924. Pages 42-55.

Strausberg, Maura. "Gallup Leisure Activities Index." The Gallup Organization, Princeton, NJ. 1989.

Strauss, Michael. "Prep School Sports." *New York Times:* 12/30/57

Talese, Gay. "Frisbees, Yo Yos, Goo-Goos, Etc." *New York Times Magazine:* 8/11/57. Page 24.

"The Frisbees are Flying-it must be spring." *Middlebury College-News Letter:* Spring 1976. Pages 33-34

"The Frisbie Co. Joins The Wagner Family." *The Pie-O-Neer* Vol. 11 No. 3: Oct. 1956. Page 3.

"The Name's Frisbee." *Newsweek: Life And Leisure-Games:* 7/8/57 Page 85.

John Stewart, Hartley P. Walker, Douglas Daniels, A.O. Innis. "Tossing The Frisbee."

Newsweek: (Letters) 8/5/57 Pages 2, 6.

Ultimate And The Ultimate Players Association Report: 1992-93.

U.S. District Court for the Southern District of NY: Civil Action, Wham-O Mfg. Co. vs Empire Plastics Corp. Case Number 63 CIV 291. 1/29/63

U.S. District Court for the Eastern District of NY: Civil Action, Wham-O Mfg. Co. vs Premier Products Company. Case Number 63C 252. 3/12/63

Wallechinsky, David and Wallace, Irving. "Tossing The Discus." *The People's Almanac #2:* William Morrow and Company, Inc. NY. 1978. Page 1091.

Ward, Geoffrey C. *Before the Trumpet: Young Franklin Roosevelt.* New York: Perennial Library, 1989. Page 247.

Wilhelm, Douglas. "Famed Flying Frisbee Feted on its 50th." T*he Boston Globe:* 6/4/89. Pages 29-30.

Wilkinson, Frederick. *Edged Weapons:* 1970 Double & Co. Inc. Garden City, NY. 1970.

Willis, Bruce D. *Catalog of Wham-O Professional Model Frisbee Brand Flying Disc.* 11/22/83.

World Flying Disc Federation (WFDF) *The Official Rules of Flying Disc Sports 1997.*

"Yale Does Not Understand FRISBEE!" *Princeton Alumni Weekly:* Vol. LVII. 7/5/57.

ACKNOWLEDGMENTS

Alfred University: Laurie L. McFadden
Amherst Alumni News Magazine: Terry Y. Allen
Andrew Taylor: Alameda, CA
Anthony Grzan: S. Plainfield, NJ
Archival Outlook-The Society of American Archivist
Arthur Viren: Roseburg, OR
Atlantic Magazine
Australia Patent Office: Canberra, Australia
Austria Patent Office
Balis Reference Center
Bay Sports Review: Berkeley, CA
Bennington College: Connie
Bill Callan: Monroe, CT
Bob Zeinert: Macdona, TX
Bryan Frederick: Williams College, MA
Buckingham Browne & Nichols School
Buffalo And Erie County Historical Society
Cambridge Chronicle Newspaper
Camp Agawam For Boys: Scott Malm
Camp Algonquin: Randy Osborn
Camp Stewart For Boys: Kathy Ragsdale
Canada Patent Office: Ottawa, Canada
Capital Information Search: Victor C. Manos
Carmella La Conte: San Diego, CA
Celin Schoen: Hobart, NY
Charles "Bill" Nichols Jr.: East Norwalk, CT
Chicago Metallic: Lake Zurich, IL: Mel Eberspacher
Columbia High School: Joan Stewart
Connecticut Historical Society: Martha H. Smart
Connecticut Post: Mena Turro
Connecticut State Library: Carolyn M. Picciano
Connecticut State University Library: Stephen Kwasnik
Curtis L. Frisbie: Dallas, TX
Dale Mitchell: Lexington, OH
Dartmouth College Alumni Magazine
Dartmouth College Library-Baker Library: Jane Chisaki
Dartmouth College Special Collections: Barbara L.Krieger
David Bedell: Bridgeport, CT
David Caruba: Enfield, CT
Daytona Beach News-Journal: Catherine Harley
Debgay Pinucci, Holyoke, MA
Dr. Orton D. Frisbie: Bandera, TX
Frank Deford: Westport. CT
French Patent Office: Paris, France
FTC Watch: Washington Regulatory Reporting Associates
Gallup Organization, Princeton, NJ: Maura Strausberg
German Patent Office: Munich, Germany
Goldy Norton: Los Angeles, CA
Greenwich Times Newspaper: Greenwich, CT
Hamilton College: Frank K. Lorenz
Hartford Courant: Marty Petty
Harvard College Library: Mary S. Smith

Harvard Magazine: Chenoweth Moffatt
Heekin Family: Cincinnati, OH
Historical Society of Princeton, NJ: Patricia L.Bruttomesso
Home News Publishing Company: Betty Selingo
Houghton County Historical Society:William Barkell
Howard University Library: Leida I.Torres
Jean Frisbie Johns: Rotonda West, FL
Johan Lindgren: Cambridge, UK
John D. Bowker: Sun City Center, FL
John Robes: Nashua, NH
John "Z" Weyland:Venice, CA
Jon M. Davis: Houghton, MI
Keith Armstrong: San Francisco, CA
Ken Cramer: Hanover, NH
Kent State University: Carolyn J. Radcliff
Kimball Union Academy: Joan E. Bishop
King & Low-Heywood Thomas School: Gloria Koster
L.A. Public Library: Rita L. Potok, Romaine Ahlstrom
Laura Cleavinger: Cincinnati, OH
Lenny Silverman: Belmont, MA
Library of Congress: Prints and Photographs Division
Library of the Boston Athenaeum: Stephen Z. Nonack
Life Magazine Photo Archives
Los Angeles Times Research and Reprint Service
Maplewood Memorial Library, NJ: Rowland Bennett
Mark J. Epstein: Short Hills, NJ
Marquette County Historical Society, Inc: Linda K. Panian
Marty Hapner: Santa Cruz, CA
Mary Witkowski: Bridgeport Public Library
Massachusetts Institute of Technology:Agnieszka Meyro
Metropolitan Toronto Library: Nancy Grossman
Miami University-Ohio: C. Martin Miller
Michael James Cronen: Oakland, CA
Michigan State University: Mary M. Jones
Michigan Technological University: J. Robert Van Pelt Library
Middlebury College: Bob Buckeye
Milford Citizen Newspaper: Milford, CT
Moses Brown School: Frank E. Fuller
NASA: Patricia M. Riep-Dice
National Air And Space Museum:Tom Newman
National Archives at College Park: Jeffery T. Harley
National Archives & Records Administration
NAVSURFWARCENDDIV Public Affairs-Crane IN: Curt Brown
Nebraskaland: Nebraska Game and Park Commission
Nebraska State Historical Society: Paul J. Eisloeffel
New Haven Colony Historical Society: James W. Campbell
New Haven Free Public Library: Shirin Jamasb
New Haven Register, New Haven, CT
New Haven Register: Mary M. McMullen
New Milford Times: Denise Dowling
New Rochelle Public Library: Michelle Watts
Newsday Inc. Library: Carole Anne Weik
Newsweek Magazine
New Times Weekly: San Luis Obispo-Jeff McMahon
New York Daily News Library

New York Post: Laura Harris
New York Public Library
New York Times Library
Ohio State University: Linda Krikos
Patents, Trademarks & Designs Office: Canberra, Australia
Pennsylvania State University Library: Laura Gordon-Murname
Peter Henricksson: Stockholm, Sweden
Peter Robes: White River Junction, VT
Philadelphia Inquirer and Daily News: Dana W. White
Phillips Exeter Academy: Edouard Desrochers
Pomfret School: Judith A.L. Jackson
Port Chester Public Library: Mary M. De Bellis
Princeton Public Library: Marc Donatiello
Princeton Weekly Bulletin
Professor Fred Crews: UC Berkeley, CA
Professor William Loomis: UC San Diego, CA
Programmers Information Network: Amy R. Hurd, Sara L. Hensley
Providence College-Phillips Memorial Library: Jane M. Jackson
Putman W. Blodgett: Lyne, NH
Rainbow Molding Inc. El Monte, CA: Ken Price
Reader's Digest: Elinor Allcott
Rensselaer Polytechnic Institute-Folsom Library: Gretchen Koerpel
Rhode Island Historical Society Library: Maureen Taylor
Ridgefield Press Newspaper
Robert A. Everett: Tulsa, OK
Rose M. Protzman: Perry, OH
Russell Everett: El Cerrito, CA
Rutgers State University: Edward Skipworth
San Jose Mercury News: San Jose, CA
Scan Art: Richmond, CA
Seppo Nieminen: Kauhajoki, Finland
Smithsonian Institution Archives: Paul Theerman
Smithsonian Institution Libraries: Amy A. Begg
Smithtown News
State of Connecticut: State Senator Gary D. Lebeau
Stewart I. Edelstein: Southport, CT
St. Michael The Archangel Church: Fr. George Maslar
St. Thomas Beckett Rectory: Father Kenneth Frisbie
Sue & Tom Frisbie: Corvallis, OR
Table Talk Pies: Tom Robo
Terry McSweeney: CopyMat: Alameda, CA
Timothy MacKey: St. Cloud, MN
Tom Schlueter, Disc Golf Journal
The Trentonian News: Trenton, NJ
Ultimate Players Association: Colorado Springs, CO
U.S. Military Academy West Point: Paul Nergelovic
United Kingdom Patent Office: London, England
University City Light: La Jolla, CA
University of La Verne: Eric Borer
Yale University: Eustace D. Theodore

INDEX

PHOTO CREDITS

Front Cover: The Annual Smithsonian Frisbee Disc Festival. Courtesy: Wham-O, Inc.
Bob Beckerer: FPC-03
Donn Blake: MA-08, MA-09
Kevin Cotchen: AT-41
Jerone Gundrun: FPC-10
Kevin Sparkman: AT-25, AT-44, AT-44A
Wil West: FPC-02, FPC-02A, FPC-02B, FPC-14
All Other Photos: Victor A. Malafronte

THE COMPLETE BOOK OF FRISBEE
The History of the Sport & the First Official Price Guide

ORDER FORM
(PLEASE PRINT CLEARLY)

Name_____

Address_____

City_____**State**_____**Zip**_____

Phone (___)_____

E-mail_____

Please send_____book(s) @: $19.95 each: $_____

California residents add local sales tax: $_____

Shipping & handling: $3.00 per book: $_____

TOTAL: $_____

Books will be sent via priority mail as soon as check clears (7-10 days.)

Money orders will enable books to be sent via priority mail the next day, in most cases.

**Canadian orders-per book total: $27.95 (U.S.)
Books will be sent via global priority mail.**

If you wish, please request a personally autographed book by the author, the Original World Frisbee Champion!

For bookstore, dealer and distributor pricing, please contact the author directly by e-mail: frisbee@pacbell.net or call: 510-814-9639

Please send your payment and order form to:

**American Trends Publishing Co.
909 Marina Village Parkway, #321
Alameda, California 94501**